4.00

Survey of I Corinthians

Survey
of
I Corinthians

By
JIMMY ALLEN

JIMMY ALLEN
Harding College
Searcy, Arkansas 72143

Dedication

To

DR. JAMES D. BALES

Servant of Christ
Student of the word
Preacher of the gospel
Defender of the faith
Author of good books
Colleague in Bible teaching
Dear brother, friend and teacher

Harding College Bible Faculty [1974-1975]—Back row, Malone, Jones, Huffard, Pfeiffer, Shackelford, Allen, McKinney; front row, Helsten, Pollard, Hays, Sanders, Pryor, Isom; missing, Bales, Warren.

Author's Preface

For several years I have taught the Corinthian epistles as an instructor at Harding College. This book is the result of my research on the first letter. Originally, the material was intended to be a syllabus for my students. However, since there is no comparable contemporary work among our people, it was felt that this publication might help to fill a need. If, even to a limited extent, the volume accomplishes that end, the endeavor will have been worthwhile.

Many books of this kind are criticized as being too light for experienced students of the Bible and too heavy for beginners. In writing, I sought for a balance which would appeal to both groups. Hopefully, anyone will be able to study these notes with profit.

Some of the simpler passages have been dealt with in an almost cursory fashion. On the other hand, in-depth observations are offered for the more difficult sections. Obviously, then, the work is not even. Frankly, I do not know how to avoid that outcome. Because of differences in the material covered and one's own interests, more attention must necessarily be given to some areas than others.

Lack of organization is a weakness which characterizes some teachers. A long time ago, I resolved that my teaching would be structured or organized. Information presented systematically is more readily learned. The unusual format of this book is given in the hope that the reader will always be able to relate the part (*i.e.* whatever is being studied at the time) to the whole of the epistle.

Although I am indebted to scores of people who have written and lectured on this epistle, the conclusions drawn are

my own. I have striven to be honest and consistent with the
sacred text. Ezra "set his heart to study the law of the Lord,
and to do it, and to teach his statutes and ordinances" (Ez.
7:10). His example has been my pattern in working with I Corinthians.

Contents

Neale Pryor speaking at chapel.

I.

Background Information

and Bibliography

I. The City of Corinth.

A. In the second century before Christ, Corinth and a number of other Greek cities, known as the Achaian League, fought to gain independence from Rome. Since Corinth was the head of the League, it received the full fury of Rome's military might in 146 B.C. when it was destroyed by General L. Mummius Achaiacus. For a hundred years, the city lay in ruins. The only thing left today from that old community is part of the temple of Apollo. In 46 B.C. Corinth was rebuilt by Julius Caesar.

B. In the first century, Corinth was a seaport city of approximately 500,000 people. It was located at the head of the isthmus which joined northern Greece to the Peloponnesian Peninsula. Its eastern seaport was Cenchrea and its western seaport was Lechaeum. It was called "Corinthus Bimaris" or Corinth of the two seas because it served the Aegean and Adriatic Seas. Since the isthmus is only about four miles across at its narrowest point, small ships were sometimes transported overland by means of rollers rather than sail around the southern tip of the Peloponnesus. Obviously, a canal was needed there then. Such an effort was first begun by Nero during his reign. Later, Jews captured in the fall of Jerusalem worked on the project. However, the Corinthian Canal did not become a reality until 1893. Today it can ac-

commodate only ships of small tonnage (the water is twenty-
six feet deep). The canal's walls look to be two hundred feet
high in some places.

C. Corinth was an extremely evil place. The city's name
and wickedness were synonymous terms. To say that one was
behaving like a Corinthian was to accuse him of gross immorality. Behind the city stood Acro-Corinth, a hill on which
was erected a temple to Aphrodite or Venus, the so-called
goddess of love. Before the destruction of the old city in 146
B.C., a thousand priestesses, dedicated to "sacred prostitu-
tion" (what a contradiction in terms!) lived in that temple. A
guide at Corinth said the prostitutes had "follow me" written
on their shoe soles so that when they walked in the sand the
men would know who they were and follow them to the
temple. Hundreds of years earlier, Solomon had described such
a follower as being like an ox going to slaughter (Prov.
7:21-23). According to R. C. H. Lenski, "Venus worship was a
mark of the new city likewise although we have no account of
the females connected with the new temple" (*Interpretation of
I and II Corinthians*, p. 12).

Asclepius was the Greek god of healing. In ancient times,
likenesses of diseased members of the body were made and
placed in his temple with the hope that healing would follow.
There is a little museum at the edge of Corinth's ruins. A small
room, located about midway in the building and not generally
open for the public, is filled with images of human organs
found in the ruins of the city. From a visit to that room, one
can easily conclude that venereal disease must have been
rampant in Corinth. Paul's assessment of the Gentile world
(Rom. 1:26-32) is an apt description of the community to
which I Corinthians was written.

II. Paul's Visits to Corinth.

    A. First Visit (Acts 18:1-18).

       1. On the second missionary journey, Paul went to
Corinth alone from Athens which was located forty-five miles
to the east (18:1).

       2. At Corinth, he met Priscilla and Aquila (18:2).

         a. They were Jews originally from Pontus in north-
ern Asia Minor.

b. They had been driven from Rome by Claudius, who was then reigning as emperor.

(1) According to Suetonius (who lived during the first and second centuries A.D.), the Jews were driven out of the city during the ninth year of Claudius (50 A.D.) because of riots instigated by a Jew named Chrestus.

(2) Chrestus may be a reference to Christ. If that view is correct, the riots likely took place among the Jews because Jesus had been preached as the Messiah predicted in the Old Testament. However, Chrestus may have been a Jew with that name about whom we know nothing.

3. Paul's support while in Corinth.

a. The Corinthians did not pay him during his labors in their city (I Cor. 9:12, 15; II Cor. 11:8).

b. He made tents with Priscilla and Aquila (18:3). Later, in speaking to the Ephesian elders at Miletus, he said, "Yea, ye yourselves know, that these hands have ministered unto my necessities, and to them that were with me" (Acts 20:34). The Hebrews felt if a boy was not taught to work, he was trained to steal. Regardless of their profession, Jewish boys were taught a trade. That is why Paul, a learned rabbi, knew how to make tents.

c. He also received support from Macedonia, a Grecian province north of Corinth (II Cor. 11:9). The brethren who came from Macedonia with the funds were Timothy and Silas (Acts 18:5).

4. Paul was joined by Timothy and Silas at Corinth (18:5).

a. They had been left in Berea with orders to meet him at Athens (Acts 17:15).

b. Possibly, they went to him in Athens only to be sent back to Thessalonica (I Thess. 3:1-2).

c. However, they may not have gone to Athens. That would mean the "we" of I Thess. 3:1 is an editorial we (*i.e.* he used the plural in reference to himself). If this is correct, he sent word back to Berea instructing them to return to Thessalonica and they later joined him at Corinth.

5. The establishment of the Corinthian church.

a. The church was begun by Paul, Silas and Timothy (18:5).

    b. It was founded upon the preaching of Jesus as Christ (18:5; I Cor. 2:1-2).

    c. Results of the preaching.

    (1) Paul went to the Jews first (18:5; Rom. 1:16) but they rejected the message and he turned to the Gentiles (18:6; Acts 13:46). A stone (probably once located over a door) with the inscription, "Synagogue of the Hebrews," has been found in the Corinthian ruins. It is dated between 100 B.C. and 200 A.D. Perhaps it is a part of the very synagogue entered by Paul.

    (2) Many Gentiles accepted the gospel (18:7-8).

    (a) To become a Christian, one must hear, believe, and be baptized (18:8; Mk. 16:16). Crispus' conversion included baptism too (I Cor. 1:14).

    (b) It seems that Titius Justus (18:7, RSV) became a disciple. Generally, Romans had three names. Some think Justus' third name was Gaius (I Cor. 1:14; Rom. 16:23).

    (c) Crispus and Sosthenes are each called a "ruler of the synagogue" (18:8, 17). Perhaps they had several rulers of the synagogue in Corinth as in Pisidian Antioch (Acts 13:15). They may have been rulers in different synagogues or maybe after Crispus was converted, Sosthenes was appointed.

    (d) A Sosthenes is included in the salutation of I Corinthians (1:1). Possibly, this is the same man mentioned in Acts 18:17. In 1964, I found an inscription in the ruins of Corinth with the name of Sosthenes on it.

    6. Paul remained in Corinth for eighteen months (18:11).

    a. He was fearful and, apparently, ready to leave the city (18:9; I Cor. 2:3-5).

    b. God intervened by a vision, told him not to be afraid and, literally, to keep on speaking (18:9-10).

    (1) Other visions which Paul had.

    (a) On the road to Damascus (Acts 26:19).

    (b) In Jerusalem, following his conversion (Acts 22:17-21).

    (c) On the second journey at Troas (Acts 16:9).

    (d) In prison at Jerusalem (Acts 23:11).

(2) It seems that God granted him visions at extremely crucial times in his life.

7. Incident involving Gallio.

a. Because of the statement, "And Gallio cared for none of these things" (18:17, KJV), he is sometimes considered as an example of indifference. That is a gross misuse of the verse. Really, Gallio was kind to Paul by refusing to become involved in a religious matter (18:14-17).

b. Sosthenes was beaten (18:17). By whom?

(1) Greeks who saw that the Jews were trying to mistreat an innocent man (KJV).

(2) Roman lictors to drive him from the tribunal (RSV).

(3) Fellow Jews because they felt he bungled the case (RSV).

c. The place where this happened is called judgment seat, tribunal or bema. It still stands today.

d. More information on Gallio.

(1) He was the brother of Seneca, a well-known Roman philosopher.

(2) He was the adopted son of L. Junius Gallio and that accounts for his name.

(3) He killed himself in 65 A.D. Seneca was implicated in a plot to assassinate Nero. Although Gallio was innocent, Nero ordered him and Seneca to commit suicide or be killed. Gallio chose to take his own life.

8. The date for Paul's first visit to Corinth is fairly well determined in two ways.

a. The year Claudius drove the Jews from Rome was 50 A.D.

b. The Gallio inscription found in Delphi, Greece, indicates that he was made pro-consul of Achaia, the province where Corinth was located, in 51 A.D. Pro-consuls served for only one year and their terms of office began in July.

c. The date for Paul's first visit to Corinth is 50 to 52 A.D.

9. I and II Thessalonians were likely written from Corinth in 51 A.D. After returning to Thessalonica from Berea or Athens, Timothy later joined Paul in Corinth (see no. 4

above). On the basis of his report and some later develop-
ments, the Thessalonian epistles were written (I Thess.
3:1-10).

10. Erastus, a brother in Christ, was the city treasurer
at Corinth (II Tim. 4:20; Rom. 16:23). In the city's ruins, an
inscription has been found bearing the name of Erastus which
indicates that he laid a pavement at his own expense. Some
scholars think this is the Erastus referred to in the New
Testament.

B. Second Visit.

1. An account of this visit is not recorded in Acts,
however, it can be learned in II Corinthians (2:1-4; 12:14;
13:1-2).

2. Apparently, during Paul's ministry at Ephesus on
the third missionary journey, he learned of trouble at Corinth
and made a trip straight across the Aegean Sea to the city (see
a map).

3. Upon his arrival at Corinth, he experienced considerable difficulty with the brethren. It looks as though one
man had stirred up the congregation against him (II Cor.
2:5-8; 7:12).

4. Paul then returned to Ephesus and wrote his severe
letter to the Corinthians (II Cor. 2:3-4; 7:8-12).

5. The date for the second visit is ca. 54-55 A.D.

C. Third Visit (Acts 20:1-3; II Cor. 12:14; 13:1).

1. While in Macedonia (II Cor. 2:13; 7:5-7; 8:1; 9:2-4),
and before arriving in Greece or Achaia where Corinth was
located, he wrote our II Corinthians (likely, he was in Philippi
at the time).

2. He then went to Corinth and found that the trouble-
some situation was much improved.

3. While there, he wrote the letter to the Romans
(Rom. 15:26-27; Acts 20:1-4; 24:17).

4. Some Jews plotted against his life and he left (Acts
20:3).

5. The date for the third visit is ca. 55-56 A.D.

III. The Corinthian Correspondence.

  A. Corinthians A.

    1. It is mentioned at I Cor. 5:9.

    2. Its subject was that brethren were not to company (*i.e.* have fellowship) with fornicators who were church members (I Cor. 5:9-10).

    3. This letter was written about 53 A.D.

    4. The epistle has been lost.

  B. Corinthians B.

    1. This is our I Corinthian letter.

    2. It was written in response to a report from the house of Chloe (I Cor. 1:11) and a letter from the disciples at Corinth in which they had raised a number of questions for Paul to answer. Notice the expression, *"Now concerning* the things whereof ye wrote unto me" (I Cor. 7:1, 25; 8:1; 12:1; 16:1).

    3. The date for this epistle is about 54-55 A.D.

  C. Corinthians C.

    1. Likely, this is the severe letter mentioned in II Corinthians (2:3-4; 7:8, 12).

    2. Apparently, it was written following Paul's painful visit to Corinth (II Cor. 2:1-4).

    3. The date for the epistle is ca. 54-55 A.D.

    4. Some identify this letter with our I Corinthians.

      a. They think the offender of II Cor. 2:5-8; 7:12 is the incestuous man of I Cor. 5:1-7.

      b. Reply:

        (1) The basis for writing this letter, "out of much affliction and anguish of heart . . . with many tears" (II Cor. 2:4), better fits the situation described above than the circumstance out of which I Corinthians was written.

        (2) The epistle mentioned in II Cor. 2:1-4 was sent *in lieu* of a visit by Paul. However, I Corinthians was written as a *prelude* to Paul's visit (I Cor. 16:5-6).

    5. Others have identified this epistle with II Cor. 10-13. They feel that II Corinthians originally consisted of only nine chapters. They maintain that the severe letter (II Cor. 10-13) was written before II Corinthians and later added to it. There is *no textual evidence* to support this view.

    6. If the reasoning given above is correct, Corinthians C is also lost.

7. How does one deal with the matter of lost New Testament letters?

a. It should be admitted that we do not have every word written by inspiration in the first century. Obviously, we do not have the epistle referred to at I Cor. 5:9. Some think the epistle from Laodicea (Col. 4:16) is another lost letter. However, that does not necessarily follow. In the opinion of many scholars, the epistle from Laodicea is what we call Ephesians. The expression "at Ephesus" in Eph. 1:1 is lacking in many of the manuscripts (see RSV). There is a possibility that Ephesians is really a general epistle like James. Or, it could be the epistle from Laodicea. Of course, the epistle from Laodicea may not have been written by an inspired person.

b. God's providence has given the faith (Jude 3) which contains all things that pertain to life and godliness (II Pet. 1:3-4), thoroughly furnishes Christians for every good work and makes them complete (II Tim. 3:16-17). Everything essential for a full and complete communication from Almighty God is included in the New Testament.

c. Undoubtedly, inspired material which we do not have is duplicated in other New Testament writings. The message of Christ has not passed away (Lk. 21:33). We can place our utmost confidence in the word of God!

D. Corinthians D.

1. This is II Corinthians.

2. It was written in response to Titus' report concerning the situation at Corinth as he had found it (II Cor. 7:5-13).

3. It was written from Macedonia (II Cor. 2:12-13; 7:5; Acts 20:1-3).

4. The date for the book is ca. 55-56 A.D.

IV. A Reconstruction of Events and Letters

Dates

50-52 A. Paul's first visit to Corinth. He remained for eighteen months.

52 B. Apollos went to Corinth from Ephesus (Acts 19:1).

53 C. Paul, from Ephesus, wrote Corinthians A which dealt with the matter of refusing fellowship to Christians involved in sexual immorality (I Cor. 5: 9).

54 D. Paul received a report from Chloe's house concerning division in the Corinthian church. He also received a letter from Corinth asking a number of questions.

54-55 E. From Ephesus, Paul wrote Corinthians B (*i.e.* I Corinthians) in response to the report and letter he had received from Corinth.

54-55 F. Paul then sent Timothy and Erastus into Macedonia (Acts 19:22). He intended to follow them (Acts 19: 21; I Cor. 16:5-6), however, it seems that his plan was not carried out since he stayed in Asia for a while (Acts 19:22).

54-55 G. Paul learned of trouble in Corinth and crossed the Aegean Sea to deal with it. He then returned to Ephesus.

54-55 H. When back at Ephesus, Paul wrote the severe letter or Corinthians C to the church at Corinth (II Cor. 2:3-4).

55 I. Either the severe letter was carried by Titus or Paul sent him later to learn how the brethren had received it (II Cor. 2:12-13; 7:6-8). Apparently, Titus made his journey across the Aegean Sea to Corinth and was to return by land to meet Paul at Troas (II Cor. 2:12). This is implied from the fact that Paul, not finding Titus at Troas, went into Macedonia.

55-56 J. Paul left Troas and went into Macedonia where he met Titus who comforted him with a favorable report about how the Corinthians had responded to his severe letter (II Cor. 7:5-7).

55-56 K. Paul was united with Timothy in Macedonia (Acts 19:22; II Cor. 1:1).

55-56 L. Paul wrote Corinthians D (*i.e.* II Corinthians) in Macedonia (II Cor. 2:12-13; 7:5).
55-56 M. Paul made his third visit to Corinth (Acts 20:1-3; II Cor. 12:14).

V. Introduction to I Corinthians.

A. Author—Paul (1:1). Perhaps Sosthenes was his stenographer.

B. Place where written—Ephesus (16:8).

C. Date—ca. 54-55 A.D.

D. Occasion.

1. Report about division from the house of Chloe (1:11).

2. A letter containing questions received from the Corinthians (7:1; 8:1; 12:1; 16:1). The letter was probably sent to Paul by Stephanas, Fortunatus and Achaicus (16:17).

E. Theme—Church Problems.

F. Chapter Outline of the Book.

1. Division and Worldly Wisdom (1).
2. Wisdom of God (2).
3. The Folly of Following Men (3-4).
4. Sexual Immorality (5).
5. Going to Law with Brethren (6).
6. Marriage (7).
7. Eating Meats Offered to Idols (8, 10).
8. Paul's Defense of His Apostleship (9).
9. Disorders in Worship (11).
   a. Wearing of the Veil (11:1-16).
   b. The Lord's Supper (11:17-34).
10. Spiritual Gifts (12-14).
    a. The Gifts of the Spirit (12).
    b. How Long the Gifts were to Last (13).
    c. How the Gifts were to be Regulated (14).
11. Resurrection of the Dead (15).
12. Contribution (16).

BIBLIOGRAPHY

Adcock, A. K., *At the Feet of Paul*

Alford, H., *Commentary on the Epistles of St. Paul*

Baird, W., *The Corinthian Church—A Biblical Approach to Urban Culture*

Barrett, C. K., *A Commentary on the First Epistle to the Corinthians*

Barclay, W., *Letters to the Corinthians*

Barnes, A., *Notes on I Corinthians*

Beet, J., *A Commentary on the First Epistle to the Corinthians*

Conybeare, W. J. and Howson, J. S., *The Life and Epistles of St. Paul*

DeHoff, G. W., *Sermons on First Corinthians*

Dods, M., *The First Epistle to the Corinthians*

Driver, S. R. and Plummer, A., *The First Epistle of St. Paul to the Corinthians*

Drummond, H. J., *The Greatest Thing in the World*

Edwards, T. C., *A Commentary on the First Epistle to the Corinthians*

Farrar, F. W., *The Life and Work of St. Paul*

Farrar, F. W., *The First Epistle of Paul to the Corinthians*

Foster, J. J., *Epistles of St. Paul the Apostle to the Corinthians*

Goudge, H. L., *The First Epistle to the Corinthians*

Grosheide, F. W., *Commentary on the first Epistle to the Corinthians*

Hayes, D. A., *The Heights of Christian Love*

Hodge, C., *Exposition of the First Epistle to the Corinthians*

Hodge, C., *Exposition of the Second Epistle to the Corinthians*

Hughes, P. E., *Commentary on the Second Epistle to the Corinthians*

Jones, J. D., *The Greatest of These*

Kelcy, R., *First Corinthians*

Kennedy, J. H., *The Second and Third Epistles to the Corinthians*

Lange, J. P., *Commentary on the Holy Scriptures—Corinthians*

Lattey, C., *Readings in First Corinthians*

Lenski, R. C. H., *Interpretation of I and II Corinthians*
Lipscomb, D., *A Commentary on the New Testament Epistles* (vols. II, III)
Luck, G. C., *First Corinthians*
McGarvey, J. W., *Thessalonians, Corinthians, Galatians and Romans*
Menzies, A., *The Second Epistle of the Apostle Paul to the Corinthians*
Meyer, H. A. W., *Epistle to the Corinthians*
Moffatt, J., *The First Epistle of Paul to the Corinthians*
Morgan, G. C., *The Corinthian Letters of Paul*
Morris, L., *The First Epistle of Paul to the Corinthians*
Olshausen, H., *St. Paul's First and Second Epistles to the Corinthians*
Plummer, A., *Commentary on the Second Epistle of St. Paul to the Corinthians*
Robertson, A., *First Epistle of St. Paul to the Corinthians*
Robertson, F. W., *Expository Lectures on I and II Corinthians*
Ruler, A. A. V., *The Greatest of These is Love*
Stanley, A. P., *The Epistles of St. Paul to the Corinthians*
Strachan, R. H., *The Second Epistle of Paul to the Corinthians*
Tasker, R. V. G., *The Second Epistle of Paul to the Corinthians*
Thompson, J., *The Second Letter of Paul to the Corinthians*

Unpublished Theses*

Fulks, B. M., *I Corinthians Thirteen*
Goebel, D., *The Problem of I Corinthians 16:2 and Different Attempts to Solve it*
Johnson, J. R., *Worship in the Church at Corinth*
Noonan, J. R., *The New Testament Doctrine of Love*
Parker, J., *An Exegesis of I Corinthians 15:20-49*
Starling, N. W., *An Exegesis of 2 Corinthians 8:1-24*

---

* Harding College libraries in Searcy, Arkansas and Memphis, Tennessee.

II.

CHAPTER ONE

Division and Worldly Wisdom

Structure

I. Introduction (1:1-9).

A. Salutation (1:1-3).

1. Paul was called to be an apostle of Christ by the will of God (1:1).

a. Jesus appeared to Paul on the road to Damascus (Acts 9:15-16) to qualify him for the apostleship (Acts 1:22; 26:16-18). Apparently, his call came shortly after his conversion in Damascus (Acts 9:17-22; 22:12-16; Gal. 1:15-17).

b. The statement appears here to show that he was writing by apostolic authority and because the authenticity of his apostleship had been questioned by some (9:1-3; II Cor. 10-13). He also made a defense of his apostleship in the first two chapters of Galatians.

2. Sosthenes, our brother (1:1). For more information about him, see the introductory material.

3. To the church of God at Corinth (1:2).

a. "Church of God" appears eight times in the KJV (Acts 20:28; I Cor. 1:2; 10:32; 11:22; 15:9; II Cor. 1:1; Gal. 1:13; I Tim. 3:15). Acts 20:28 is "church of the Lord" in ASV.

23

"Churches of God" appears three times in the New Testament (11:16; I Thess. 2:14; II Thess. 1:4).

b. Other designations for the church are "churches of the saints" (14:33), "churches of Christ" (Rom. 16:16), "church of the firstborn" (although Jesus is the firstborn from the dead, the expression here does not refer to him since the language in the original is firstborn *ones*) (Heb. 12:23), "churches of Asia" (16:19), "churches of Galatia" (16:1; Gal. 1:2), "churches of Judea" (Gal. 1:22), "church of the Laodiceans" (Col. 4:16), "church of the Thessalonians" (I Thess. 1:1) and "the church" (most of the time it is described in this way) (6:4; 11:18; Eph. 1:22).

c. Any expression which sets forth biblical truth concerning the church may be used in reference to it. It is the New Testament church, blood-bought church, rock-founded church, Hadean-proof church, age-lasting church, first century church, universal church, apostolic church, Spirit-filled church, Godly church, Christly church, sanctified church, holy church, etc.

d. There are at least two ways in which born again people can become denominational.

(1) By using a biblical expression solely and exclusively to name the children of God. The word denomination is from the Latin "denomen" which means to name. When people name themselves by using only one biblical designation for the church, they are denominational. Those who speak of "Church of Christ" homes, "Church of Christ" members, "Church of Christ" preachers, "Church of Christ" teaching and "Church of Christ" colleges are denominational in their thinking and speech whether they realize it or not. It is very difficult for one to convince another of the sinfulness of denominationalism while embracing it himself. Our words betray us. Many have become denominational who profess opposition to denominationalism. Brethren can avoid falling into this trap by using many different expressions (all in harmony with the word of God) in reference to those who constitute the church.

(2) By applying a scriptural expression to only a part of those who have been born again. When this is done, a biblical designation is given an unbiblical application. All any sect claims to be is a *part* of God's family. However, the

church of the New Testament includes *all* who have obeyed the fundamentals of the gospel. When one speaks of the church, unless all of the reborn are included (although some may rightly be outside his immediate fellowship), he is denominational in his language. This does not mean one endorses any unscriptural teaching or practice because he recognizes that a given person or faction is to be included in God's universal church.

4. To the sanctified in Christ who are called to be saints (1:2).

a. This statement, in connection with Paul's condemnation of the sin in the church at Corinth, clearly refutes the view that sanctification means sinless perfection (held by several Holiness groups).

(1) Those who hold the erroneous concept mentioned above teach that one is saved, baptized in the Holy Spirit, sanctified and then made sinlessly perfect.

(2) Another illustration which indicates that such is false can be seen in the fact that Aaron and his sons were *sanctified* (Ex. 29:44) but Nadab and Abihu, two of those sons, *sinned* and were destroyed (Lev. 10:1-2).

b. This statement also refutes the Roman Catholic concept of sainthood.

(1) Catholic theologians admit that all of God's people are saints but they also have a special use for the word. The qualifications necessary for one to be a saint in this unique way are death, miracles wrought through the intercession of the dead one and investigation and canonization by the church.

(2) The saints to whom Paul wrote were alive (Phil. 1:1; Col. 1:12; Acts 9:32, 41; 26:10; Rev. 13:7, 10). There is no biblical authority for the unique way Catholics use the word.

c. The church is sanctified and saints compose its membership.

(1) Saint is from the Greek "hagios." One sanctified has been set apart for the Lord (Ex. 13:2, 12). He is holy, peculiar or different not on the basis of moral character but by virtue of his belonging to God (Ex. 19:16). "This sainthood is

not an attainment, it is a state into which God in grace calls men" (W. E. Vine, *An Expository Dictionary of New Testament Words,* vol. II, p. 226). Someone has said that faithful Christians are "positionally perfect and experientially imperfect." Of course, every saint should strive to live the righteous life.

(2) Obviously, one must be a member of the church to be a saint and thus to be saved (Eph. 1:22-23; 5:23, 25-26).

5. With all in every place who call on the name of Jesus Christ our Lord (1:2).

a. Every place may be limited to every place in Achaia (II Cor. 1:1).

b. Call upon the name of Jesus Christ our Lord.

(1) This does not mean prayer to the Lord which refuses to obey his will (Matt. 7:21; Lk. 6:46).

(2) It does mean obedience in a prayerful attitude.

(a) It is involved in obedience to the first principles of the gospel which includes baptism (Acts 2:21, 38; 22:16; Rom. 10:13; I Pet. 3:21 in RSV).

(b) It is also involved in the obedience which characterizes the Christian life (Acts 9:14, 21; II Tim. 2:22). It is used this way in the verse under consideration.

6. Grace and peace (1:3)

a. That was Paul's customary greeting (II Cor. 1:2; Rom. 1:7). In addressing Timothy and Titus, he used "grace, *mercy* and peace" (I Tim. 1:2; II Tim. 1:2; Tit. 1:4). Likely, this reflects the great love he had for them.

b. Grace always appears before peace in the greeting. There may be significance in the order. Men cannot have God's peace until they first experience his saving grace.

c. Grace was the Greek greeting and peace ("Shalom" in Hebrew) was the Jewish greeting.

B. Commendation (1:4-9).

1. Paul commended before he condemned. John did the same in writing to the seven churches in Asia. Probably, inspired men made that approach for at least two reasons.

a. It is only fair to commend people for their good points as well as denounce them for their bad ones.

b. Others will more likely listen to criticism if their good traits are also acknowledged.

2. Paul thanked God on their behalf (1:4-7).

a. Because they had been given God's grace by Jesus Christ (1:4).

b. Because they had been enriched in Christ by spiritual gifts (1:5-7).

(1) They were not lacking in any of the gifts (1:7; 12:8-10).

(2) The purpose of the gifts was to confirm the word of God (1:6; Mk. 16:20; Heb. 2:1-4).

3. The faithfulness of the Godhead (1:8-9).

a. Jesus would confirm or sustain (RSV) them blameless (guiltless, RSV) until his coming (1:8). Such was done by his blood on the condition that they walked in the light of truth (1 Jno. 1:7).

b. God had called them into the fellowship of his Son (1:9). That call came by the gospel, God's power to save (II Thess. 2:14; Rom. 1:16).

c. *Paul's point:* As God had been faithful to call them, Jesus would be faithful to sustain them to the end.

C. This section (1:1-9) shows that Paul was dominated by thoughts of Deity. God appears six times. Christ is used nine times. Lord appears five times (six in RSV). One of his favorite expressions, "our Lord Jesus Christ" (or "Jesus Christ, our Lord"), is used five times.

II. Division (1:10-17).

A. Plea for unity (1:10-11).

1. Strong plea.

a. Beseech (KJV) or Appeal (RSV).

b. "By the name of our Lord Jesus Christ" (*i.e.* by his authority, Acts 4:12). "In this Epistle Paul has already used the name of Jesus nine times, thus emphasizing its virtue before he uses it as a symbol of supreme authority: as Chrysostom says, 'he nails them to this name' " (J. W. McGarvey, *Commentary on Thessalonians, Corinthians, Galatians and Romans,* p. 52).

2. The plea itself.

a. Negatively—"That there be no divisions among you."

b. Positively—"Be perfectly joined together." "He wishes them to be *knit together*. The word he uses is a medical word which is used of knitting together bones that have been fractured, or joining together a joint that has been dislocated. The disunion is unnatural and must be cured for the sake of the health and the efficiency of the body of the Church" (W. Barclay, *The Letters to the Corinthians*, p. 15).

(1) "Ye all speak the same thing." This can be achieved today by speaking where the Bible speaks and remaining silent where the Bible is silent. Men should bind upon one another only those things clearly revealed in Scripture.

(2) Be of "the same mind." If each saint has the mind of Christ (2:16, Phil. 2:5), they will be of the same mind.

(3) Be of "the same judgment." Judgment ("gnome" in Greek) refers to opinion. For ideal and perfect unity, Christians who express themselves should have the same opinion. When opinions differ, it is better that men hold them as private property and remain silent. Opinions pressed upon others as God's word have been productive of many useless divisions in the body of Christ.

3. The plea was based on a report from Chloe's house (1:11).

a. Chloe (a feminine word in Greek) was a well-known Christian woman at Corinth.

b. Were those of Chloe's house unchristian in reporting the divisions to Paul? When is it right to report others? To whom should such reports be made? What standard should disciples follow—one authorized by Jesus or one composed by gangsters?

B. The Corinthian brethren were divided because they followed men (1:12-13).

1. They were good men who taught the truth. It is wrong to be divided over favorite preachers.

2. A *theory* concerning the division. The intellectuals followed Apollos (see Acts 18:24), the Jews and humbler classes followed Peter and the Gentiles and those who strongly emphasized grace followed Paul.

3. It has been suggested that some had a wrong attitude in being a part of the Christ group (II Cor. 10:7). However, they were probably correct in their views.

    a. Consider the questions—"Was Paul crucified for you or were you baptized in the name of Paul?"

    b. *Paul's point:* Two events were necessary for the Corinthians to belong to him—his crucifixion on their behalf and their being baptized in his name. Since Christ had been crucified for them and they had been baptized in his name, they did belong to him (1:12).

C. Those whom Paul had baptized at Corinth (1:14-16).

    1. Crispus (see Acts 18:8).

    2. Gaius (see introductory material on Acts 18:7). Is he the same as the one to whom III John was written?

    3. Household of Stephanas.

        a. They were the first converts in Achaia (16:15). Perhaps Paul baptized them before Timothy and Silas arrived at Corinth (see Paul's first visit in the introductory material). Others have suggested that he baptized them elsewhere in Achaia and they later moved to Corinth.

        b. Other household conversions.

        (1) Lydia and her household (Acts 16:15).

        (2) The jailor and his household (Acts 16:33-34).

        c. Household conversions do not uphold the view of infant baptism.

        (1) There are many households which have no infants.

        (2) The baptism of the great commission must be preceded by teaching (Matt. 28:18-20), belief of the gospel (Mk. 16:15-16) and repentance (Lk. 24:46-47; Acts 2:38). Since infants cannot be taught and are incapable of belief and repentance, they are not subjects of New Testament baptism.

    4. He may have baptized some he could not recall. It is not important to know whom you have baptized or who baptized you. God keeps the record. Furthermore, the validity of one's immersion does not depend on the administrator. What is important is the sinner's sincere acceptance of Christ as Lord and Savior.

D. Paul's mission was to preach the gospel (1:17).

1. False position drawn from this verse: Major premise—Christ sent me not to baptize. Minor premise—Christ did send me to preach the gospel. Conclusion—Therefore, baptism is no part of the gospel. Since baptism is not a part of the gospel, it is not essential to salvation (Rom. 1:16).

2. In light of this position, "ad hominem" or to the man conclusions can be directed to those who deny the necessity of baptism for salvation but believe one must be baptized for church membership. There are very few who do not maintain that some "form" of baptism is essential to church membership.

a. If Paul was not sent to baptize, he was not sent to make (supply the name of the denominationalist who made the argument above). If he had lived from the first century until now, he would not have made one.

b. If baptism is no part of the gospel, then making (supply the name of the denominationalist who made the argument) is not part of the gospel.

c. If baptism is no part of the gospel, then the (supply the name of the denominationalist who made the argument) church is not a gospel church since one must be baptized to get into it.

3. Some questions for those who deny that baptism is essential to salvation.

a. If Paul was not sent to baptize, did he sin in baptizing Crispus, Gaius and the household of Stephanas (1:14, 16)?

b. If Paul had been sent to baptize, would this mean baptism is essential to salvation? John the Baptist was sent to baptize (Jno. 1:33). Was his baptism necessary for salvation? Those under the great commission were sent to baptize (Matt. 28:18-20). Is the baptism of the great commission essential to salvation? Did Paul labor under the great commission?

4. What 1:17 does not say.

a. That baptism is no part of the gospel. Wherever Paul went, he taught people to be baptized (Acts 16:13-15, 31-34; 18:8; 19:1-6). In telling them to be baptized, he was preaching the gospel or he was teaching something other than the gospel, in which case he placed himself under God's condemnation (Gal. 1:6-9). Jesus said that as a result of gospel preaching men would know to believe and be baptized (Mk. 16:15-16). Hence, baptism is a part of the gospel!

b. That Paul was thankful there were only a few baptized in Corinth. If he was thankful that only a few were baptized, would he not have been more grateful had *none* been baptized? If he was thankful that only a few had been baptized, then he was grateful that only a few (supply the name of the denominationalist who made the argument above but believes baptism is necessary for church membership) had been made. Every believer in Corinth had been baptized (1:14; Acts 18:8). What Paul said was that he was glad he had baptized only a few personally lest some claim they had been baptized in his name.

5. What 1:17 means.

a. A corrected syllogism: Major premise—Christ sent me not to baptize. Minor Premise—Christ did send me to preach the gospel. Conclusion—Therefore, to baptize is no part of to preach the gospel.

b. The false syllogism given earlier is illogical because of the introduction of "baptism" in the conclusion, a word which does not appear in the major or minor premises. Logically, nothing can appear in the conclusion which is not in either premise. To place in the conclusion what is not in the premise is known as a "fourth term" fallacy. The word which should be used in the conclusion is baptize (verb) rather than baptism (noun).

c. Explanation of 1:17.

(1) This may be an ellipsis (*i.e.* omission of words which must be supplied). If this view is correct, the meaning would be "Christ sent me not *only* to baptize, but *also* to preach the gospel" (for other elliptical statements, see Jno. 6:27; 12:44; I Tim. 5:23).

(2) It is more likely that Paul was saying Christ did not send him to personally baptize but he did send him to personally preach. As a general rule, Paul relied on others to do the baptizing (see Jno. 4:1-2). I have preached in meetings with more than two hundred baptisms without once getting into the water. The brethren called me to preach rather than to baptize. However, in every sermon, I urged the unsaved to be baptized.

d. Really, 1:17 shows the importance of baptism. "Paul's thankfulness that he baptized so few at Corinth is not an undervaluing of baptism, though this is a favorite argument of anti-immersionists. He does not deny that he preached baptism, but only says that he did not there (generally) administer the rite with his own hands. He does not deny that the 'Lord sent him to preach' baptism, but does deny that his great mission was to baptize. It is evident from the narratives of Acts 16 and 18 that he did preach baptism, at Corinth and elsewhere, as a part of the gospel, and that those who believed under his preaching were immediately baptized. But he preferred, when practicable, that someone else should officiate, just as now an 'evangelist' (so called) might for the best of reasons, prefer that pastors should do the baptizing, while himself strenuously insisting on baptism in his preaching. The bearing of this passage on the subject in hand is exactly opposite to the inference drawn from it. It is this: Baptism was such an important thing in the view of the early Christians that Paul congratulated himself in having baptized so few at Corinth, lest some should say that he 'baptized in his own name'—lest the faith and reference due to Christ might be 'divided'—and a part be transferred to the distinguished administrator. How could this have been, if baptism had been a mere symbol of no vital consequence?" (J. W. Wilmarth, "Baptism and Remission," *Baptist Quarterly*, July, 1877, pp. 312-313).

III. Man's Wisdom Versus God's Wisdom (1:18-31).

A. Conflict between man's wisdom and God's wisdom (1:18-26).

1. The introduction of this thought is at 1:17b where it is pointed out that man's wisdom makes the cross of Christ of none effect.

2. Two classes of people (1:18).

a. Those who were perishing. To them, the preaching of the cross was foolishness (Greek "moria" from which we get moron and moronic). They were not saying the gospel is laughable but stupid, dull and insipid. They felt the message was not challenging to people of their high intellectual caliber.

b. Those who were being saved. To them, the word of the cross was God's power (Greek "dunamis" from which we get dynamite, dynamo and dynamic). God's power is described as Christ (1:24), Christ crucified (2:2, 5), word of the cross (1:18) and the gospel (Rom. 1:16). The cross is God's power since it is the means by which we are saved. It is also a power because it expresses God's love which causes rebellious men to surrender their hearts to his will (II Cor. 5:14; I Jno. 4:19).

3. The inability of human wisdom to save (1:19-26).

a. Such is taught in the Old Testament (1:19; Isa. 29:14).

b. Rhetorical questions—"Where is the wise? Where is the scribe? Where is the disputer of this world?" (1:20). Wise is a general term which can be applied to both Jews and Gentiles. Scribe refers to a Jew trained in the law (Matt. 7:29). A debater or disputer was a Gentile questioner, sophist or philosopher. The writer was saying that those people were not in God's family. Although they rejected the Lord's way as foolishness, they failed to provide a way by which men could be reconciled to God.

c. The world by wisdom knew not God (1:21) because its approach was wrong (1:22-23).

(1) The Jews required signs (Matt. 12:39; 16:4) and Christ was a stumblingblock to them (I Pet. 2:7-8).

(2) The Greeks (i.e. Gentiles) sought wisdom and Christ was foolishness to them. Because Paul preached Jesus and the resurrection, Athenian philosophers called him a babbler (Acts 17:18).

(3) To those who were not worldly oriented but sensitive to the will of God, Christ was the power and wisdom of God (1:24).

d. An appeal to their own experience (1:26). Not many of the wise, mighty and noble are called.

(1) A Christian lady of noble birth once said she had been saved by an "m." She explained that Paul taught not many noble are called rather than not any.

(2) Some of the powerful people of the first century did accept the gospel. Erastus, city treasurer at Corinth (Rom. 16:23), Sergius Paulus, pro-consul of Cyprus (Acts 13:12), Dionysius, a judge in the court of the Areopagus at Athens

(Acts 17:34), the treasurer of Ethiopia (Acts 8:35-40) and some in Caesar's household (Phil. 4:22) became Christians. Nevertheless, the mighty ones were few and far between in the apostolic church.

      e. *Conclusion:* God's way is superior to man's way (1:25; see Rom. 11:33-36).

B. Why God has chosen foolish things (1:27-31).

    1. The contrast between God's way and man's way (1:27-28).

      a. God chose the foolish things to confound the wise.

      b. God chose the weak things to confound the mighty.

      c. God chose the base things, despised things and things which are not to bring to nought things that are.

    2. Why God made those choices (1:29-31).

      a. To exclude human boasting (1:29; Eph. 2:8-9; Rom. 3:27).

      b. To cause men to glory in the Lord (1:31; Eph. 3:21; Gal. 6:14).

III.

CHAPTER TWO

The Wisdom of God

Structure

I. Central Theme of God's Wisdom (2:1-5).
  A. What Paul preached (2:1-2).
    1. Negatively—He did not use excellency of speech (lofty words, RSV) or enticing words of man's wisdom (2:1, 4). He did not make a worldly-wise approach to his hearers. No attempt was made to overpower them with eloquence.
    2. Positively—He preached Jesus Christ and him crucified (2:2) which was a demonstration of the Spirit and power (2:4). This does not mean Paul discussed no theme other than the personality of Christ. He also preached repentance (Acts 20:21), faith (Acts 20:21), baptism (Acts 18:8), kingdom of God (Acts 20:25), necessity of leading a life worthy of God (I Thess. 2:11-12), anything that was profitable (Acts 20:20) and the whole counsel of God (Acts 20:27). However, all of his preaching revolved around Christ. Jesus was the center and circumference of his presentation. For other illustrations, study Philip's preaching Christ to the Samaritans (Acts 8:5, 12) and to the Ethiopian (Acts 8:35-40). In each instance, matters other than the Lord's personality were set forth but they were all Christ-related.

B. Paul's condition while preaching at Corinth (2:3).

1. Weakness. He had a lack of confidence in himself.

2. Fear (see Acts 18:9-10). He was afraid they would not *hear* him and that some would *hurt* him.

3. Much trembling. He may have literally trembled like Belshazzar (Dan. 5:6) or he may have used the expression figuratively to suggest the anxiety he had experienced (II Cor. 7:15).

C. Why Paul preached Christ and him crucified (2:5).

1. Negatively—That their faith might not stand in the wisdom of men.

2. Positively—That their faith might stand in the power of God.

D. Some practical lessons.

1. The basis for division at Corinth was worldly wisdom which expressed itself in following men. Since Paul did not preach worldly wisdom, he was not responsible for the divisions.

2. To convert people, we must preach Christ and him crucified! Evangelistic preaching is not Christ as an example, a good man, a great prophet or a master teacher but Christ crucified.

3. God's power is in Jesus and him crucified. If Christians are to be powerful, their teaching and faith must be centered in the crucified and risen Lord. Faith in a lovely church edifice, a local congregation, a strong church program, a fluent preacher or one's parents is powerless and unavailing.

4. Success in converting others does not depend solely on our skill as teachers and preachers. The power is in the message!

II. *God's Wisdom Revealed by the Holy Spirit* (2:6-13).

A. The wisdom Paul preached (2:6-9).

1. Negatively—Not the wisdom of men (2:6, 13).

2. Positively—The wisdom of God in a mystery or hidden wisdom (2:7).

a. Old fashioned Calvinism teaches that the gospel (or wisdom of God in a *mystery*) cannot be understood by the unconverted. A Calvinist once said an unsaved man might as well be reading an almanac as the Bible. That viewpoint is incorrect.

(1) Questions—Why did Paul preach to the Corinthians what they could not understand in their unsaved condition? Why make any attempt at fulfilling the great commission by preaching the gospel to the lost world today?

(2) The message was God's hidden wisdom or mystery at one time because it had not been revealed (2:7; Eph. 3:9) but it is no longer a mystery or hidden because it has now been revealed (2:10; Rom. 16:25-26). Vine, in defining "mustarion," the original word translated as mystery, wrote: "In the New Testament it denotes, not the mysterious (as with the English word), but that which, being outside the range of unassisted natural apprehension, can be made known only by Divine revelation, and is made known in a manner and at a time appointed by God, and to those only who are illumined by His Spirit. In the ordinary sense a mystery implies knowledge withheld; its Scriptural significance is truth revealed. Hence the terms especially associated with the subject are 'made known,' 'manifested,' 'revealed,' 'preached,' 'understand,' 'dispensation' " (vol. III, p. 97). Of course, the gospel is a "mystery" to some because they are blinded by Satan (II Cor. 3:14; 4:3-4), however, that is not Paul's meaning here.

   b. The mystery or hidden wisdom of God.

     (1) Was ordained before time began (2:7).

     (2) Was ordained for the glory of the saints (2:7).

     (3) Did not originate in the mind of man (2:9).

     (4) Is wonderful beyond human imagination (2:9). Repeatedly, this verse has been misapplied to heaven. In context, it refers to God's message or revelation.

     (5) Is salvation through Christ for *both* Jews and Gentiles (Eph. 3:6; Rom. 16:25-26).

B. The wisdom Paul preached was made known by the Spirit (2:10-13).

   1. The Spirit is competent to reveal God's wisdom because he knows the mind of God (2:10-11). The omniscience of the Spirit is here affirmed.

   2. The Spirit has revealed God's mind (2:10-11) through the *apostles* and *prophets* (Eph. 3:3, 5) who are called "us" in 2:10.

3. Inspired men taught the message in words of the Spirit (2:13). In Weymouth's translation, the verse says, "This we also utter, not in language which man's wisdom teaches, but in that which the Spirit teaches, *adapting spiritual words to spiritual truths*" (emphasis mine, J.A.). A footnote in the RSV gives the latter part of the verse as "interpreting spiritual truths in spiritual language." In the commentary already cited, McGarvey wrote: "Here again we have a clear claim to inspiration, and not only so, but verbal inspiration. Paul did not reason after the manner of worldly philosophers, but imparted his truth under the guidance of the Spirit, who taught him the words to use, so that he taught spiritual truths with spiritual words, a fitting combination" (p. 61). Obviously, the supervision of the Holy Spirit went beyond the concepts imparted even to the words employed by inspired writers. New Testament penmen claimed *plenary, verbal, inspiration* for their writings.

a. Plenary is from the Latin "plenus" which means full. All scripture is fully inspired by God (II Tim. 3:16).

b. Verbal refers to words. "Knowing this first, that no prophecy of the scripture is of any private interpretation. For the prophecy came not in old time by the will of man: but holy men of God spake as they were moved by the Holy Ghost" (II Pet. 1:20-21). "The men who spoke from God are here declared, therefore, to have been taken up by the Holy Spirit and brought by His power to the goal of His choosing. The things which they spoke under this operation of the Spirit were therefore His things, not theirs" (B. B. Warfield, *Inspiration and Authority of the Bible,* p. 137). The inspired writers made no mistakes. They were guided into all truth (Jno. 16:13). Their message was inerrant.

c. "Inspiration of God" appears only one time in the New Testament (II Tim. 3:16). The expression is from the Greek "theopneustos" which means God breathed (see Gen. 2:7). The message, therefore, has resulted from God's breathing.

d. "The Church, then, has held from the beginning that the Bible is the Word of God in such a sense that its words, though written by men and bearing indelibly impressed upon them the marks of their human origin, were written, nevertheless, under such an influence of the Holy Ghost as to be also the words of God, the adequate expression of His mind and will. It has always been recognized that this conception of co-authorship implies the Spirit's superintendence extends to the choice of the words by the human authors (verbal inspiration), and preserves its product from everything inconsistent with a divine authorship—thus securing, among other things that entire truthfulness which is everywhere presupposed in and asserted for Scripture by the Biblical writers (inerrancy)" (Warfield, p. 173).

III. Reception of God's Wisdom (2:14-16).

A. Who is the natural (KJV) or unspiritual (RSV) man?

1. The Greek is "psuchikos" which is defined as "belonging to the 'psuche,' soul (as the lower part of the immaterial in man), natural, physical, describes the man in Adam and what pertains to him" (Vine, vol. III, p. 103). The word appears in Jas. 3:15 and Jude 19 and is translated in both places as sensual in KJV and unspiritual and worldly in RSV. Apparently, it refers to one who is governed by the instincts of the sensuous nature (*i.e.* he acts as though he does not have a spirit created in the image of God).

2. Interpretations.

a. Any unconverted man. This is the view of Calvinism. Vine, in the latter part of his definition, inclined in that direction. Many in the Protestant world believe that the unsaved person cannot understand the things of the Spirit until he receives a direct and miraculous operation of the Spirit on his heart to free him from his "totally depraved" nature. They maintain he can then understand the gospel and yield to the invitation of Christ. This concept is incapable of being supported by the word of God.

b. Any unconverted man who rejects the message of the Spirit. This point of view can be supported from the context and the definition above.

c. An uninspired man. Some think 2:14-16 is discussing the contrast between an uninspired and an inspired person. If the definition for "psuchikos" given above is correct, it would be virtually impossible to accept this interpretation.

B. Who is the spiritual man?

    1. The Greek is "pneumatikos" which means "one who is filled with and governed by the Spirit of God" (J. H. Thayer, *Greek-English Lexicon of the New Testament,* p. 523).

    2. Interpretations. In contrast to the interpretations given to the unspiritual man, this person may be:

        a. Any converted man.

        b. Any man who accepts the Spirit's teaching.

        c. An inspired man.

C. Study of the context.

    1. The natural man.

        a. Receives not the things (or gifts) of the Spirit.

        b. The things (or gifts) of the Spirit are foolishness to him.

        c. He cannot understand the things of the Spirit because they are spiritually discerned.

        d. Is he

        (1) Any unconverted person? No, for there are many unconverted people whom the statements in "a," "b," and "c," will not necessarily fit.

        (2) An uninspired person? No, for the statements in "b" and "c" will not necessarily fit him.

        (3) The unconverted who rejects the Spirit's teaching. Yes, for all of the statements above will fit him.

    2. The spiritual man.

        a. Judges all things.

        b. Has the mind of Christ.

        c. Is to be judged by no one. Judge has been taken in at least two different ways.

        (1) Some feel that he is judged of no one in the sense of another determining that he is in need of instruction. From this understanding, the following has been offered: No one can instruct the Lord. The spiritual man has the mind of the Lord. Therefore, no one can instruct the spiritual man. This leads to the conclusion that the spiritual man is an inspired person.

        (2) "The spiritual man cannot be discerned or *estimated aright* [emphasis mine, J.A.] by those who are not spiritual" (C. Hodge, *Commentary on I Corinthians,* p. 45).

d. Is he

(1) Any converted man? That is possible but not likely.

(2) An inspired man? Perhaps but there is much in the context against the view.

(3) The one who accepts the Spirit's teaching. Yes, because everything in the context will fit him. Hodge's definition of judge (*i.e.* estimated aright) must be accepted, if this view is correct.

3. Raymond Kelcy beautifully summed up the matter concerning the natural and spiritual man as follows: "In view of Paul's discussion in chapter one, it is evident that the 'natural' man is the worldly-wise man whose horizon is bound by the interests of this life. In such a man there is a complete absence of spiritual discernment. It is the spiritually-minded man who has the ability to discern things spiritual for, . . . such a man has ability to discern or judge all things. He is able to recognize the spiritual and to place the material things in their proper place. He is able to discern the true status of the 'natural' man, and he himself is judged of no one, that is, the natural man knows nothing about the spiritual man and knows nothing about the wealth he possesses" (*First Corinthians,* p. 15).

IV.

CHAPTER THREE

The Folly of Following Men

Structure

I. It is Carnal to Follow men (3:1-4).

A. Description of those involved in the divisions of the church (3:1-4).

1. They were not spiritual (3:1). That had been their condition shortly after their conversion and during the time Paul had worked in Corinth. It is implied that he then had further indication of their not being spiritual. Spiritual is the plural form of the same word appearing in 2:15. Obviously, they had been spiritual to the point of initially accepting the gospel, in contrast with those who had rejected it (that is the point in 2:14-16). Furthermore, they had been spiritual during the early days after their conversion because they had possessed the mind of Christ (2:16) and had experienced the Christian unity known to those governed by the Spirit of God (see Thayer's definition of "pneumatikos" given earlier). On the other hand, they had not been spiritual in the sense of

43

being full-grown, spiritually mature men and women (see Gal. 6:1). As a matter of fact, they were only babes in Christ during that period immediately following their conversion (3:1). The divisions which had arisen in the church after Paul's departure surely indicated that those in the various parties were not then being governed by the Spirit of God. Hence, the implication is that they were not then spiritual.

2. They were carnal or men of the flesh (3:1, 3).

a. It should be noted that carnal does not translate "psuchikos," used at 2:14 to describe the natural man who rejected the gospel. Had Paul used that word, it would have meant those addressed were not even in Christ.

b. The words translated as carnal (KJV) are the plural forms of "sarkinos" (3:1) and "sarkikos" (3:3). Possibly, they are used interchangeably but that is doubtful. It seems more likely that the second is an intensification of the first. Due to their short time in the church, they were "sarkinos" (*i.e.* weak, earthly and lacking in spirituality) in that they acted like ordinary men composed of *flesh* and blood and they were "sarkikos" (*i.e.* dominated by the lower nature and opposed to the spiritual) in that they behaved as rebellious men ruled by their own stubborn wills. Lenski described the differences in these words: "He makes a fine distinction when he now calls the Corinthians 'sarkikoi.' At one time, in their early days, they were 'sarkinoi,' still largely made up of flesh because their spiritual part was still in the infant stage. They could then not help it, they were 'fleshy' in heart, mind, and life and yet giving promise that they would soon outgrow that stage. But something has interfered with their development, Paul finds that they are now 'sarkikoi,' 'fleshly,' people who ought to obey the true spiritual norm and yet by a choice of their own obey the norm of the flesh. The difference between the two terms is: 'fleshy,' and you cannot help it; 'fleshly,' and you can but do not help it. 'Fleshy,' you carry a bad load but will soon be rid of most of it; 'fleshly,' you follow a bad norm and refuse to get rid of it. Paul approves of neither condition but cannot especially blame them for the former whereas he must decidedly blame them for the latter" (p. 124).

c. Proof of their carnality: They were guilty of envy, strife and boasting about belonging to the parties of men (3:3-4).

d. Envy (or jealousy), strife, dissension and the party spirit are works of the flesh and those who practice such will not inherit the kingdom of God (Gal. 5:19-21, RSV). Obviously, some of the Corinthians were in danger of eternal condemnation. Practically speaking, there is no difference between those who are "sarkikoi" or carnal (3:3) and those who are "psuchikoi" or natural (2:14). The former is used in reference to men who rebelled against the Lord after having become his children; the latter describes men who rebelled against God and never became his children. Really, the attitude of the two groups was identical.

3. They were babes in Christ (3:1-2).

a. Proof: In the past Paul had fed them with milk because of their spiritual infancy and inability to partake of meat (or solid food) and they were still in the *same* condition (for other passages dealing with the milk and meat of the word, see Heb. 5:12-14 and I Pet. 2:2).

b. Explanations of the difference between meat and milk.

(1) Content of the message—Meat being the deep and profound truths of God's word and milk pertaining to the surface and simple matters in the Bible.

(2) Method of presentation—Meat being a simple statement of the facts and milk being an involved explanation for simplification.

II. *The Place of Teachers in God's Plan* (3:5-9).

A. Teachers were:

1. Ministers or servants through whom they had believed (3:5).

2. Men gifted, endowed or assigned by God to teach (3:5; 4:7; Rom. 12:6-7).

3. Not anything in themselves (II Cor. 12:11), apart from Christ (Jno. 15:5) and in comparison to God who gives the increase (3:6-7).

4. One (KJV) or equal (RSV) (3:8). If the word (Greek "en") is taken as "one," it is to be understood that teachers

were one thing or instrument in God's hand for the accomplishment of his will. They were not to be considered as leaders of rival factions. Rather than magnifying their individual differences, the Source and purpose of their work should have been considered. If the word is taken as "equal," it is to be understood that teachers were equal before the Lord and one should not have been placed above another by the Corinthians.

5. Men who will be rewarded according to their labors (3:8) rather than by fame, talent or success in reaching people with the gospel.

6. Laborers together with God (3:9). They do not work alone (Matt. 28:20).

B. The Corinthian Christians belonged to God (3:9).

1. They were God's husbandry (field, tilled land or vineyard). That goes back to the figure of planting and watering (3:6-7).

2. They were God's building (structure or temple). That looks forward to what is to follow (3:10-17; Eph. 2:19-22; I Pet. 2:5).

C. *Point of this section* (3:5-9): Teachers are God's instruments. Christians are God's people. Therefore, instead of honoring teachers, honor God!

III. Christ, the True Foundation (3:10-15).

A. Paul, a wise master builder, had laid the true foundation during the time he worked at Corinth (3:10-11).

1. He accomplished that task by faithfully preaching Jesus Christ (3:11; 2:1-2). As a general rule, he did not build upon another man's foundation (Rom. 15:20).

2. He did his work according to the grace (commission, RSV) of God given to him (3:10). Since the Greek aorist tense is used, it must be understood that the grace was given to him in the *past*. The expression has been explained in the following ways:

a. The grace given to him when he was saved from his sins (see Acts 22:16; Eph. 2:8-9).

b. The grace given to him in making him an apostle (Rom. 15:15-16). The RSV rendition, based on an alternate reading, readily lends itself to this view.

c. The grace he received in being used by God for the establishment of the Corinthian church. Kingdom work is God's favor to his people.

B. Two ways to build (3:12).

1. Gold, silver and precious stones (materials used in great temples). Some think this figure is to be understood as a reference to the doctrine of Christ. Likely, however, it refers to Christ-centered Christians. They had been founded in Jesus initially and all future building was to have him as their center.

2. Wood, hay and stubble (materials used in shacks which burned easily). If the figure immediately above is taken to mean the doctrine of Christ, this should be understood as the false doctrines of men. However, it probably refers to teacher-centered Christians. Although they had been built on Christ, they now had their loyalty in men and were divided into warring factions.

3. *Warning:* Men should take heed how they build on Christ as the foundation (3:10).

C. Every man's work will be tested by fire (3:13-15).

1. At the day of judgment (1:8; 3:13).

2. Work in these verses should be understood as the work done by a teacher in the lives of others. He works for the purpose of leading them into the experience of eternal salvation (if he is God's man).

a. His work survives (gold, silver and precious stones do not easily burn) and he is rewarded if they go to heaven (3:14; I Thess. 2:19-20).

b. His work is burned (contemplate what happens to wood, hay and stubble in a fire!) and he suffers loss, if they fail to go to heaven (3:15). Furthermore, his labor on their behalf will have been wasted (Phil. 2:16; Gal. 4:11).

c. The teacher can lose his reward (*i.e.* the people with whom he worked) and still be saved (3:15). It should be added that some have thought the word translated as saved means "preserved" for the lake of fire. Hence, they saw the teacher's damnation in the verse. "Some of the Fathers gave to this beautiful verse the shockingly perverted meaning that 'the workman would be *preserved alive* for endless torments.'

'salted with fire' in order to endure interminable agonies. The meaning is impossible, for it reverses the sense of the word 'saved;' and makes it equivalent to 'damned;' but the interpretation is an awful proof of the distortions to which a merciless human rigorism and a hard, self-styled orthodoxy have sometimes subjected the word of God" (F. W. Farrar, *The First Epistle of Paul to the Corinthians*, pp. 94-95).

3. Reply to erroneous views based on this section (3:13-15).

a. Impossibility of apostasy (*i.e.* once saved, always saved)—Work does not refer to an individual's personal life of sin. The passage does not remotely imply that lying, stealing, swearing, adultery, etc., will be destroyed while the participant in such activity will be eternally saved.

b. Purgatory—The section says absolutely nothing about refining one's character through the fires of Purgatory.

IV. The Penalty for Destroying God's Temple (3:16-17).

A. This is a continuation of the figure of building begun at 3:9. Temples are constructed of gold, silver and precious stones. Saints are the temple of God. Therefore, they should be gold, silver and precious stones. Since gold, silver and precious stones represent Christ-centered Christians, by implication, the author meant the Corinthians should have been centered in Jesus (rather than in men as party leaders).

B. Paul used a second person, plural (3:16) and taught that the church is the temple of God (II Cor. 6:16; Eph. 2:21) or shrine in which the Lord dwells. Since all agree that tobacco, alcohol and drugs have a deteriorating effect upon man's body, these verses have been cited to denounce their uses. This cannot be legitimately done for the passage deals not with the physical body but with the church. However, 6:19-20 does describe the human body as the temple of the Holy Spirit, and, in light of its teaching, continual warnings against the abuse of the physical body should be made loud and clear. From 3:16-17 and 6:19-20, it is evident that the Lord dwells in his people collectively and individually.

C. The Greek word translated defile (KJV) in 3:17 is the same as the one translated destroy. There seems to be no reason for the difference in translation. The RSV, which translates the word destroy each time, is to be preferred.

D. *The Point:* By worldly wisdom, the Corinthians had exalted their teachers and divided the church. Those who did such were destroying the church and would be destroyed by God. Farrar translated the thought as "God shall ruin the ruiner of the temple" and then added, "St. Paul was, perhaps, thinking of the penalty of death attached to anyone who desecrated the temple of Jerusalem" (p. 95). It is extremely dangerous to participate in a *needless* division of God's people (Rom. 16:17-18). However, it is sometimes necessary to be involved in division to please the Lord (Lk. 12:51). The fundamentals of God's truth must never be compromised in the name of unity.

V. Do Not Glory in Men (3:18-23).

A. The possibility of self-deception (3:18; Gal. 6:3; Jas. 1:26; I Jno. 1:8).

1. Men can deceive others (Eph. 5:6), be deceived by others (II Tim. 3:13) and deceive themselves.

2. Had they continued to glory in men (thus rejecting Paul's teaching, 3:21), the Corinthians would have placed their wisdom above the wisdom of God (3:19-20) and been guilty of self-deception (3:18).

B. To be wise and well-pleasing to God, one must be a fool in the eyes of the world (3:18; 4:10; 1:25-28). What God calls wisdom, the world calls foolishness. What the world calls wisdom, God calls foolishness.

C. The wisdom of the world is foolishness with God (3:19-20).

1. Two Old Testament quotations (Job 5:13; Ps. 94:11) are offered as proof to sustain that affirmation.

2. By pledging party loyalty to Paul, Peter and Apollos, the Corinthians were following the wisdom of the world and thus engaging in foolishness.

D. Do not glory in men (3:21-23).

1. Because such is worldly wisdom and in conflict with God's will (implied).

2. Because all things are yours (3:21-22). God gave them richly all things to enjoy (I Tim. 6:17) and he caused all things to work for their benefit (Rom. 8:28).

   a. What belonged to the Corinthians (see Rom. 8:38-39).

      (1) Peter, Paul and Apollos (or all gospel teachers).

      (2) The world — This may be a reference to the world as a present possession or to the new earth in the hereafter (Rom. 4:13; 8:19-22; II Pet. 3:13).

      (3) Life and death — Life in union with Christ is the only real life. Jesus came that men might experience the abundant life (Jno. 10:10). Those without Christ do not really live; they only exist. Since all are dominated by death, the figure which generally enters the mind is that of death possessing the human family. However, in respect to the redeemed, Paul reverses the figure. Even death belongs to Christians! Death is a precious possession for the saints (Ps. 116:15). Death conquered by the resurrection of Jesus Christ has become the servant of believers (15:21-22, 45). Death is dire loss for the disobedient but it is great gain for those who love the Lord (Phil. 1:21).

"So live that when thy summons comes to join
  The innumerable caravan that moves
  To the pale realms of shade, where each shall take
  His chamber in the silent halls of death,
  Thou go not like the quarry slave at night,
  Scourged in his dungeon, but sustained and soothed
  By an unfaltering trust approach thy grave
  Like one who wraps the drapery of his couch
  About him and lies down to pleasant dreams."

(From *Thanatopsis,* by W. C. Bryant).

      (4) Present and future — Day to day life belongs only to God's children. Any other kind of life is really death, regardless of its appearances to the worldly-wise. Who but Christians have a future? It has been said, "I may not know what the future holds, but I know who holds the future." The destiny of every person reaches beyond time into eternity. There is a heaven awaiting the disciples of Christ (Rev. 22:14).

b. *Paul's point:* Since all things were theirs, why should the Corinthians deprive themselves by laying hold on only a small part (*i.e.* their teachers) of the whole?

3. Because they belonged to Christ who belongs to God (3:23). Hence, they should have boasted in the Lord, their rightful owner (by virtue of creation and redemption), rather than in men (1:29, 31; Gal. 6:14).

V.

The Folly of Following Men

Structure

I. Do Not Judge Your Teachers (4:1-5).

A. The place of teachers in God's plan (4:1-2). This is a continuation of the thought in 3:5-9.

1. Servants of Christ (4:1).

a. Servants in 3:5 is from the Greek "diakonos," meaning servant, attendant or minister (Thayer, p. 138). Servants in 4:1 is from "huperetes." This is the only time the word appears in Paul's writings. The word has been defined as "an under-rower, or common sailor; and then, subordinate servant of any kind" (Hodge, p. 64) or a "subordinate official waiting on his superior (originally an under-rower in a war galley)" (Vine, vol. I, p. 273). Farrar suggested that teachers are "diakonoi" in relation to men and "huperetai" in relation to Christ (p. 132).

b. There was quite a difference in Paul's view and the Corinthians' view of gospel preachers. He indicated they were similar to galley slaves rather than heads of rival parties!

2. Stewards of the mysteries of God (4:1).

a. Stewards is from "oikonomos" which denotes "the manager of a household or estate ('oikos,' a house, 'nemo,' to arrange)" (Vine, vol. IV, p. 74). Such people were usually slaves or those who had been freed from slavery.

b. As stewards, teachers must be faithful or trustworthy (4:2).

(1) To God who has entrusted them with the message.

(2) To the people as dispensers of the message. They must "tell it like it is."

(3) It is not necessary for a person to be brilliant, eloquent, famous or successful (as the world judges success) in his work of preaching. He must simply be faithful. Perhaps Noah was lacking in all of these man-made qualifications but he was a faithful steward of God's teaching. In the judgment, he could fare better than one who has converted thousands to Christ.

3. Obviously, it was right for the Corinthians to judge their teachers in the sense of seeing them as Paul described them. However, they were wrong by judging in the sense of exalting some and humiliating others (which always occurs when people are divided into factions).

B. Concerning the matter of judging (4:3-5).

1. Who is to judge?

a. Not the Corinthians (4:3, 5). Although all things were theirs (3:22), that did not give them the right to judge as they had done.

b. Not a human court (4:3, RSV). Literally, the expression is "of man's day" or "by human day," meaning a day of earthly trials.

c. Not even Paul (4:3). Paul knew nothing against himself (4:4, RSV). He was not making the claim of sinless perfection. He knew he was less than perfect (Phil. 3:12-13) and described himself as chief of sinners (I Tim. 1:15). It was in the matter of his faithfulness as a minister (4:2) that he knew nothing against himself, however, that did not mean he was acquitted (4:4, RSV). Since it is virtually impossible for one to see himself as he is, no man is qualified to judge himself (see Ps. 19:12-13; I Jno. 3:20-21).

d. The Lord is to judge (4:5). This is a reference to the Lord Jesus Christ (II Cor. 5:10).

2. Why is the Lord alone competent to judge (4:5)?

a. He has all the information necessary to render a correct judgment (*i.e.* he "will bring to light the things now hidden in darkness," RSV).

b. He can "disclose the purposes of the heart" (RSV). Christ knows whether one is sincere or not (Phil. 1:15-16).

3. When will this judgment occur (4:5)? At the coming of the Lord.

4. What will be the result of judgment (4:5)? Then every man will receive his praise or commendation from God.

5. *The point:* Teachers are to receive their commendation from the Lord and not from men. This may imply degrees of reward. If that is correct, some will be more highly honored than others. However, such is a prerogative of God rather than man.

II. Do Not be Puffed Up (4:6-7).

A. In a figure, Paul transferred (KJV) or applied (RSV) this to himself and Apollos (4:6).

1. Some have thought Paul applied the matter of division to himself and two of his colleagues when, actually, the parties at Corinth were built around other men. That would mean he denounced the divisions without specifying the party leaders. Likely, such is incorrect for whatever he had in mind was limited to himself and Apollos but Peter's name is also mentioned in connection with the divisions (1:10-15). Probably, Paul had reference to the section at 3:5-9 where he wrote of himself and Apollos under the figure of planting and watering.

2. The truth concerning the place of teachers in God's plan was applied to Paul and Apollos that the brethren might learn not to think of men above that which is written ("that in us ye might learn not to go beyond the things which are written"—ASV) (4:6).

a. This is a reference to what Paul himself was writing. What he wrote constituted scripture (II Pet. 3:15-16). Scripture in the New Testament is a technical word meaning inspired writing (Jno. 10:35; I Tim. 5:18). The scripture from

Paul's pen is as binding on God's people in the Christian era as was the Old Testament scripture during the Mosaic period.

b. *The point:* In his inspired writing, Paul taught the Corinthians not to go beyond God's word by honoring one teacher above another. Of course, those loyal to Christ will never deliberately go beyond his teaching in any realm (II Jno. 9; Rev. 22:18-19).

B. Since knowledge without love puffs up (8:1), the Corinthian practice of favoring one teacher and opposing another (4:6) may have been based on a conceited misconception of what they thought was superior learning.

C. The rebuke (4:7).

1. Who sees anything different in you (RSV)? As far as basic human needs are concerned, they were all alike as we are today. An honest reception of God's word as taught by Peter, Paul or Apollos would have fulfilled those needs. Their differences were imaginary.

2. What have you that you did not receive (RSV)? Even if differences among them did exist, all they had came from God. Hence, they should have honored him rather than their teachers.

3. *Conclusion:* The basis for their division was egotism. To illustrate, one might have said, "All of you know I am talented and educated. It is Apollos who holds my attention and challenges me to think. I simply cannot support the work of a crude and unlettered fisherman like Peter. You can put me down as an Apollosite." That kind of statement reveals more about the speaker than Apollos. One who would use such language is glorying in himself rather than in his so-called favorite preacher.

III. *Contrast Between the Corinthians and the Apostles* (4: 8-13).

A. There is a great deal of irony, sarcasm or satire in this section.

1. At times Elijah (I Kgs. 18:27), Isaiah (Isa. 44:1-20) and Jeremiah (Jer. 10:3-5) employed a similar approach.

2. By scriptural example, sarcasm is justified when the view opposed is not only wicked but foolish and when one is

motivated by the desire to convict and convert rather than to simply cause pain. However, all Christians need to be extremely cautious in using this method. Uninspired persons rarely use sarcasm successfully.

3. Paul was sarcastic because of their conceited, worldly-wise attitude that expressed itself in the divisions which had racked the Corinthian congregation.

B. Paul wished the Corinthians were then reigning (4:8-9).

1. Satirically, he depicted them as being full, rich and already reigning (4:8). They were full with self-satisfaction and rich with intellectual pride (McGarvey, p. 69). With similar language, John described the Laodicean church (Rev. 3:17-18). The Corinthians were already reigning in the sense of being as happy as kings (Farrar, p. 134), being independent of the apostles (McGarvey, p. 69) or being participants in "the full blessedness of the Messiah's reign" (Hodge, p. 72).

2. Two reasons why he wished they were then reigning.

a. The apostles would be reigning with them (4:8).

b. The apostles would be free from persecution (4:9).

(1) The expression describing the apostles as "a spectacle unto the world, and to angels, and to men" is an allusion to the Roman arena of that day. Spectacle is from the word "theatron" (it also appears in Heb. 10:33), meaning theater or place of assembly (Vine, vol. IV, p. 59). The picture is one of men and angels watching the apostles from the stands as they were being tormented and killed.

(2) That the apostles were last and appointed to death has been understood as a reference to:

(a) Prisoners captured in battle and condemned to die in the arena (by fighting wild animals or other men). They were *last* in a Roman general's victorious procession which marched through the streets of Rome.

(b) "Gladiators who were condemned to die, and who came into the arena *last* [emphasis mine, J.A.] after the spectators had been sated with other exhibitions and bloodless performances" (M. Dods, *The First Epistle to the Corinthians*, p. 106). Before the conflict began, they addressed the audience by saying, "We who are about to die salute you."

C. Contrast between the Corinthians and the apostles (4: 10). In this verse, Paul returned to his use of irony.

1. Apostles—fools, weak, despised. That was the world's assessment of them and their work. Truthfully, the world was not worthy of them (see Heb. 11:38).

2. Corinthians—wise, strong, honorable. That was how the brethren viewed themselves! However, the correct conclusion was diametrically opposite to the one they had reached.

D. The suffering of the apostles (4:11-13; II Cor. 11:23-33).

1. The words used to describe their hardships are hunger, thirst, ill-clad, buffeted, homeless, reviled, persecuted, slandered (RSV). Dods applied the language to Paul and added, "Here is the finest mind, the noblest spirit, on earth; and this is how he is treated: driven from place to place, thrust aside as interrupting the proper work of men, passed by with a sneer at his rags, refused the commonest charity, paid for his loving words in blows and insolence. And yet he goes on with his work, and lets nothing interrupt that" (p. 107).

2. Their suffering explains why the unregenerate considered them as fools (4:10). Surely, they asked, "Who but fools would undergo such persecution and agony?"

3. How they responded to mistreatment.

a. When reviled, they blessed; when persecuted, they endured; when slandered, they conciliated (4:13, RSV). They literally followed the teaching of the Sermon on the Mount (Matt. 5:38-48).

b. In contrast to that reaction, many disciples tend to imitate their enemies. If the opposition is harsh and severe, they respond in like manner. In such cases, they allow the enemies of the cross rather than Jesus to dictate the standard by which their conduct will be regulated. What do they more than others?

E. How the apostles were regarded by some (4:13).

1. Filth or refuse of the world.

2. The offscouring of all things. "The words rendered *filth* and *off-scouring*, signify, the former, what is carried off by rinsing, and the latter, what is scraped off. They both express the general term of refuse" (Hodge, p. 74).

IV. A Personal Message of Love and Warning (4:14-21).

A. Why Paul had used irony (4:14).

1. Not to make them ashamed. This has two possible explanations.

a. It may be an ellipsis (see definition at 1:17). The meaning would then be "I do not write this *simply* to make you ashamed but *also* to admonish you" (RSV).

b. The design of the writing had not been to produce shame although that may have been its effect.

2. To warn or admonish them.

a. He had the right to engage in that activity because they were his children. The verb "noutheto," translated admonish (RSV) means to put in mind or warn and it is generally used to express parental admonition and instruction. The noun form "nouthesia" appears in Eph. 6:4 where fathers are commanded to bring up their children in the *admonition* of the Lord.

b. It is the father's obligation to admonish his children and one who fails in this respect has shirked his duty. "Admonition differs from remonstrance, in that the former is warning based on instruction; the latter may be little more than expostulation. For example, Eli remonstrated with his sons, I Sam. 2:24, he failed to admonish them, 3:13, LXX" (Vine, vol. I, p. 31).

B. Paul was spiritual father to the Corinthians (4:15).

1. Possibly, they could have ten thousand instructors (countless guides, RSV). Instructor is from "paidagogos" (it appears in Gal. 3:24-25) which means "a guide, or guardian or trainer of boys, literally, a child-leader (*pais,* a boy, or child, *ago,* to lead)" (Vine, vol. II, p. 265). "Among the Greeks and Romans the name was applied to trustworthy slaves who were charged with the duty of supervising the life and morals of boys belonging to the better class. The boys were not allowed so much as to step out of the house without them before arriving at the age of manhood" (Thayer, p. 472).

2. However, Paul was their only father.

a. He had begotten them by means of the gospel (Jas. 1:18; I Pet. 1:23 in ASV).

b. Through an honest reception of the message they experienced begattal. Later, their faith moved them to be baptized (Acts 18:8) at which time they were born again of water and the Spirit (Jno. 3:3-5).

C. As their father, Paul urged them to imitate him (4:16; Phil. 4:9).

1. He did not mean they were to follow him in the sense of building a party around himself. Earlier, he had clearly denounced such (1:10-15). He wanted them to follow him as he followed Christ (11:1).

2. How many Christian fathers could, in good conscience, ask their children to imitate them as they imitate Christ? "Do as I say but not as I do" carries very little weight with young people. As the Chinese say, "One picture is worth ten thousand words."

D. Timothy had been sent to remind the Corinthians of Paul's ways (4:17).

1. Timothy was his "beloved and faithful child in the Lord" (RSV). He is also called his "own son in the faith" (I Tim. 1:2, KJV). Apparently, Paul converted him on his first missionary journey while at Lystra (Acts 14:8-18; 16:1-5).

2. If the Corinthians were going to imitate him, they needed one of Paul's faithful sons to remind them of his ways.

E. Paul's reply to his enemies (4:18-21).

1. Their description—puffed up or arrogant (4:18).

2. Their charge—He will not come here again (4:18).

3. His response to their charge (4:19-21).

a. "I will come to you shortly, if the Lord will" (4:19; see Jas. 4:13-15). He did go there two more times (see introductory material).

b. "I will find out not the talk of these arrogant people but their power" (4:19, RSV).

(1) Power may refer to miraculous ability but that is doubtful.

(2) Likely, he had in mind their power based on character, dedication, teaching, good works and influence with others (4:20; II Tim. 3:5). There is much talk about Christianity but too little practice of it.

c. How shall I return (4:21)?

(1) With a rod (like a father ready to punish them because of their impenitence)?

(2) In love and a spirit of meekness or gentleness (if they repented of their partyism and wrong attitude toward him as an apostle of Christ)?

VI.

CHAPTER FIVE

Sexual Immorality

Structure

I. 5:1-8 — Purge Out the Old Leaven.

II. 5:9-13 — Limitation of Christian Fellowship.

I. Purge Out the Old Leaven (5:1-8).

A. The sin under consideration was one of incest (a man was living with his father's wife) (5:1).

1. Under the law of Moses one could not marry his mother, stepmother, sister, half-sister, granddaughter, great granddaughter, aunt (blood relation), aunt (by marriage), daughter-in-law or sister-in-law. Furthermore, he could not marry a mother and daughter or two sisters (Lev. 18:6-18). Herod Antipas violated that law by marrying his brother's wife (Matt. 14:4). The only exception to the foregoing legislation was the Levirate (which means "concerning a brother") law. In that instance, a man was to marry the wife of his dead brother to perpetuate the name of him who had died (Deut. 25:5-10).

2. The kind of incest in the Corinthian church did not exist among the pagans (5:1).

a. In early times, Roman law would allow an individual to marry as close as a second cousin. By the time Paul wrote I Corinthians, one could legally marry a first cousin. Claudius Caesar (41-54 A.D.) married his brother's daughter but he had to get permission from the Roman Senate to do so.

b. Cicero (106-43 B.C.) "alludes to such a crime in the words, 'Oh, incredible wickedness, and—except in this woman's case—unheard of in all experience!' ('Pro Cluent.,' 5)" (Farrar, p. 165).

c. Suetonius accused Nero of being sexually involved with his mother, however, because of his extreme bias against the emperor, many scholars discount his accusation.

3. The sin was actually or commonly reported (5:1).

a. Apparently, the wickedness was well known to the unbelievers in Corinth who had an acquaintance with the church. What sort of influence do you suppose that ungodliness had in the lives of the unsaved? Untold thousands have left this life unprepared to meet God because of the hypocrites in the church.

b. It seems that Paul had learned about it from those of Chloe's house (1:11). Again, when is it right to tell? Of course, tale-bearing is wrong (Lev. 19:16), however, telling those who are in a position to correct an evil situation is right.

4. Some conclusions:

a. Undoubtedly, the woman was the brother's stepmother rather than his mother. The thought of it being his mother is almost too horrible to contemplate. Furthermore, in the Old Testament a man's stepmother is called his "father's wife" (the very expression used to describe the one in the sinful relationship) and a clear distinction is made between her and his mother (Lev. 18:7-8).

b. The woman was probably not a member of the church since no judgment was passed on her (5:12).

c. It cannot be determined whether the Christian man's father was dead or alive. If he was still alive, he and the woman may have been separated or divorced or the son may have taken the woman from his father.

d. It is impossible to tell if the brother and woman were legally married or simply living together.

B. The attitude of the Corinthians was one of arrogance (5:2).

1. The word translated as puffed up or arrogant is "phusioo," which means "to bear oneself loftily, to be proud" (Thayer, p. 660). The word also appears in 4:6, 18, 19; 8:1; 13:4).

2. Meaning?

a. They were so conceited about their supposed wisdom (discussed in the first four chapters), they overlooked the existence of an enormous evil in their midst.

b. They were so broadminded (they came from a moral background which was the lowest in the then known world), they were not shocked by the sin.

C. The Corinthians should have mourned because of their brother's sin (5:2).

1. Mourn is from "pentheo" which is also used to express the disciples' sorrow over the death of their beloved Lord (Mk. 16:10). The Corinthians ought to have grieved in a similar way due to the wickedness of their brother. According to Chrysostom, they should have engaged in mourning and supplication as they would had disease or pestilence appeared among them (*Homilies on First Corinthians*, 15).

2. "An easy-going attitude to sin is always dangerous. It has been said that our one security against sin lies in our being shocked at it. Carlyle said that men must see the infinite beauty of holiness and the infinite damnability of sin. When we cease to take a serious view of sin we are in a perilous position. It is not a question of being critical and condemnatory. It is a question of being wounded and shocked and hurt. It was sin that crucified Jesus Christ; it was to free men from sin that Christ died. No Christian can take an easy-going view of sin" (Barclay, p. 48).

D. The solution to the problem was withdrawal (5:3-5).

1. Paul had already pronounced judgment (5:3).

2. It was then time for the church to exclude the sinful brother (5:4-5).

a. It was to be done by the authority or in the name of Christ (5:4).

b. It was to be done in the assembly (5:4).

c. The brother was to be delivered to Satan (5:5).

(1) That probably means he was to be officially placed in the realm over which Satan rules (Jno. 12:31; Col. 1:13). Practically speaking, he already belonged to the Devil.

(2) For a similar situation, consider Hymenaeus and Alexander whom Paul delivered to Satan (I Tim. 1:19-20).

d. Reasons why he was to be delivered to Satan.

(1) For the destruction of the flesh (5:5). What does this mean?

(a) That Satan might inflict physical punishment on him.

(b) That Paul might miraculously inflict punishment as he did to Elymas (Acts 13:8-12).

(c) Through excommunication, the brother would be led to repent and destroy the fleshly relationship between himself and the women. This seems to be the correct interpretation.

(2) That his spirit might be saved in the day of the Lord (5:5).

(a) There are three salvations set forth in the New Testament. First, there is salvation from past sins which one receives when he is baptized (Mk. 16:16). Second, there is a present salvation which the Christian possesses as he faithfully serves the Lord (II Pet. 1:10). Third, there is an eternal salvation given when the disciple enters heaven (Mk. 10:30; II Pet. 1:11). It is the latter salvation that Paul had in mind here.

(b) This indicates that withdrawal should be practiced not to hurt but to help the one who has been overcome by sin. It is the last step taken in church discipline (see Matt. 18:15-17) and when correctly done, some rebellious brethren can be saved by it. May the Lord give his church the courage to obey this forgotten commandment.

(3) To save the church (5:6). A little leaven leavens the whole lump (see Heb. 12:15). It is evil's nature to diffuse itself. When ungodliness is tolerated, its deteriorating effect will influence additional saints. However, when discipline is exercised against wickedness, others in the church are led to fear (Acts 5:11).

E. The leaven illustration (5:6-8).

1. The figure is that of the Passover Feast which was near at the time Paul wrote I Corinthians (16:8).

2. As a lamb was offered in the Jewish Passover (Ex. 12:1-6), Christ was sacrificed as the paschal lamb for Christians (5:7; Isa. 53:7; Jno. 1:29; I Pet. 1:19).

3. Followers of Christ at Corinth were to celebrate the feast.

a. By being purged of the leaven of malice and wickedness (5:7-8). At the beginning of the Passover, the Hebrews were commanded to rid their homes of all leaven (Ex. 12:15). Apparently, leaven was a symbol of Egypt's corruptions to them. Putting it away was a type of their sanctification. In Paul's illustration, leaven represents evil. If the Corinthians were to be purged of the leaven of evil, they had to exclude the immoral brother from their fellowship.

b. By having the traits of sincerity and truth (5:8).

(1) Sincerity is from "eilikrineia" which appears only two other times in the New Testament (II Cor. 1:12; 2:17). In ancient times, it meant that "which is cleansed by much rolling and shaking to and fro in the sieve" or what was "held up to the sunlight and in that proved and approved" (R. C. Trench, *Synonyms of the New Testament*, p. 298).

(2) Truth is from "aletheia." According to Thayer, it means "sincerity of mind and integrity of character, or a mode of life in harmony with divine truth" (p. 26). Hodge wrote: "In its subjective sense, it means that inward state which answers to the truth; that moral condition which is conformed to the law and character of God" (p. 88).

II. Limitation of Christian Fellowship (5:9-13).

A. In a former letter Paul had told them not to associate with immoral men (5:9).

B. Because they had misunderstood him, he explained (5:10-11).

1. That he was not speaking of men of the world for it would be impossible to have no association with them (5:10).

2. That they were to have no company with *brethren* who engaged in immorality (5:11).

C. They were not to eat with an ungodly person who had been excluded from the fellowship of the church (5:11).

1. What does this mean?

a. Some think it refers to eating the Lord's Supper with him. In my judgment, that view is incorrect. How could the faithful keep the unfaithful from partaking of the Supper?

Some, while thinking they are right, are so adamant in their rebellion they cannot be kept from the Lord's table other than by physical force. Surely, Paul was not recommending that procedure. As far as communion is concerned, each is to examine himself (11:28).

b. Likely, the reference is to a common meal. Because of fear, Peter withdrew from eating with the Gentiles lest certain Jews get the idea that he was in fellowship with them (Gal. 2:11-14). Saints should not eat with an excommunicated person in their home, his home, a restaurant or any other place. They are not to socialize with him at all. They can be with him *only* for the purpose of warning him (II Thess. 3:15). Obviously, all of this follows only if the withdrawal has taken place according to the teaching of God's word.

2. Why was it to be done? To save the soul of the erring church member. Think of how lonely and wretched one would feel away from the warmth, strength and encouragement of his brothers and sisters in Christ. If an excluded individual has any sensitivity left in his soul, this action will bring him to repentance and a sense of responsibility. Because a few churches practice it, a number of backsliders have been saved who otherwise would have been eternally lost.

D. God, rather than saints, judges those outside the church (5:12-13).

E. Christians are to withdraw from the immoral, greedy, idolaters, revilers, drunkards and robbers (5:11, RSV; see also 6:9-11; Gal. 5:19-21; II Thess. 3:6). In spite of this instruction, some are actually advocating fellowship for practicing homosexuals!

F. Some random thoughts on fellowship.

1. God's people cannot have fellowship with:

a. Those who have never been born again of water and the Spirit because they are not God's children (Jno. 3:5).

b. Those who deny that Jesus came in the flesh (II Jno. 9-11). By an extension of the principle, this would apply to those who deny any truth connected with the person of the Lord (*i.e.* his virgin birth, miraculous ministry, atoning death, bodily resurrection from the dead, etc.).

c. Those who live ungodly lives (Eph. 5:11-12; I Cor. 5:3-5).

d. Those guilty of factionalism (Tit. 3:10; Rom. 16:17; Gal. 5:19-21).

e. Those who, in the realm of liberty, violate the consciences of their brethren (Rom. 14:1-15:13). For further discussion, see my *Survey of Romans,* pages 111-114.

2. Fellowship is not to be withdrawn simply because of incorrect belief but because of the *practice* of that which violates God's will.

3. All error is not to be placed in the same category. Holding the view of a representative indwelling of the Holy Spirit in Christians cannot be placed in the same category with a denial of the inspiration of the Bible.

4. Attitude has a great deal to do with fellowship. Some are what they are by disposition (I Tim. 6:3-5) and some are what they are by conviction. The former are simply arguments looking for an issue. Making concessions will not please them for they have the spirit of Diotrephes (III Jno. 9). No attempt should be made to please men with contentious attitudes. However, almost anything (in harmony with the New Testament) should be done in behalf of brethren whose convictions are genuine and sincere.

5. Christians can have fellowship without 100 per cent agreement in *all* areas. As a matter of fact, that is the only kind of brotherhood that will ever exist.

6. Saints should be willing to sacrifice their opinions for the unity of God's church.

7. One cannot be biblically out of fellowship with one congregation and biblically in fellowship with another congregation. Elders should be very cautious about receiving people who have been withdrawn from elsewhere. If the withdrawal was handled scripturally, every New Testament church in the land should honor it. To do otherwise is to rebel against the will of God.

8. One cannot be biblically out of fellowship with one of God's churches and in fellowship with God. How can he be right with God having been delivered to Satan?

9. One should be excluded from the church not so much because of what he has done but due to his impenitent attitude toward what he has done. If the immoral brother at Corinth had repented and put away the woman, Paul would not have commanded his exclusion from the congregation. Regardless of what one has done, if he is broken-hearted and penitent about it, he is to be kept in the local brotherhood.

VII.

CHAPTER SIX

Going to Law with Brethren

Structure

I. Going to Law with Brethren (6:1-11).

A. The Hebrews were taught to settle their differences among themselves.

1. Hodge quoted a Rabbinical source which declared: "It is a statute which binds all Israelites, that if one Israelite has a cause against another, it must not be prosecuted before the Gentiles" (p. 93).

2. Farrar explained *why* they held that view. "Even the Jews were bound to settle their civil disputes before their own tribunals. The ideal Jew was *jashar*, or 'the upright man,' and Jews could not consistently seek integrity from those who were not upright" (pp. 191-192).

B. Engaging in law suits against one another was a part of the Greek way of life.

1. "The Greeks were naturally and characteristically a litigious people. The law courts were in fact one of their chief amusements and entertainments. Going to law was integrally bound up with Greek life. . . . The Greeks were in fact famous, or notorious, for their love of going to law" (Barclay, pp. 55-56).

71

2. Since Corinth was a Greek church, it is not surprising that the people had brought their tendency to engage in law suits into the body of Christ with them. Paul was utterly overwhelmed by such conduct and asked, "Dare any of you, having a matter against another, go to law before the unjust?" (6:11).

C. When differences arise between brethren, they are to be handled within the church (6:2, 5; Matt. 18:15-17).

D. The Corinthians were involved in two errors.

    1. Going to law with one another (6:7).

    2. Going to law with one another before unbelievers (6:1, 6).

E. The saints will judge the world (6:2).

    1. Question—"Do you not know?" That expression is used in reference to an important truth which they knew but disregarded. It occurs ten times in I Corinthians (3:16; 5:6; 6:2, 3, 9, 15, 16, 19; 9:13, 24) and only three other times in Paul's writings (Rom. 6:3, 16; 11:2).

    2. Meaning of the saints will judge the world.

        a. They will judge the world *through* Christ as their representative. He and they are part of the same spiritual body.

        b. They will be associate judges of the world *with* Christ.

        c. By their righteous lives, they will condemn the world (see Heb. 11:7; Matt. 12:41-42).

F. The saints will judge angels (6:3). Meaning?

    1. They will judge the wicked angels (II Pet. 2:4; Jude 6) in the same way they judge the disobedient world.

    2. They will judge good angels in the sense of ruling over them in heaven. The saints will reign with Christ (II Tim. 2:12; Rev. 2:26-27). The first explanation better fits the context than this one.

G. *The point of 6:1-3:* If saints are qualified to judge the world and angels, they must also have the ability to handle their own differences without going to law with their fellow-Christians before unbelievers. Actually, they were allowing those to judge them whom they are to judge!

H. Is there not a wise man among you (6:4-6)?

1. A difference in translations (6:4).

a. "Least esteemed *in* the church" (KJV). Get those who are least qualified within the congregation to judge rather than going outside the fellowship to be judged by unbelievers.

b. "Least esteemed *by* the church" (RSV). This could be interpreted in the same way as the expression in the KJV. However, it may mean such matters were not to be taken before outsiders who were least esteemed by the members of the church.

c. "Do you set to judge who are of no account *in* the church?" (ASV). If you would not think of using simpletons in the church to make a judgment, how much worse to go outside the brotherhood for a judgment!

2. "I speak to your shame" (6:5). That expression appears only one other time in I Corinthians (15:34).

3. "Is there . . . not a wise man among you" (6:5)? They had been exalted by their worldly wisdom to the point of being divided into factions but they could not find one wise enough among them to hand down a fair decision between two disputing brethren! The legs of the lame are not equal!

I. Conclusions drawn from their sinful action (6:7-11).

1. Lawsuits between saints are defeat (RSV), fault (KJV) or defect (ASV).

a. The word in the original is "hettema." It appears only two other times in the Bible (Isa. 31:8, LXX; Rom. 11:12). At Isaiah 31:8 it is used concerning a defeat of Assyria. In Romans 11:12 it is translated as diminishing (KJV), failure (RSV) and defection (Phillips).

b. Meaning? According to the NEB, the Corinthians fell below their standard in going to law against one another. Trench held essentially the same view in stating that they had come short of their duty (p. 232). Thayer thought they suffered loss as respects salvation (p. 281). Another took it in the sense of defeat and added, "The idea being that, in going to law with brethren, one is vowed to 'utter defeat' whichever side wins. If you win you defraud your brother: if your brother wins he defrauds you" (Ernest Gordon, *Notes from a Layman's Greek New Testament*, p. 220).

2. It is better to be defrauded than to have lawsuits (6:7).

3. The Corinthian Christians were guilty of wrong-doing (6:8).

4. They would not inherit the kingdom of heaven for engaging in such activity (6:9-11).

a. Be not deceived (6:9; 15:33; Gal. 6:7). See notes at 3:18.

b. This is a reference to God's eternal kingdom (II Tim. 4:1). See remarks concerning three salvations at 5:5.

c. The words in the list which had application to the problem are thieves, greedy, robbers (RSV) or thieves, covetous, extortioners (KJV). In having lawsuits with fellow-disciples, they were guilty of some or all of these activities.

d. Read 6:9-11 and consider what some of the Corinthians had been. Obviously, there is hope even for the homosexual if he will sincerely turn to Christ. Incidentally, one might be surprised if he knew the history of every member in the congregation where he has membership.

e. How the Corinthians had been saved from their past sins (6:11).

(1) They had been washed from their filth by the blood of Jesus when they were baptized (Rev. 1:5; Eph. 5:25-26; Tit. 3:5-7; Heb. 10:22; Acts 22:16).

(2) They had been sanctified from their former pollutions when they were washed in the waters of baptism (Eph. 5:25-26). One is sanctified when he is initially set apart for the Lord's service (see remarks on 1:2). However, sanctification is also a process (Jno. 17:17). In other words, a saint can become more and more dedicated to God with the passing of time. This is what takes places as Christians mature in the faith.

(3) They had also been justified, acquitted or made righteous when their faith led them to be baptized into Christ and the benefits of his death (Rom. 5:1, 9; 6:3). The washing, sanctification and justification happens simultaneously when one obeys the first principles of the gospel.

J. Questions over this section (6:1-11).

1. Is it wrong to go to court if a brother brings suit against you (Rom. 12:18)? How could a Christian avoid such?

2. Is it wrong for two parties in the same congregation to go to court over church property? Should those loyal to New Testament teaching allow a few who become modernists to take a $250,000 plant from them? Really, this passage does not *specifically* deal with that problem. This is not to say its principles are to be totally ignored.

3. Is it wrong to go to court with people outside the church? Paul did (Acts 25:6-12). Of course, believers should do their best to avoid it.

4. When does one cease to be a brother? If one who has not attended church in ten years attempts to defraud a devoted Christian, does Paul's teaching here apply? Is there any difference between a backslidden brother and one who has never been in the kingdom of God? Since Paul's teaching in I Cor. 6:1-11 was read in the assembly at Corinth, it seems that anyone who made no attempt to faithfully attend church services would hardly be a brother under consideration.

II. *Against Sexual Immorality* (6:12-20).

A. Corinthian arguments favoring fornication (6:12-13).

1. "All things are lawful" (6:2).

a. In recent translations, the above expression is set apart in quotes to show that Paul was citing a Corinthian statement.

b. Reduced to a syllogism, the Corinthians reasoned as follows: Major premise—All things are lawful. Minor premise —Fornication is a thing (*i.e.* action). Conclusion—Therefore, fornication is lawful.

c. Basis for their reasoning.

(1) It may have come from Gnosticism. The Gnostics taught that adultery and other sexual sins were lawful, if one had a proper understanding of God's word. In his writings, the Apostle John dealt with that early heresy (Rev. 2:4; I Jno. 1:8; 3:9). According to Gnosticism, fleshly activities did not impair one's relationship with the Lord. They said as the essential nature of a diamond was not affected by being in the mud so a Christian's inner nature redeemed by Christ could not be affected by ungodliness. Antinomianism (*i.e.* against law) is the name for that point of view. It is clearly refuted in

the New Testament (II Pet. 2:20-22). Since Gnosticism arose later in the first century, it is not likely that the Corinthians had then been influenced by their thought and teaching.

(2) Their argument was probably based on a perversion of Paul's teaching concerning law and grace. It is true that faithful saints are not under law in the sense of being condemned for their failures (Rom. 6:14; 8:1-4; Gal. 5:23). However, this does not mean they can engage in any and all activities with impunity. Disciples are responsible for keeping God's commandments (Jno. 14:15, 21, 23) or observing his law (9:21; Gal. 6:2; Jas. 1:25; 2:12). The Corinthians had misunderstood freedom in Christ (Gal. 5:13). Their view is called libertinism. Really, liberty is found in doing right (the Harding College motto). Naturally, all things are lawful in the area of indifference, however, the Corinthians had erred in applying that rule in the realm of sinful activity.

2. "Food is meant for the stomach and the stomach is meant for food" (6:13, RSV).

a. That is the first part of an argument from analogy. Apparently Paul did not complete the analogy for they knew the rest of it anyway. The latter part was "Fornication is meant for the body and the body is meant for fornication." They had placed fornication in the same category with eating. Accordingly, they believed that both were harmless physical activities. Although such is foreign to sensitive saints of our day, when the background of the Corinthians is contemplated, it is not difficult to see how they held that viewpoint.

B. Paul's reply to their arguments (6:12-14).

1. All things are lawful is limited (6:12).

a. To those things which are expedient (KJV) or helpful (RSV).

b. To those things which do not enslave.

c. Conclusion: Fornication is destructive rather than helpful and it is enslaving. Hence, all things are lawful had been misapplied to sexual immorality.

2. "Food is meant for the stomach and the stomach is meant for food" (6:13-14).

a. The relationship between the stomach and food is temporary since God will destroy both. Eating, understanding that it is to be done temperately (overeating seems to be a prevalent sin of the righteous. They strongly oppose drunkenness but must turn sideways to get through a door. A glutton is simply one drunk on food), does not have an eternal effect on the body which is to be raised from the dead (6:14). However, it is clearly implied that fornication has a deadly effect on the body's relationship to God in this life and in the life to come.

b. The body is not meant for sexual immorality. To use it in that way is to pervert its purpose. Pens were made for writing and spoons were made for eating soup. Try to write with a spoon or eat soup with a pen! Those efforts are innocent parlor play in comparison to the man or woman who attempts to find fulfillment in adultery. "He who commits adultery has no sense" (Prov. 6:32, RSV).

c. The body is meant for the Lord and the Lord for the body. Obviously, honorable sexual fulfillment betwen a man and woman in marriage (Heb. 13:4) does not violate the body's supreme obligation to God.

C. Additional arguments against sexual immorality (6:15-20).

1. Fornication is a misuse of the body (6:15, 19-20).

a. Christians do not belong to themselves but to the Lord who bought them by his death (6:9; Acts 20:28; Eph. 5:25; I Pet. 1:18-19). Prior to their redemption, they had been sold to sin (I Kgs. 21:20, 25; Rom. 7:14). The ransom price was both paid and received by God the Father (Isa. 53:11). It most certainly was not given to Satan. He was hurt rather than helped by the Lord's death and resurrection (Heb. 2:14). Since the saved are God's possession by creation and redemption, they look to him for guidance as to life's purpose.

b. Believers are members of Christ's body (6:15; 12:12, 27; Rom. 6:13, 19). The head directs the members in their proper function. Fornication is not one of those proper functions.

c. The body should be used to glorify God (6:20; Rom. 12:1-2).

(1) The expression, "and in your spirit, which are God's" (KJV), is lacking in manuscript support and does not appear in many translations.

(2) The point is that since the body is to be used for God's glory and since fornication does not glorify God, a child of God cannot commit fornication.

2. Immoral union violates a Christian's union with Christ (6:16-17).

a. There is an actual union or affinity between Christ and the Christian. Christ lives in a child of God (Gal. 2:20). The union between the Savior and the saved is as real as the union between a vine and its branches (Jno. 15:4-7). When one is biblically baptized, he is united with Christ (Rom. 6:3, 5; Gal. 3:27). In light of this truth, upheld many times in the New Testament, how anyone could argue for a representative indwelling of Christ in the form of his word is difficult to understand. If the believer is in Christ, Christ must also be in him. The expression "one body" or "one flesh" (6:16) is figurative but it refers to an actual union. In like manner, "one spirit" (6:17) is figurative but it describes an actual union between Jesus and his followers.

b. One flesh and marriage cannot be used interchangeably as some have done. According to their position, one is married to the first individual with whom he has sexual union (appeal is made to Matt. 19:1-9).

(1) All marriages are characterized by the one flesh relationship but not all one flesh relationships are marriage. All horses are animals but not all animals are horses. As animals is a larger category than horses, so marriage is a larger category than the one flesh relationship.

(2) For two Christians to be married, at least three qualifications must be met. First, they must will that it be marriage. Two people might be forced to stand before a preacher or Justice of the Peace and exchange matrimonial vows but they cannot be coerced into the marriage bed. Second, they must obey the laws of the land regulating marriage (Rom. 13:1-7). Third, they must engage in sexual union or the one flesh relationship (Matt. 19:5). A man and woman should love one another when they marry, however, they could be married in God's sight without love. People have married for many reasons other than love (money, fame, power, position, etc.). In parts of the first century world (and in some places today), marriages were arranged for young people by their parents. Since, in some cases, they hardly knew each

other, they entered the union without romantic love but they were married nevertheless.

3. Fornication is a sin against the body (6:18). Meaning?

a. It hurts the body physically as no other sin. "It wastes the bodily energies; produces feebleness, weakness, and disease; it impairs the strength, enervates the man, and shortens life. . . . Perhaps no single sin has done so much to produce the most painful and dreadful diseases, to weaken the constitution, and to shorten life as this. Other vices, as gluttony and drunkenness, do this also, and all sin has some effect in destroying the body, but it is true of this sin in an eminent degree" (A. Barnes, *Notes on First Corinthians*, p. 107).

b. It hurts the body morally and spiritually as no other sin. "This does not teach that fornication is greater than any other sin; but it does teach that it is altogether peculiar in its effects upon the body; not so much in its physical as in its moral and spiritual effects. The idea runs through the Bible that there is something myserious in the commerce of the sexes, and in the effects which flow from it. Every other sin, however degrading and ruinous to the health, even drunkenness, is external to the body, that is, external to its life. But fornication, involving as it does a community of life, is a sin against the body itself, because incompatible, as the Apostle had just taught, with the design of its creation, and with its immortal destiny" (Hodge, pp. 105-106).

c. It hurts the body's future state as no other sin. "Now, other sins, even drunkenness and gluttony, are sins without the body; *i.e.*, sins against those parts of the body that shall not inhere to it in the future state (Rev. 7:16), and hence do not strike directly at that future state; but fornication joins the whole body in sinful union to a body of death, so that it becomes one flesh with the condemned harlot; thereby wholly severing itself from the mystical body of life in Christ, and thus it does strike directly at the body's future state" (McGarvey, p. 78).

d. It is the only sin which *directly* alienates the body from Christ. "But he means that this is the only sin in which the present connection of the body with Christ and its future destiny in Him are directly sinned against. This is the only sin, he means, which by its very nature alienates the body from Christ, its proper Partner. Other sins indirectly involve separation from Christ; this explicitly and directly transfers allegiance, and sunders our union with Him. By this sin a man detaches himself from Christ; he professes to be united to what is incompatible with Christ" (Dods, p. 156).

e. It hurts the human personality (*i.e.* body stands for the whole person) as no other sin. "The relation of fornication to one's body is unique; the sin strikes at the very roots of a man's being and is against his very personality. No other sin desecrates the person *within* as does the sin of fornication" (Kelcy, p. 27).

f. It is the only sin in which the body is the instrument of sin. " 'Without the body.' Literally, *outside.* The body is not the instrument, but the subject. But in fornication the body is the instrument of the sin, and 'inwardly as well as outwardly is made over to another' " (M. R. Vincent, *Word Studies in the New Testament,* p. 217).

4. Sexual immorality is a desecration of the Spirit's temple (6:19).

a. Possibly, as a background for this verse, Paul had in mind the desecration of the Jewish temple by Antiochus Epiphanes in 168 B.C. At that time "the temple was formally dedicated to Zeus, the supreme god of Olympus; and swine's flesh was sacrificed on the altars of the temple" (H. E. Dana, *The New Testament World,* p. 80; see also R. H. Pfeiffer, *History of New Testament Times,* p. 13).

b. If the desecration of a temple made of stones was a heinous evil (it led to the Maccabean Revolution), how much worse to profane the body in which God's Holy Spirit dwells?

5. Flee or shun fornication (6:18).

a. The young Christian must flee fornication and other youthful lusts (2 Tim. 2:22).

b. When Joseph was tempted by Potiphar's wicked wife, he fled from her (Gen. 39:6-12). Men cannot reason or argue with this sin. Either they flee from it or they are trampled by it. An ancient Greek poet said that in escaping it he felt as though he had escaped "from a mad and furious master."

VIII.

CHAPTER SEVEN

Marriage

Structure

I. Responsibilities of Marriage (7:1-7).

A. At this point, Paul began to answer questions which the Corinthians had raised in their letter to him (7:1). Apparently, they had asked, "Is it advisable for a saint to enter the marriage relationship? Should one abstain from sexual union even in marriage? After becoming a Christian, should one continue to live with his or her unconverted mate?"

B. It is good or well (RSV) for a man not to touch a woman (7:1). Meaning?

1. The word translated as good or well is from "kalon." It can be understood in one of two ways.

a. The single state is expedient, profitable, wholesome, honorable or excellent. If that is its meaning, this indicates that the married do not occupy a more honorable state than the unmarried.

b. "Kalon" is sometimes used comparatively meaning better (Matt. 18:8-9). If that is its meaning, Paul was saying, under the circumstances, it is better for single Corinthians to remain unmarried.

81

2. Not to touch a woman is a reference to sexual relations (Gen. 20:6; Prov. 6:29). Paul was speaking of sexual union within marriage (7:2).

3. Paul's teaching at 7:1 is an exception to the general rule that it is not good for man to be alone (Gen. 2:18).

a. Later, he urged young widows to marry (I Tim. 5:14) and said that forbidding to marry would be one of the characteristics of the apostasy (I Tim. 4:1-3).

b. G. Campbell Morgan wrote: "No attempt is made here to state the Christian doctrine of marriage in its fullness and completeness. That must be sought elsewhere, and will be found if we study his Ephesian and Colossian letters, and those to Timothy. There we have specific instructions on the marriage relationship. Here it looks as though Paul considered the marriage state a little lower than the state of celibacy. However, he cannot be interpreted in that way, for do not forget that when he was writing to Timothy he spoke of 'forbidding to marry' as a 'doctrine of demons' " (*The Corinthian Letters of Paul*, p. 27).

4. Why it was good or better for a man not to touch a woman (*i.e.* not to get married).

a. Not because Paul was a hater of women as some have charged. He was so concerned about the welfare of wives, he commanded their husbands to love them as Christ loves the church (Eph. 5:25).

b. Not because celibacy is more moral than marriage. That false concept arose during the first three hundred years of the church's existence and is the basis for the celibacy of the Roman Catholic priesthood today. Jerome (340-420 A.D.) wrote: "If it is good for a man not to touch a woman, it must be bad to do so, and therefore celibacy is a holier state than marriage. . . . I suspect the goodness of a thing which the greatness of another evil enforces as a lesser evil" (as quoted by Farrar, p. 233). In that quotation, he not only wrested the verse from its context but he also plainly contradicted the fact that the marriage bed is honorable and undefiled (Heb. 13:4).

c. It was good for men not to marry for two reasons.

(1) Because of the present or impending distress (7:26, 29-31). Distress translates "ananke" which means a

"necessity imposed either by the external condition of things, or by the law of duty" (Thayer, p. 36). In 7:26 it obviously refers to a necessity imposed by external conditions (see also Lk. 21:23; I Thess. 3:7; II Cor. 6:4; 12:10). It is very difficult to know exactly what distress Paul had in mind. Some have thought he believed the Lord's second coming was then at hand. History has proved the incorrectness of that position. Furthermore, Paul plainly taught that the second coming of Jesus was *not* imminent (II Thess. 2:1-12). It has been suggested that the distress was fulfilled in the destruction of Jerusalem in 70 A.D. Unless it can be shown that the Corinthian saints were Jews (Acts 18:5-8 indicates they were not), this interpretation carries little weight. The best explanation is the view of persecution and oppression which the Corinthians were to soon experience (perhaps during the time of Nero). However, one is hard-pressed to support that viewpoint with historical evidence. Paul was saying in light of their coming hardships, it was good for single people to remain unmarried.

(2) Because some could do a greater work for the Lord (7:32-34). With a wife and family, Paul could not have done the great work he did. However, this concept must be understood in the light of 7:7 which teaches that not everyone is gifted to live the celibate life.

C. People should marry to avoid fornication (7:2).

1. Some have felt this to be a low view of marriage. Really, Paul was looking at the matter from a highly practical viewpoint. Sexual desire is one of man's strongest drives. Unless one has a legitimate release for that urge, temptations can be almost overwhelming (living in a monastery or nunnery does not change human nature either). As indicated in Morgan's quotation above, Paul does not here give all of God's revelation on marriage. If one wants to see a "higher" view, let him read Eph. 5:22-23 where the apostle taught that the relationship between husband and wife should be like that of Christ and his church.

2. To support the Roman Catholic view that birth control is a violation of God's will (abortion is not included as birth control since it is the destruction of life already begun but birth control is a process which keeps life from beginning), it

must be proved that reproduction is the *only* reason for having sexual relations. However, 7:2 clearly shows that the fulfillment of sexual desire is one reason for marriage. Hence, birth control cannot be evil.

3. Two other reasons given in the Bible for marriage are companionship (Gen. 2:18) and the bearing of children (I Tim. 2:15; 5:14). If a healthy Christian couple refuses to adopt children or have any of their own, unless there are extenuating circumstances (*e.g.* doing mission work in an extremely dangerous area), are they in obedience to the will of God?

D. The husband controls his wife's body and the wife controls her husband's body (7:3-6).

1. The language upholds the monogamous view of marriage. There is no talk of the husband and his wives or of a wife and her husbands. Surely, polygamy ought not to be tolerated among Christians even in heathen lands.

2. Marriage partners are not to refuse one another (7:5). There may be times when one has a sexual need the other does not feel. At such times, the child of God should remember that he does not have control of his body. It is not right for one to refuse the other sexual privileges to get his or her way. At this point, some married couples in the church have made tragic mistakes. Of course, men and women should not expect to have "heaven" in the bedroom while experiencing "hell" in the rest of the house. Sexual compatibility is simply an expression of the good attitudes which dominate a marriage.

3. Sexual restraint is to be practiced only by mutual agreement (7:5).

a. Lest they be tempted by Satan due to a lack of self control.

b. If a couple agree to practice restraint as an aid to prayer (fasting in KJV is lacking in manuscript support and is likely no part of the original. Apparently, an ascetic added it at a later date), that was to be only for a time or season.

4. Paul spoke by permission or concession (7:6).

a. This does not mean he was giving his uninspired opinion. That statement was penned by God's inspiration as well as all of the others in the same context (II Tim. 3:16).

b. What did he mean when he wrote of *this* as a matter of concession?

(1) Some think he meant marriage is permitted but not commanded. Although that is true, it is doubtful that is what Paul meant here.

(2) Likely, he meant sexual restraint as an aid to prayer was permitted but not commanded. In other words, a husband and wife do not have to restrain their sexual lives even for prayer. They can practice both.

E. Some are specially gifted by God to live a celibate life (7:7; see also Matt. 19:11-12). As was pointed out earlier, they are exceptions to the general rule (Gen. 2:18).

II. *To Christians Married to Unbelievers* (7:8-24).

A. A word to the unmarried and widows (7:8-9).

1. It was good or well for them to remain single (7:8) due to the impending distress (7:26).

a. From 7:8 some have inferred that Paul was a widower (F. W. Farrar, *Life of St. Paul,* pp. 75-82).

(1) "It is not necessary to assume that Paul had never been married. Marriage was regarded as a duty among the Jews, so that a man was considered to have sinned if he had reached the age of twenty without marrying. The Mishna fixed the age of marriage at seventeen or eighteen, and the Babylonish Jews as early as fourteen. A rabbinical precept declared that a Jew who has no wife is not a man. It is not certain, but most probable, that Saul was a member of the Sanhedrin (Acts 26:10). If so, he must have been married, as marriage was a condition of membership" (Vincent, pp. 217-218).

(2) "We may be fairly certain that at some time Paul had been married. We may be certain of that on several grounds. Paul was a Rabbi and it was his own claim that he had failed in none of the duties which Jewish law and tradition laid down. Now orthodox Jewish belief laid down the obligation of marriage. If a man did not marry and have children, he was said to have 'slain his posterity,' 'to have lessened the image of God in the world'. Seven were said to be excommunicated from heaven and the list began, 'A Jew who has no wife;

or who has a wife but no children.' God had said, 'Be fruitful and multiply,' and, therefore, not to marry and not to have children was to be guilty of breaking a positive command of God. The age of marriage was considered to be eighteen; and therefore it is in the highest degree unlikely that so devout and orthodox a Jew as Paul once was would have remained unmarried. On particular grounds there is also evidence that Paul was married. He must have been a member of the Sanhedrin for he says that he gave his vote against the Christians (Acts 26:10). It was a regulation that members of the Sanhedrin must be married men, because it was held that married men were more merciful. It may be that Paul's wife died; it is even more likely that she left him and broke up his home when he became a Christian, so that he did indeed literally give up all things for the sake of Christ. At all events he banished that side of his life once and for all and he never remarried" (Barclay, pp. 67-68).

(3) It cannot be conclusively proved that Paul was ever married. The reference to his casting his vote against Christians (Acts 26:10), mentioned in both of the quotations above, does not necessarily mean he was a member of the Sanhedrin. It is possible that he voted for the death of saints as a leader in one of the Jewish synagogues.

2. However, if they had difficulty in maintaining self-control, it was better (not "kalon" but "kreisson") for them to marry than to burn or to be aflame with passion (7:9).

B. A word to believers joined in marriage (7:10-11).

1. When Paul said, "I command, yet not I, but the Lord" (7:10), he meant that Jesus had personally set forth the truth which applied to the marriage of two believers (Matt. 5:32; 19:9; Mk. 10:11-12; Lk. 16:18).

2. Ideally, they were not to separate. However, if they did separate, they were to remain unmarried or be reconciled to one another (7:10-11). For a similar approach, see I Jno. 2:1-2 where the ideal situation is given and the exception follows.

3. Paul did not mention fornication as the exception given by Jesus (nor did he refer to it in Rom. 7:1-4). It had no direct bearing on the problems at hand but it must be assumed that he was aware of the exception.

C. To Christians married to unbelievers (7:12-24).

    1. They were to remain with their unbelieving companions (7:12-14).

        a. "To the *rest*" (7:12) is a reference to mixed marriages.

        b. "Speak I, not the Lord" (7:12) does not mean Paul was giving his uninspired opinion. He meant that by his authority as an apostle of Christ, he was dealing with a problem to which the Lord did not personally speak during his ministry.

        c. These verses (7:13-14) were probably in response to the Corinthian view that Christians should separate from their unbelieving mates lest they be polluted (a concept upheld by the law of Moses). In light of his Jewish background, one might have expected Paul to say that the saint was "desanctified" by the sinner, however, he declared that the sinner was sanctified by the saint! Hence, the saint was to remain with the sinner (7:13).

        (1) Apparently, the unbeliever was sanctified by the believer because of their union with one another. As gold was sanctified by its union with the temple (Matt. 23:16-17) and a gift was sanctified by its union with the altar (Matt. 23:18-19), the unsaved was sanctified by his union with the saved.

        (2) What is the meaning of this sanctification?

        (a) It does *not* mean the unbeliever was saved simply by virtue of his being married to a believer.

        (b) Perhaps he was sanctified in the Jewish sense of no longer being considered unclean. Under the law, those who were not in covenant relationship with God were regarded as unclean and during the days of Ezra, Hebrews were made to separate from their foreign wives because the holy race had been corrupted by such relationships (Deut. 7:1-5; Neh. 9:2; 13:3; Ez. 9:2; 10:1-44).

        (c) It has been suggested that the believer exerted a sanctifying influence on the unbeliever by leading him to Christ through a godly life (I Pet. 3:1-2).

        (d) It may mean that because of the pure life of the believer, the unbeliever was sanctified or set apart from the practice of wickedness which was so characteristic of Corinth.

(e) Some think the marriage relationship between believer and unbeliever was sanctified in the sense of being approved by God so there was no need for the two to be separated.

d. What is meant by "Otherwise, your children would be unclean, but as it is they are holy" (7:14, RSV)?

(1) It does not mean that children are born into the family of Christ. Babies are not born in the family of Christ or the family of Satan. At birth they are not lost because they have committed no sin (and they are not under damnation because of Adam's transgression, all argument to the contrary not withstanding). Neither are they saved because having done no evil, they have not experienced forgiveness. Babies are *safe*. If they die in infancy, they go into the next life to be with God. Adults who faithfully serve God can join those little ones in heaven (II Sam. 12:23). Paul's words do not refer "to life within the covenant and to the right to baptism" for infants (F. W. Grosheide, *Commentary on the First Epistle to the Corinthians,* p. 165). Such an interpretation "does not accord with the scope and design of the argument. There is not one word about baptism here; not one allusion to it; nor does the argument in the remotest degree bear upon it" (Barnes, p. 117). Incidentally, Barnes was a believer in infant baptism but he knew 7:14 cannot be used in support of the practice.

(2) It can be taken to mean that children were holy in the same sense as the unbeliever was sanctified (a different form of the same word is used to describe each). If the unbeliever was set apart from heathen vices by the believer, the children were set apart from those same practices. If the unbeliever was led to Christ by the sanctifying influence of the believer, the children were led to Christ by that same influence. If the unbeliever was to be considered as ceremonially clean because of his relationship to the believer, the children were also clean because of their relationship to the believer. If the marriage between the believer and unbeliever was sanctified in the sense of having God's endorsement, the children were also holy because they had God's approval as being the product of a legitimate union.

(3) Perhaps Paul was making an "ad hominem" (*i.e.* to the man) argument. If that be true, he was turning their position against them. In other words, he was saying, "Your separation would be a proclamation to all that you regard the marriage as invalid and improper. From this it would follow that the offspring of such a marriage would be illegitimate. But you are not prepared to admit this; you do not believe it. Your children you esteem to be legitimate, and they are so. The marriage tie, therefore, should be regarded as binding, and separation unnecessary and improper" (Barnes, p. 118).

2. If the unbeliever departed, the Christian was not bound (7:15-16).

a. What is meant by not bound or not under bondage (7:15)?

(1) It does not mean:

(a) Bondage to bed and board (*i.e.* bound to maintain a home with the unbeliever). "Now if freedom from obligations to bed and board is all that Paul has in mind in verse 15, we should expect him to say virtually the same thing in verse 15 as he says in verse 11. But that is precisely what he does not say. In verse 15 we find a terseness and severity of terms which viewed from the standpoint of the separation envisioned, are indicative of decisiveness and finality—'let him (or her) depart,' that is, 'let him (or her) be gone' " (J. Murray, *Divorce*, p. 74).

(b) Bondage to Christianity for God's people are always bound to be faithful to Christ regardless of the circumstances.

(c) One is bound to go to such lengths as to compromise his faith with an unbeliever. "If the believing partner were under obligation to prevent the departure, he would be subject to the unbeliever and would virtually abandon his or her faith since only by doing that could a divorce be prevented" (Grosheide, p. 166). Where in the Christian message would a disciple of Christ find even the slightest hint that he could ever compromise the faith?

(2) Apparently, the correct view is that the believer is no longer bound in marriage if deserted by an unbelieving companion. This interpretation is taken for the following reasons.

(a) If the unbeliever consents to remain with the believer, they are bound (7:13), however, if he leaves, they are not bound (7:15). "But the one part of the verse should be allowed to explain the other. An obligation which is said to exist in one case, Paul denies exists in another. If the unbelieving is willing to remain, the believer is bound by the marriage contract; but if she be unwilling, he is not bound" (Hodge, p. 119).

(b) If two believers separate, the bond between them continues to exist and they must remain unmarried or be reconciled (7:10-11), however, there is a striking difference between what was said to them and to the believer who was abandoned by an unbelieving companion. In the latter case, there is not a command or even an implication that he or she is to remain unmarried.

(c) If bound in 7:27, 39 means marriage bond, its opposite, not bound, would surely mean freedom from the marriage bond. If not, why not? A similar application can be made to 7:15.

(d) The opposite of being bound to a wife in 7:27 is being loosed or free from a wife. There is no difference in being loosed from a mate and not being bound to him (7:15).

(e) If Paul was saying the same thing in 7:12-15 that he said in 7:10-11 (i.e. that the individual was to remain unmarried or be reconciled to his mate), it seems that he needlessly repeated himself. He could have simply made the application at 7:10-11 and dropped the matter. Furthermore, if he was giving the same instruction in each instance, how does one explain "yet not I, but the Lord" (7:10) and "to the rest speak I, not the Lord" (7:12)? If both sections mean the same thing, Paul was applying what the Lord personally taught in both situations and his statement, "to the rest speak I, not the Lord," becomes meaningless.

(3) Objections to the above interpretation.

(a) A difference in Greek words. Since Paul used a form of "douloo" for bound in 7:15 and a form of "deo" for bound in 7:27, 39, the marriage bond cannot be contemplated in 7:15 as it is in 7:27, 39. *Reply:* According to Vine, "doulos" (slave or bondman) is from "deo" (Vol. I, p. 139). Thayer stated that most scholars derive "doulos" from "deo" (pp.

157-158). Since, "douloo" is the verb form of "doulos," it follows that it is also derived from "deo." Hence, the two words translated as bound in the RSV are closely akin and the distinction made between them to avoid the conclusion of freedom from the marriage bond at 7:15 vanishes.

(b) Since Paul never used a form of "douloo" elsewhere in reference to the marriage bond, it cannot refer to marriage in 7:15. *Reply:* To say the least, that objection is inconclusive. To illustrate, Paul generally used "doulos" and "diakonos" to describe God's people as servants. However, one time he used "huperetes" for servant (4:1). Paul's reason for using it then was to show the abject lowliness of teachers before Christ (*i.e.* like galley slaves) in contrast to the exalted position given to them by the Corinthians. He also had good reason for using a form of "douloo" in 7:15 to describe the marriage bond. That word is actually stronger than the one he normally used concerning the marriage bond (Vincent, vol. III, p. 219). He deliberately chose it to show that if the unbeliever departed, the believer was really and truly no longer bound to him. That is why the language of finality, "let him depart," is employed (in contrast to the language of 7:11 where the marriage bond was not broken).

(c) Since Jesus gave only one reason for remarriage (*i.e.* fornication) at Matt. 5:32; 19:9, this explanation contradicts his teaching. *Reply:* No one thinks that because Paul gave death as another reason for remarriage (7:39; Rom. 7:1-4), he contradicted the Lord's teaching in Matthew. That being the case, if an additional reason for remarriage (*i.e.* desertion of a believer by an unbeliever) is given in 7:12-15, why should this be construed as contradicting Matt. 5:32; 19:9? Furthermore, the language of Jesus allowing only one reason for remarriage was applied by Paul to two believers, whereas he here spoke of a believer married to an unbeliever (see comments at 7:10, 12 again).

(4) Some added thoughts.

(a) There is no justification for the believer deserting the unbeliever and thinking that he has the right to remarry. That is a perversion of Paul's teaching.

(b) The believer has been called to peace (7:15) and must do everything in his power to make a happy home and marriage. The church member who makes life so wretched and miserable for the unbelieving mate as to drive him away is not contemplated in 7:15 and is not free to remarry.

(c) Probably, in most instance, shortly after his departure, the unbeliever will become involved in sexual immorality. This point is made for those who feel that fornication is the only way (other than death) the marriage bond can be severed.

b. The believer and unbeliever were not bound:

(1) Because God had called the saint to peace (7:15; Col. 3:15).

(2) It was not certain that the unbeliever could be converted (7:16).

3. Illustrations showing the Christian's responsibility to remain with his unsaved partner (7:17-24).

a. The illustrations: Circumcision-uncircumcision (7:18-19; Gal. 5:6; 6:15) and slavery-freedom (7:21-23).

b. *The point:* Each was to remain in the state in which he was called (7:17, 20, 24). If one was called (by the gospel, II Thess. 2:14) with an unbelieving mate, he was to remain in that state.

c. Remaining in the state in which one had been called was Paul's rule for all the churches (7:17).

III. *To the Unmarried and Widows* (7:25-40).

A. It was good or well for them not to marry (7:25-26).

1. That was Paul's inspired judgment or opinion rather than a command of God (7:25).

2. It was good for them not to marry.

a. Because of the impending distress (7:26-31).

b. Because a single person could more fully give himself to the Lord (7:32-35). Keep in mind that this is only for the few who are specially gifted by the Lord to control their passion (7:7).

B. However, it was no sin for them to marry (7:36-38).

1. Because of the strength of physical desire (7:36-37, 2, 9).

2. A difference in translations (7:36-38).

a. According to KJV and ASV, the man and woman are father and daughter.

b. According to RSV, the man and woman are male sweetheart and fiancee.

c. The lesson is the same regardless of which translation one accepts. If the engaged couple could practice self control, in light of the impending distress, it was better for them not to marry. However, if the physical need between them was strong and the father concept is correct, he was to allow his daughter to marry. If the view of the male sweetheart is right, he and his betrothed could marry without sinning.

C. The widow (7:39-40).

1. The wife is bound to her husband as long as he lives (7:39; Rom. 7:1-4). This verse sets forth the ideal state and does not take into consideration the two exceptions already discussed (7:15; Matt. 19:9; 5:32).

2. If her husband dies, she is free to marry again "only in the Lord" (7:39). Meaning?

a. She can marry only a Christian (most expositors hold this view).

(1) Proof: To be in Christ or in the Lord generally means to be a child of God. One must be baptized to get into union with Christ (Rom. 6:3; Gal. 3:27). Hence, Paul was saying the widow can marry only a baptized believer.

(2) Why would he give that kind of instruction to a widow?

(a) Because of their loneliness, widows sometimes behave foolishly and accept the first male who offers himself for marriage.

(b) Since the woman is to be in submission to the husband, she would be placing herself in a very difficult situation religiously by marrying out of Christ.

(c) By marrying an unsaved man, she would greatly hinder her future usefulness in the cause of Christ.

(d) To marry out of Christ would indicate that her commitment to the Savior is not what it should be.

b. She is to marry as the Lord directs.

(1) Proof: Only is from "monon" and can be used as an adverb (Thayer, p. 418; Vine, vol. III, p. 139). Although he accepted the view that she is to marry a Christian, Hodge wrote: "The phrase may be taken adverbially as expressing manner, *as becomes those who are in the Lord, i.e.,* in a Christian manner. She is to marry as becomes a Christian" (p. 134). The word order in Greek is "free she is to whom she wills to be married, only in the Lord." Since adverbs modify adjectives, verbs or other adverbs, if "only" is taken as an adverb, it does not modify "she" or "whom." Hence, it must modify "married." In other words, Paul was describing the manner of marriage rather than the person whom she can marry (from other New Testament teaching, we know there are persons who would not be eligible for her to marry). Phillips translates, "let her be guided by the Lord." Berkley translates, "in a Christian way."

(2) Questions.

(a) If the widow is to marry only a Christian, why is not the same requirement placed upon a young female saint who is marrying for the first time?

(b) If the widow is to marry only a Christian, why is not the same teaching directed to the widower?

(c) If the expression, "in the Lord," always describes one in union with Christ, how is Eph. 6:1 to be explained? In this passage, and others (I Cor. 11:11; Col. 3:18), the expression can mean in harmony with the Lord's instruction.

(d) Does God recognize the marriage of a Chrisian widow to an unchristian man?

(e) If a widow marries an unsaved man, must she separate from him or lose her soul because of rebellion against God's will?

(f) If a widow marries outside the New Testament church, should the congregation where she holds membership withdraw fellowship from her unless she leaves him?

(3) Any Christian, male or female, will have a happier home by marrying a child of God (assuming that the person is truly devoted to Christ). My three children have been taught not to date or marry anyone outside the kingdom

of Christ. It is my daily prayer that they will marry individuals of like precious faith. Repeatedly, my students at Harding College have heard me say they should marry Christians. True wisdom suggests that one select a mate who is like him religiously, culturally, educationally, financially and racially. Serious problems often arise when a Christian marries out of Christ. Since marriage is a union of spirits as well as bodies, it is difficult to see how a man and woman can relate at a deep, meaningful spiritual level when one loves Christ and the other does not. However, after having shown the advantages of marrying a child of God, the question still remains, "Has God made a hard and fast *law* which says that a Christian widow *must* marry a Christian man?"

IX.

CHAPTER EIGHT

Eating Meats Offered to Idols

Structure

I.   8:1-3 — Knowledge Puffs Up.

II. 8:4-6 — An Idol is Nothing.

III. 8:7-13 — Do Not Put a Stumblingblock Before a Weak Brother.

I. Knowledge Puffs Up (8:1-3).

A. From the Corinthians.

1. Paul had received a question "concerning food offered to idols" (8:1, RSV). Likely, the question was "Don't we have the right to eat meat which has been offered to idols?" Perhaps they also asked about eating such meat in an idol temple (8:10).

2. In their letter to him, they had said, "All of us possess knowledge" (8:1, RSV) concerning this matter.

B. Paul's reply.

1. He flatly contradicted their assertion by saying that all did not possess knowledge (*i.e.* have a proper understanding) on the subject (8:7).

2. Knowledge without love puffs up (8:1). Love is a reference to a love for the brethren (I Jno. 3:15), particularly those who were weak. Knowledge without love is simply a type of ignorance (see 13:1-3).

3. One who thinks he knows something does not know as he ought to know (8:2). He was saying that one who is conceited because of his knowledge is not truly a learned person. Humility would come easier if each one remembered that all of us are ignorant but in different fields.

4. Men must love God to be known by him (8:3).

a. The love of God here has reference to its expression in their love for one another as God's children (I Jno. 4:20).

b. McGarvey took knowledge in this verse to mean man's knowledge of God rather than God's knowledge of man (p. 85). It is true that one who loves God also knows him (I Jno. 4:7); however, this probably refers to God's knowledge of man (Gal. 4:9).

c. To be known by God can mean:

(1) To be recognized as belonging to him (II Tim. 2:19).

(2) To be approved by him (Nah. 1:7; Matt. 7:23).

d. It has been suggested that to fall short of God's glory (Rom. 3:23) means one is not known, recognized or approved by God.

II. An Idol is Nothing (8:4-6).

A. Apparently, the Corinthians had said, "An idol is nothing" (KJV) or "has no real existence" (RSV) (8:4). Paul agreed with them. What does the statement mean?

1. Not that the image itself did not exist. All one had to do was look and see that it was there.

2. The gods (*i.e.* the so-called divine beings contemplated by the pagans) represented by the images did not exist. Paul used idol metonymically for the personality it was supposed to represent. Later, he pointed out that idols *did* represent demons (10:20) but they were nothing as far as representing the deities envisioned by the heathen.

B. Many gods and many lords (8:5).

1. Obviously, he was referring to the pagan concept.

2. "Gods in heaven" may be an allusion to the Greek gods of mythology who supposedly resided on Mount Olympus.

3. "Gods on earth" could be a reference to men, animals and idols. All, at one time or another, have been regarded as lords or gods by men with perverted minds.

C. However, there is but one God and one Lord (8:4, 6).

1. One God, the Father (see the Jewish Shema at Deut. 6:4-5).

a. From whom are all things (he is the Creator, Gen. 1:1).

b. For whom we exist (RSV). Man's purpose in living is to serve God (Eccl. 12:13; Isa. 43:7). He can find fulfillment in no other way.

2. One Lord Jesus Christ.

a. Through whom are all things. He is the one by whom the Father created everything (Jno. 1:1-3, 14; Heb. 1:2).

b. Through whom we exist (RSV). All things are sustained by Christ (Col. 1:16-17).

III. Do Not Put a Stumblingblock Before a Weak Brother (8:7-13).

A. Description of the weak brother (8:7).

1. He was weak due to a lack of understanding and his past practice of participating in idolatrous worship.

2. He felt the meat had really been offered to an idol. Meaning?

a. "But there were others having less knowledge, and weaker consciences, who could not shake off the power of old habits, thoughts and associations, and who therefore could not free themselves from their former reverence for the idol, but looked upon it as really representing *something*—a false something, but still a reality. To such the sacrificial meat was part of a real sacrifice, and was contaminating" (McGarvey, p. 87).

b. It seems he was not persuaded that the pagan deities were nothing. He still held the superstitious feeling that the heathen gods *might* be real beings. If this interpretation is correct, it would appear that some new converts were held in the fellowship of the early church while thinking that *possibly* there were lesser deities in addition to Almighty God.

Surely, after more instruction and the passing of a reasonable amount of time such an idea was eventually eradicated.

3. In eating food which had been offered to an idol, his conscience was defiled (Rom. 14:23). That was true because he thought he was involved in worshipping something other than God.

B. Paul's instruction on the matter (8:8-10).

1. Eating or refusing to eat will make one no better or worse before God (8:8).

2. Take heed (or care, RSV) lest your liberty become a stumblingblock to the weak (8:9).

a. Stumblingblock is from "proskomma." It is "an obstacle against which one may dash his foot (akin to 'pros-kopto', to stumble or cause to stumble; 'pros', to or against, 'kopto', to strike), is translated . . . of the spiritual hindrance to another by a selfish use of liberty . . . so in I Cor. 8:9" (Vine, vol. III, p. 129). Since the word is also used concerning Christ (Rom. 9:32-33; I Pet. 2:8), in such an instance, the stumblingstone was good and those who stumbled because of it were evil.

b. The weak brother defiled his conscience in eating meat sacrificed to idols because he was influenced by another brother to do it (8:10).

(1) Some of the Corinthians had taken the position that they could eat meat offered to idols in an idol's temple (using it simply as a place for banqueting) without sinning. The language does not necessarily indicate that they had done such. It seems they had taken that view while contending for their "vaunted" liberty. McGarvey felt that "for a Christian to feast in such a place was a reckless abuse of liberty" (p. 86). Because of Paul's words in 10:21, Hodge believed they would have sinned had they eaten in the precinct of an idol's temple (p. 148). That does not follow if the eating of 8:10 is simply a meal and the eating of 10:21 is participation in idolatrous worship. However, to say the least, McGarvey's statement is correct. If they could eat in an idol's temple without sinning, they were surely getting close to it.

(2) If we engage in an activity, thinking it is right, and lead another to do it in violation of his conscience, we sin

by casting a stumblingblock in his way. "For we make men worse if by our example we teach them to act in contradiction of their conscience" (Farrar, p. 265).

C. Results of causing another to stumble (8:11-12).

1. The weak brother perishes or is destroyed (8:11; Rom. 14:15). According to Calvinism, Christ died only for those whom God predetermined to eternal salvation before the foundation of the world and all such persons will persevere faithfully until the end of life. In one short verse, Paul indicated the falsity of that system by showing that one for whom Christ died can be destroyed or lost eternally (unless one concludes he was setting forth the possibility of what is actually impossible).

2. Christ's death is made void, as far as the perishing brother is concerned (8:11).

3. Sin against the brethren (8:12) whose consciences are weak.

4. Wound the conscience of the weak (8:12). " 'What,' asks St. Chrysostom, 'can be more ruthless than a man who strikes one who is sick?' Was it not a cowardly exercise of liberty to strike the conscience of the defenseless?" (Farrar, p. 265).

5. Sin against Christ (8:12). That is true because Jesus dwells in his people (Gal. 2:20; Eph. 3:17; Col. 1:27) and suffers with them (Matt. 25:40, 45; Acts 9:4).

D. Conclusion: Forego the eating of meat sacrificed to idols for the sake of a weak brother (8:13).

1. The word translated as offend (KJV) or fall (RSV) is from the verb form of "skandalon." It means "properly, the movable stick or tricker ('trigger') of a trap, trap-stick; a trap, snare; any impediment placed in the way and causing one to stumble or fall, (a stumblingblock, occasion of stumbling)" (Thayer, p. 577). It is used at Rev. 2:14 to indicate that Balaam's advice to Balak was a snare or trap for the people of Israel. What Peter said to Jesus about his not going to the cross could be understood in the same way (Matt. 16:22-23). Christ crucified (1:23) or the cross (Gal. 5:11) was a "skandalon" to the Jews because it was contrary to their expectations concerning the Messiah. Jesus became a rock of offence ("skandalon") to them (I Pet. 2:8).

2. Causing a brother to violate his conscience could be depicted as putting a snare or trap in his way. What sensitive child of God would deliberately do that? Many are so concerned about their "rights" they have forgotten their "responsibilities" to others. If Christians were more thoughtful in this area, much which passes for modern-day recreation and entertainment would be avoided. If for no other reason, it would be done out of deference to the convictions of others.

E. Added note—How can 8:7-13 be harmonized with passages which simply condemn the eating of meats sacrificed to idols (Acts 15:29; Rev. 2:20)?

1. First, it should be noted that under certain circumstances it was right to eat such meat.

a. When one did not know it had been used sacrificially (10:25-27).

b. When eating it did not cause a brother to stumble (8:13; 10:28-29).

c. When it was not eaten in connection with heathen worship (10:14-22).

2. Harmony.

a. It has been advocated that Acts 15:29 was limited to those places among the Gentiles where eating meats sacrificed to idols was regarded as an abomination.

b. Acts 15:29 and Rev. 2:20 may deal with the eating of meats only as it pertained to pagan worship.

X.

CHAPTER NINE

Paul's Defense of His Apostleship

Structure

I.   9:1-6 — Paul, a Genuine Apostle.

II. 9:7-14 — Paul Had a Right to Their Support.

III. 9:15-23 — Paul Did Not Exercise His Right.

IV. 9:24-27 — Paul Had Purpose in His Actions.

I. Paul, a Genuine Apostle (9:1-6).

A. Background. It seems that false teachers had gone to Corinth after Paul left. Apparently, they denied his apostleship to undermine his teaching. If he were not a true apostle, his doctrine was false (an approach made by the Judaizing teachers who went to the churches of Galatia). Along with Paul, Barnabas was also attacked (9:6). The criticism of Paul fell into three areas. First, it was said that he refused to take financial support for his work because he knew he was an imposter. Barclay drew a parallel in the following words: "The enemies of Socrates and Plato had in fact taunted them because they took no money for teaching, and had hinted that they did so because their teaching was worth nothing" (p. 88). Second, it was alleged that he had not seen Jesus during his earthly ministry. Since one had to be a witness of the resurrected Savior to be an apostle (Acts 1:22), they contended he was not qualified. Third, he was not married as the rest of the apostles and the Lord's brothers. On the basis of these criticisms, it appears the Corinthians had raised questions concerning his claim to apostleship in their letter to him.

B. Paul's questions (9:1-2).

    1. Am I not free?

        a. Free from the responsibility to regulate his life in harmony with the opinions and prejudices of others (see 9:19).

        b. A freeman deserving of financial support rather than a slave who works without pay.

    2. Am I not an apostle? Have I not seen Jesus Christ our Lord?

        a. If the latter explanation is accepted for the first question, "Am I not an apostle?" likely means that as an apostle he was more entitled to wages than an ordinary teacher.

        b. However, the questions concerning his apostleship and his having seen Jesus are probably linked (as given above) since it was essential for one to have seen the risen Lord to qualify as an apostle. Christ appeared to Paul on the road to Damascus to enable him to meet that qualification (15:8; Acts 26:16-18). This must be a reference to that experience (although he did have other visions later—Acts 18:8-10; 23:11; II Cor. 12:1-10). Whether Paul ever saw Jesus prior to his crucifixion cannot be definitely determined (II Cor. 5:16 is really of no help in the matter).

    3. Are not you my work (workmanship, RSV) in the Lord?

        a. This question is based on reasoning similar to a tree being known by its fruits (Matt. 7:16-20).

        b. A seal vouches for the validity of a document. Since the Corinthian saints were the seal of his apostleship (9:2), if he were not a true apostle, they were not Christians! He was not only an apostle but *their* apostle.

C. Other proofs which Paul could have used.

    1. He had performed the signs (*i.e.* miracles which *signified* that his claim was true) of an apostle among them (II Cor. 12:12).

2. The gospel he preached was not taught to him by others but directly communicated to him by Christ himself (Gal. 1:11-12).

D. Paul's defense (9:3-6).

1. Answer (KJV) or defense (RSV) is from "apologia" (it also appears in Acts 22:1; 25:16; Phil. 1:7, 16; II Tim. 4:16; I Pet. 3:15) which means "verbal defense, speech in defense" (Thayer, p. 65).

2. Questions.

a. Do we not have a right to our food and drink (9:4, RSV)?

(1) Paul was not supported by the Corinthians while in their community (see introductory chapter).

(2) In this query, he clearly implied that he had a right to receive food and drink at their expense.

b. Do we not have the right to be accompanied by "a Christian wife" (9:5, Phillips)?

(1) "Gune," translated as wife, denotes a woman whether married or unmarried (Vine, vol. IV, p. 215). Context determines its meaning. To illustrate, at I Tim. 3:11, KJV has wives (i.e. wives of deacons) but RSV has women (which sets forth the possibility of deaconesses in the apostolic church).

(2) After showing wife to be the correct translation of "gune," Farrar dealt with the concept of celibacy held by some of the church fathers as follows: "This plain meaning . . . was so distasteful to the morbid asceticism which held celibacy in sort of a Manichaean reverence, that the scribes of the fourth, fifth, and later centuries freely tampered with the text, in the happily fruitless attempt to get rid of this meaning. They endeavored by putting the word in the plural or by omitting 'wife' to suggest that the women whom the apostles travelled with were 'deaconnesses.' Augustine, Tertullian, Ambrose, and others explain the verse as 'ministering women' (Lk. 8:2-3). The false interpretation avenged itself on the bias which led to it. Valla adopts the wilful invention that the apostles, though married, travelled with their wives only as sisters. . . . It was the cause of such shameful abuses and misrepresentations that at last the practice of travelling about with unmarried women, who went under the name of 'sisters,' 'beloved,' 'companions,' was distinctly forbidden by the third

canon of the first Council of Nice. Simon Magus might un-
blushingly carry about with him a Tyrian woman named
Helena; but apostles and true Christians would never have
been guilty of any conduct which could give a handle to base
suspicions" (p. 287).

(3) Since Paul had the power or right to be married
to a Christian woman, does this mean a saint, under no circumstances, has a right to marry a sinner? Is it a sin for a
child of God to marry outside the church? If so, must those in
such relationships separate to please God? Some readily
answer the first two queries in the affirmative but they are
hesitant to give the same answer to the third question. If an
unequal yoke exists by virtue of a believer being married to an
unbeliever, they must separate (II Cor. 6:14-17). Since no one
(to my knowledge) is willing to take that position, all among
us must believe that the marriage union itself is not an unequal
yoke. A marriage or business relationship does become an
unequal yoke when the saint must engage in evil to maintain
the arrangement. In that situation, the Christian's duty is
clear—"Come out from among them and be ye separate, saith
the Lord" (II Cor. 6:17). To contend that it is a violation of
God's word to marry an unsaved person on the basis of 9:5 is
to make too much of the language. The apostles and brothers
of the Lord, as leaders in the church, had the right to be
married only to Christians. However, this does not mean the
same restriction was bound on every church member in the
first century (see comments on 7:39). As pointed out earlier, it
is far better for a saint to marry a person of like precious faith,
yet, one must exercise caution lest he make a law where God
has made none.

(4) From 9:5, it is obvious that Peter was accompanied by his wife or leading about a sister to whom he was
not married (see Farrar's comments above). The former is a
more honorable interpretation than the latter. Surely, Paul
was not criticized for failing to lead about an unmarried
woman! Apparently, Peter had a wife during the Lord's ministry (Matt. 8:14; Mk. 1:30). In light of 9:5, Catholic appeal to
Matt. 19:27-30 to prove he gave up his wife for the Lord's
cause is a distortion of the passage. According to Romanism,

Peter, a married man, was the first pope. If so, why is not today's pontiff allowed a wife (see I Tim. 4:1-3)?

(5) The brothers of the Lord were James, Joses, Simon and Judas (Matt. 13:55). There was a time when they did not believe in Jesus as the Christ (Jno. 7:3-5), however, following his resurrection, they became his disciples (Acts 1:14).

c. Do we not have a right to refrain from working for a living (and be supported by fellow-Christians) (9:6)?

(1) The two categories of 9:5 are apostles and brothers of the Lord. Since Barnabas was not a brother of Christ, it seems that Paul identified him as an apostle (see Acts 14:4, 14). An apostle was "one sent forth ('apo,' from; 'stello,' to send)" (Vine, vol. I, p. 63). The two unnamed brethren of II Cor. 8:23 are described as apostles (in the Greek) of the churches. Epaphroditus was an apostle or messenger of the Philippian church (Phil. 2:25). Perhaps Barnabas was an apostle in the sense of having been sent forth to preach the gospel by the church at Antioch. However, since he was specially commissioned by the Holy Spirit (Acts 13:1-4), he may have been more than simply an apostle of the church (see Gal. 2:9). For additional references to apostles (other than the twelve), read Rom. 16:7; I Thess. 2:6.

(2) Because of the references to Peter and Barnabas (9:5-6), one might be led to ask if they had ever been to Corinth. The book of Acts is silent on the question. If they had never been there, why did their names enter the discussion? Perhaps they are mentioned because they were well known by Christians everywhere.

II. Paul Had a Right to Their Support (9:7-14).

A. Wages for labor is the foundation of employment (9:7). He illustrated that truth with a soldier, vinedresser and shepherd.

B. The law of Moses provided wages for service (9:8-10; Deut. 25:4).

1. The figure is that of an ox trampling wheat or barley under its feet at the threshing floor to separate the grain from the stalk.

2. The statement about the ox was made altogether (KJV) or entirely (RSV) for our sake (*i.e.* that men might understand the importance of paying a fair wage to their employees). From a cursory look at 9:10 some might conclude that God has no concern for animals but that is not the case.

    a. "Pantos" is the word translated as altogether or entirely. It can also be translated as "chiefly, mainly, principally, doubtless" (Barnes, p. 158) or "doubtless, surely, certainly" (Thayer, p. 476) or "doubtless, assuredly" (Vincent, vol. III, p. 231).

    b. The way it is translated elsewhere in the New Testament.

        (1) Lk. 4:23 — "surely" (KJV); "doubtless" (RSV).

        (2) Acts 18:21 — "by all means" (KJV).

        (3) Acts 21:22 — "must needs" (KJV); "certainly" (RSV).

        (4) Acts 28:4 — "no doubt" (KJV, RSV).

    c. God is concerned about animals and provides for them (Ps. 104:21, 27-30; Matt. 6:26; Lk. 12:24). The point is that he is more concerned about men. Phillips translates: "Now does this imply merely God's care for oxen, or does it include his care for us too? Surely, we are included! You might even say the words were written for us." Luther felt the language was written entirely for our sake since we can read and animals cannot!

3. Illustrations (9:10). — As the plowman and thresher labor in hope of sharing in the harvest, preachers of the gospel have the right to expect to be paid for their work.

  C. The law of exchange demands support (9:11).

    1. The principle of sowing spiritually and reaping materially as seen in other passages.

    a. Gentile brethren in Macedonia and Achaia gave to the poor among the saints in Jerusalem because they were spiritually indebted to the Jews (Rom. 15:25-31).

    b. Christians at Philippi, spiritually indebted to Paul because he had led them to Christ, supported him financially in his work of preaching (Phil. 4:15-17).

    c. Saints in Antioch, who were spiritually indebted to the Jews (in the same sense as Macedonia and Achaia — Rom.

15:25-31), sent funds to help disciples of Christ in Judea (Acts 11:27-30).

d. Children of God in Macedonia, who were spiritually indebted to Paul for his having taught them the gospel, helped him financially while he was in Corinth (II Cor. 11:8-9).

2. There is not a case in the New Testament of individuals or churches sending money to other individuals or churches where the principle of spiritual indebtedness does not exist. Those opposed to the kind of cooperation employed to maintain such programs as World Radio and Herald of Truth contend that there is a pattern in the New Testament for church cooperation. If that view is correct, the concept of spiritual indebtedness is part of the pattern. That would mean one church could not send funds to another church to do anything unless the sending church was indebted spiritually to the receiving church. That view must be accepted or one must abandon his contention of "pattern" cooperation.

D. The fact that they had supported others indicated Paul had a right to their support too (9:12).

E. Those employed in temple service shared in the sacrificial offerings (9:13; Num. 18:8-13; Deut. 18:1).

F. The Lord ordained or commanded that preachers should live by the gospel (9:14). Apparently, this is a reference to Matt. 10:10 or Lk. 10:7 or to both.

III. Paul Did Not Exercise His Right (9:15-23).

A. He was not then writing for their financial assistance (9:15). He could have shamed them for not supporting him but he preferred death rather than being deprived of his ground of boasting (*i.e.* preaching without pay).

B. With or without support, Paul was compelled to preach the gospel (9:16-18; cf. Acts 4:20).

1. He could not glory in preaching (9:16) since the work had been thrust upon him by God and was not of his own choosing (9:17). Had he made the choice, he would have been rewarded by experiencing the fulfillment of a self-chosen labor. Instead, he had been entrusted with a commission or

stewardship by the Lord (9:17; I Thess. 2:4) and it was mandatory that he obey. This is not to say he preached against his will. Other passages show that he considered preaching a joyous labor (Rom. 1:13-15; Eph. 3:8; I Thess. 2:17-20). "The difference, therefore, here between ('ekon' and 'akon'), 'willingly' and 'unwillingly,' is not the difference between cheerfully and reluctantly, but between optional and obligatory" (Hodge, p. 162). Paul was saying he could not boast in simply fulfilling what was his duty (see Lk. 17:10).

2. Paul's reward came in *choosing* to forego his right of financial support through preaching the message without charge (9:18). He felt he had no choice concerning his call to the apostleship but he could choose to preach without pay. Apparently, he was rewarded in at least three ways. First, he knew he had sacrificed his needs in the interest of others. Second, he realized he had not fully used his God-given privileges. Third, he had confidence that his motives for preaching were free from any financial consideration.

3. Further observations.

a. Some, in emulation of Paul, think they should engage in secular pursuits to make a living and preach without pay where the church is weak or non-existent. This is a noble aspiration which few have fulfilled. In most cases, such people become involved in full-time "tent-making" and preach a little "on the side." Paul spent most of his time in sharing the good news of redemption and very little time in working with his hands. Not many men with families to support can maintain that kind of balance. Alexander Campbell was able to do it only because he was independently wealthy.

b. Some churches have been hurt by hearing preachers whom they did not pay. Members grew accustomed to receiving something for nothing and failed to practice biblical liberality. Later, even Paul ironically apologized to the Corinthians for having wronged them in this matter (II Cor. 12:13). Most preachers need to be married but Paul was an exception. Most preachers must also be supported financially although Paul was an exception.

C. Why Paul, generally, did not receive financial support (9:19-23).

1. That he might glory (*i.e.* have confidence in his selfless motivation) in preaching without pay (9:15).

2. That he might make the gospel free of charge (9:18).

3. That he might reach the most people with the gospel (9:12, 19-23).

   a. He was free from all men but he was the slave of all (9:19; 10:33). He practiced what he preached. In chapter eight, he instructed the strong to surrender their rights in the interest of the weak. In this chapter, he related how he followed the same principle in the interest of the lost. Paul yielded his rights only in areas of indifference. He did not compromise the gospel or do wrong out of deference to the view of others. He sought primarily to please God rather than men (Gal. 1:10; Acts 5:29).

   b. To the Jews, he became as a Jew (9:20).

   (1) To a Jewish audience, he described himself as a Pharisee (Acts 23:6).

   (2) He kept Jewish feasts (Acts 20:16).

   (3) He observed Jewish vows (Acts 18:18; 21:26).

   (4) He circumcised Timothy (Acts 16:3). However, when Judaizers attempted to make circumcision essential to salvation, he would not yield to them for an hour and he refused to circumcise Titus, a Gentile (Gal. 2:1-5). Expediency was the only consideration in the case of Timothy, but a gospel principle was at stake in the case of Titus. He also rebuked Peter for playing the part of a Jew among Gentile Christians at Antioch (Gal. 2:11-14).

   c. To those under the law, he became as one under the law (9:20).

   (1) The difference between Jews and those under the law has been explained as follows:

   (a) Jews viewed nationally and those under the law viewed religiously.

   (b) Jews by origin and those under the law as Gentiles proselyted to the Jewish faith.

   (c) Jews by race and those under the law as rigid Jews or Pharisees.

   (d) Those under the law simply being an elaboration or explanation of his former statement about Jews.

(2) The expression, "though not being myself under the law" (RSV), does not appear in KJV, however, it does have strong support in the Greek manuscripts, early versions of the New Testament and quotations from the church fathers. It is carried in the later translations of the New Testament. For the doctrine of freedom from law, see Rom. 6:14; 7:1-7.

d. To those outside the law, he became as one outside the law (9:21).

(1) This is a reference to Gentiles who were outside the law of Moses but not totally without law (Rom. 2:12-16).

(2) Perhaps to guard himself against the charge of antinomianism, he added that he was "under the law of Christ." Christians are under grace rather than a legal system but this does not mean there are no rules for them to follow.

e. To the weak, he became weak (9:22). He honored their views by refusing to do anything which would cause them to stumble (8:7-13; Rom. 14:1-15:13).

f. His purposes for such activity.

(1) To gain more disciples for the Lord (9:19).

(a) Ordinarily, men are not critical of those who work without pay. In that situation the laborer is obviously not seeking his own welfare (how many times have evangelists been denounced as preaching "just for the money they make"?).

(b) Yet, in Paul's case, his method was turned against him in an attempt to overthrow his claim as an apostle. Although he was not paid for his work by the Corinthians, it was alleged that the contribution commanded for the poor saints in Jerusalem (16:1-2) actually went into his own pockets. He was accused of being crafty in not taking pay for his preaching and making a profit by means of guile (II Cor. 12:16-18).

(c) If a man does or does not take money for preaching, he will be criticized by some. It is simply impossible to please everyone. Jesus beautifully depicted this truth when he described the reactions of the people to the different approaches employed by himself and John the Baptist (Matt. 11:16-18).

(2) To personally share in the blessings of the gospel (9:23). "Apostle though he was, he had his own salvation to work out. He was not himself saved by proclaiming salvation to others, no more than the baker is fed by making bread for others or the physician kept in health by prescribing for others. Paul had a life of his own to lead, a duty of his own to discharge, a soul of his own to save; and he recognized that what was laid before him as the path to salvation was to make himself entirely the servant of others" (Dods, p. 213).

IV. Paul Had Purpose in His Actions (9:24-27).

A. He illustrated with athletics.

1. Background. "The isthmus of Corinth was the scene of the Isthmian games, one of the four great national festivals of the Greeks. The celebration was a season of great rejoicing and feasting. The contests included horse, foot, and chariot racing; wrestling, boxing, musical and poetical trials, and later, fights of animals. The victor's prize was a garland of pine leaves, and his victory was generally celebrated in triumphal odes called 'epinikia,' of which specimens remain among the poems of Pindar. At the period of Paul's epistles the games were still celebrated, and the apostle himself may very probably have been present" (Vincent, vol. III, p. 235).

2. Athletes are characterized by purpose (9:24-25).

a. Runners participate in a race to win the prize (9:24).

b. Athletes practice temperance or self-control in all things to obtain a corruptible crown or perishable wreath (9:25). In describing the training of runners who took part in the Isthmian races, Vincent wrote: "The candidate for the races was required to be ten months in training, and to practice in the gymnasium immediately before the games, under the direction of judges who had themselves been instructed for ten months in details of the games" (vol. III, p. 236).

B. Conclusion (9:26-27).

1. Paul did not run uncertainly or aimlessly but purposefully (9:26).

2. He did not box as one beating the air (9:26). This may be a reference to shadow boxing or to missing with his

punches in fighting an opponent. Paul's blows were straight and true and he did not spare. The point is he fought with purpose.

3. He pommeled his body and subdued it (9:27, RSV).

a. The word translated as pommel or buffet (ASV) is "hupopiazo" which means "literally, to strike under the eye (from 'hupopion,' the part of the face below the eye; 'hupo,' under, 'ops,' an eye), hence, to beat the face black and blue (to give a black eye), is used metaphorically . . . of Paul's suppressive treatment of his body, in order to keep himself spiritually fit" (Vine, vol. I, p. 156). There is no justification in this figure for the actual beating of the body with whips as some ascetics have done and continue to do (Col. 2:20-23).

b. Purpose for such action.

(1) Lest since he had preached to others, he should be a castaway or disqualified. "When the cedar of Lebanon trembles, what shall the reed by the brookside do?" (see 10:12). If, through carelessness, the great apostle Paul could have been lost, obviously, the same could happen to any child of God (II Pet. 2:20-22).

(2) Concerning the word "preached," McGarvey suggested the possibility of Paul's using the figure of a herald or announcer at the games who also participated in the athletic contests. It was unusual for the same man to occupy both positions. On one occasion, Nero did both (p. 96). Having announced the terms of salvation, it would have been tragic had Paul been disqualified to participate in it.

4. Paul's primary reason for including this last paragraph was to illustrate that he did have a reason in preaching without pay. Everyone should have a noble reason for his actions. Jesus went about doing good (Acts 10:38), however, the majority of today's world simply "go about."

XI.

CHAPTER TEN

Eating Meats Offered to Idols

Structure

I. Israel, an Example to Warn the Corinthians (10:1-13).

A. Background. Some of the Corinthians were quite confident they could eat meat sacrificed to pagan gods even in an idol temple (8:10). They reasoned that since they had been baptized and had partaken of the Lord's Supper, such activity would not endanger their souls. Like the Gnostics who arose a short time later and those today who believe a Christian cannot so sin as to be eternally lost, the Corinthians had a false sense of security. Repeatedly, it has been said that those who will not learn from history are determined to repeat it. There is no need to relate fiction to illustrate tragedy. History is replete with instances of calamity. Paul, by appealing to the history of Israel, sought to correct Corinthian misunderstanding.

B. Israel's blessings (10:1-4).

  1. All were baptized (10:2).

    a. The Hebrews, as spiritual fathers of Gentile Christians (10:1; Gal. 3:7, 9, 26-29), had been baptized into Moses (10:2).

      (1) In crossing the sea, the Israelites fully renounced Pharaoh and their old life of bondage. They were "born again" into Moses and freedom. They were "baptized" (metaphorically) into the authority, leadership and laws of Moses. They became his disciples and pledged to support and obey him from that time onward.

      (2) In the Christian era, men are baptized *into* union with Christ (Rom. 6:3, 5) and *into* the name of the Father, Son and Holy Spirit (Matt. 28:19).

    b. They were baptized in the cloud and in the sea (10:2).

      (1) This is probably an allusion to immersion, the one and only baptism authorized in the New Testament (Eph. 4:5; Rom. 6:4; Col. 2:12). As biblically baptized people are engulfed in water, the Hebrews were engulfed by water on two sides (Ex. 14:22) and the cloud overhead.

      (2) It is true that the cloud generally led Israel and that it stood between them and the Egyptians during the early part of that historic night of deliverance (Ex. 14:19-20), however, it actually covered them during the crossing of the sea (10:1; Num. 14:14; Ps. 105:38-39).

    c. The Hebrews were saved from Egypt the *day* they crossed the sea (Ex. 14:30). Similarly, the alien sinner today is saved when he crosses the water of baptism (Mk. 16:16). When Israel went through the water God delivered them from bondage into freedom and one scripturally baptized today is delivered from the bondage of sin into the glorious freedom of forgiveness (Rom. 6:1-7, 16-18).

    d. Some have attempted to refute this typological reasoning by saying that as the blood of the Passover lamb was shed before the Hebrews went through the water, the blood of the Savior washes away one's sins before he is baptized. That viewpoint is incorrect for the following reasons:

      (1) Israel was still in Egyptian captivity after the Passover lamb was killed and before they crossed the sea.

(2) The slaying of the Passover lamb saved only the first born Jewish males from death (Ex. 12:29-32; 13:11-15) and not the Hebrew nation from bondage.

(3) The death of the Passover lamb and the crossing of the sea, as types, correspond to the death of Jesus and one's baptism in water at which time he receives the benefits of Christ's death (Rom. 6:3) and is saved from all past sins (Acts 2:38; 22:16).

2. All ate the same supernatural or spiritual food (10:3).

a. The manna which fell upon Israel daily in the wilderness (Ex. 16:15; Jno. 6:31) was spiritual in origin—it came from God (probably gifts are called spiritual for the same reason—12:1).

b. Manna is called angel's bread (Ps. 78:25). Likely, this also refers to its heavenly origin.

3. All drank the same supernatural or spiritual drink (10:3).

a. This is a reference to Israel's drinking from a rock during the wilderness wandering (Ex. 17:6-7; Num. 20:10-11).

b. The food and drink were spiritual because of origin, however, the rock (i.e. Christ) was spiritual because of his nature (he was spiritual rather than physical).

c. The rock which followed them was a type of Christ (10:4). As water was provided by the rock, Jesus now provides men with living water (eternal life—Jno. 4:14; indwelling Spirit—Jno. 7:38-39).

d. How did the rock follow the Hebrews (10:4)?

(1) According to a Jewish tradition, the rock actually moved through the wilderness with them. "Paul appears to recall a rabbinic tradition that there was a well formed out of the spring in Horeb, which gathered itself up into a rock like a swarm of bees, and followed the people for forty years; sometimes rolling itself, sometimes carried by Miriam, and always addressed by the elders, when they encamped, with the words, 'Spring up, O well!' " (Vincent, p. 239). Surely, Paul did not hold that view, although he may have had the tradition in mind when he penned these words.

(2) The supply of water from the rock followed them since they had enough to last for some time (Ps. 105:41).

(3) The best explanation is they drank from the rock provided by the Lord and the anti-type of the rock, Christ himself, followed them and provided for their needs.

e. 10:4 proves the pre-incarnate existence of the personality now known as Jesus Christ. Other passages upholding this truth are:

(1) 10:9 has Christ in KJV. The manuscript evidence favors the reading of Lord, however, Christ does appear in Codex Beza, some of the early versions of the New Testament and in some quotations from church fathers.

(2) An alternate reading for Lord in Jude 5 is Jesus, however, it must be admitted that some have understood this as a reference to Joshua. For a similar case, see Heb. 4:8 in KJV.

(3) Heb. 11:26 indicates that Moses suffered reproach for Christ. Although Christ is an anacronism (*i.e.* connecting the Person active in delivering the Hebrews from bondage with a name that came later in history), this verse supports the point being made.

(4) In the Old Testament "Yahweh" (the Hebrew word translated as Lord or Jehovah) is used in reference to God alone. However, in the New Testament, Yahweh passages are applied to Jesus (see Isa. 6:1-6 and Jno. 12:37-41; Isa. 40:3 and Matt. 3:3; Joel 2:32 and Acts 2:21). Obviously, this proves that Christ is God.

(5) The One whom we adore as Lord and Savior existed before Abraham (Jno. 8:58). God the Son is co-eternal with God the Father (Jno. 1:1-3, 14).

4. *Paul's point in 10:1-4:* As Israel was baptized and partook of spiritual food and drink, the Corinthians had been baptized and had partaken of the bread and fruit of the vine in the Lord's Supper.

C. Nevertheless, most of the Hebrews were overthrown in the wilderness (10:5-10).

1. Most (RSV), from "pleion," rather than many (KJV) is preferred (10:5). As a matter of fact, of the 603,550 men twenty years of age and older who left Egypt, only Joshua and Caleb entered the promised land (Num. 1:3; 2:32; 14:29-30; 26:64-65). It is hoped that the mortality rate among present day Christians is not as high!

2. Overthrown (10:5) is from "katastronnumi" (found only here in the New Testament) which means "to strew over (the ground); to prostrate, slay (cf. our 'to lay low')" (Thayer, p. 337). It is a combination of "('kata,' down, 'stronnumi,' or 'stronnuo,' to spread)" (Vine, vol. III, p. 135). The NEB translates, "for the desert was strewn with their corpses" (see Num. 14:29, 32). Dods compared the fate of Israel with Napoleon's grand army which was strewn across Russia in its retreat from Moscow (p. 237).

3. Ways in which Israel displeased God (10:6-10).

a. They lusted or desired evil (10:6). This may be a general description of Israel's attitude during the wilderness wandering followed by specific illustrations (idolatry, immorality, etc.). However, it could refer specifically to their lust or strong craving for the fleshpots of Egypt, for which God destroyed many of them by a plague (Num. 11:4-6, 33-34). The latter interpretation is particularly appropriate in view of how some Corinthian Christians desired to participate in idolatrous feasts.

b. They were idolaters (10:7; Ex. 32:1-35).

(1) Since Paul was leading up to the question of eating meats in idolatrous worship, Exodus 32 is especially relevant (it would be worthwhile to read that entire chapter).

(2) Paul quoted Ex. 32:6 indicating that Israel rose up to play (KJV) or dance (RSV). Some think play is used broadly to include dancing (Ex. 32:19). Others feel dancing was the kind of play in which they engaged. A third view distinguishes between the words and suggests that the Hebrews played and danced. In Farrar's opinion, play was "used euphemistically for the worse concomitants of a sensual natural worship" (p. 323).

(3) Idolatry is not limited to the worship of heathen images. Covetousness is idolatry (Col. 3:5). Recently, I read a tract entitled "The Idolatry of Sports." Any person, activity or thing placed before God in one's life is a form of idolatry. Today, men are basically what they have always been. Idols may differ but the sin is as widespread now as ever.

c. They committed fornication or sexual immorality (10:8; Num. 25:1-18).

(1) The mastermind behind Israel's disaster at Baal-peor was Balaam, who loved the wages of unrighteousness (Rev. 2:14; Num. 31:8; II Pet. 2:15; Jude 11).

(2) Fornication accompanied the practice of idolatry (Num. 25:1-9; Acts 15:29). Canaanite religion associated the fertility of the soil with fertility in the human body. Licentiousness was not only practiced but consecrated. When men reject Almighty God, immorality always follows as night follows day (see Rom. 1:18-32).

(3) Difference in the number who were killed by the plague. It is 23,000 here and 24,000 at Num. 25:9.

(a) Perhaps each writer used a round number. Paul rounded down and Moses rounded up. This would mean there were actually between 23,000 and 24,000 who died.

(b) Maybe there were two days of the plague with 23,000 dying one day (10:8) and 24,000 dying over the two day period (Num. 25:9).

(4) The person who says he cannot be tempted sexually is so young his passions have not arisen, so ignorant he does not know what is occurring, so old they have already subsided, not normal or lying. For the vast majority, only death will totally deliver from this temptation. Not simply a fear of evil (which is extremely important) but a passionate love for purity characterizes those who do not go astray in this realm.

d. They tempted Christ (KJV) or put the Lord to the test (RSV) (10:9).

(1) Tempted or tested is from "ekpeirazo," about which Vincent wrote: "The compound word is very significant, 'to tempt out' (ek) tempt 'thoroughly;' try 'to the utmost.' It occurs in three other places: Matt. 4:7; Lk. 4:12; 10:25; and in every case, is used of tempting Christ" (p. 240).

(2) Israel tempted the Lord in complaining about their food (Num. 21:4-5). As a result, God sent fiery serpents among them and many were bitten and died (Num. 21:6). If the Lord dealt with his people who complain about their food today in a similar fashion, the disciples of Christ would be thinned out considerably!

(3) There are at least two ways to try God.

(a) In a bad sense. By distrust expressed in ungodly conduct which tries his justice and patience (Acts 5:9; 15:10; Heb. 3:9) or by foolishly and needlessly exposing oneself to danger expecting to be shielded from harm by him (Matt. 4:7). The Corinthians could have tempted God in either of these ways. They might have become guilty of discontent and impatience or they might have exposed themselves to needless danger in attending idolatrous feasts.

(b) In a good sense. By humbly yielding to God and his purposes and seeking his support in return. Gideon tried the Lord in seeking assurance of victory over the Midianites (Jud. 6:36-40). God commanded the Jews to try him (i.e. see that he would provide for their needs) through the faithful practice of tithing (Mal. 3:10-11).

e. They grumbled or murmured (10:10).

(1) Two occurrences to which this may refer.

(a) Israel complained against Moses and Aaron at Canaan's southern border after the spies had returned and submitted their distressing report (Num. 14:1-2, 27).

(b) The Hebrews murmured against their leaders because of the death of Korah, Dathan and Abiram, three rebels whom God had swallowed by the earth (Num. 16:41).

(2) They were destroyed by the Destroyer.

(a) In each instance cited above, some died by a plague (Num. 14:37; 16:41-50). Conceivably, in both cases, the Destroyer (Ex. 12:23; Heb. 11:28) was involved. If he was God's instrument each time, obviously, he used pestilence as the medium for destruction.

(b) The Destroyer may have been an angel (II Sam. 24:15-16; Acts 12:23). McGarvey suggested he was the angel of death whom the Jews called Sammael (p. 102).

D. Paul's application (10:11-13).

1. Israel's experiences serve as examples to warn Christians (10:6, 11).

a. The word translated as examples (10:6) or ensamples (10:11) in KJV is from "tupos" (type or figure). A type is an Old Testament person or event symbolizing or foreshadowing a New Testament person or event. Melchizedek was a type of

Christ (Heb. 5:10; 6:20). Lambs offered during the Mosaic period were types of Christ's sacrifice at Golgotha (Jno. 1:29). However, Israel's apostasies and attendant punishments must not be understood as having been predetermined by God simply to serve as types to us. Since "tupos" can also be taken as example (Phil. 3:17; I Tim. 4:12; I Pet. 5:3), it likely has that meaning here. The Hebrews had repeatedly turned from God and suffered catastrophe and Christians can learn from their bad exampes. We cannot live long enough to make every mistake. We should profit some by the mistakes of others.

b. The events in Israel's history, to which Paul had made reference, were written as an admonition or warning to Christians (10:11; Rom. 15:4).

c. Followers of Christ are described as those upon whom the end of the ages have come (RSV). Meaning?

(1) Christ's second coming which Paul believed was near. That interpretation is false, or by the Spirit's inspiration, Paul taught error. It is true that Jesus came in the destruction of Jerusalem, using Rome as the instrument of his wrath (Matt. 24:1-35), however, his personal coming was not "at hand" during the apostolic period (II Thess. 2:1-12).

(2) End of the Jewish dispensation.

(3) The Christian era so called because it is the last and final age of time. Or, it can be taken as the Christian dispensation from another point of view. End (literally, ends) is from "telos" which can mean "the end to which all things relate, the aim, purpose: (I Tim. 1:5)" (Thayer, p. 620). "Ellicott acutely remarks that the plural, 'ends,' marks a little more distinctly the idea of each age of preparation having passed into the age that succeeded it, so that now all the 'ends' of the ages have come down to them" (Vincent, p. 241). Hence, Paul may have meant we are now living during that time to which all previous ages aimed (see Heb. 9:26).

2. Take heed to keep from falling (10:12). The child of God who lives a life of trusting obedience will never fall (II Pet. 1:10). That concept is not "once saved, always saved" but the security of faithful saints. Paul did not here reflect upon that precious point of view. He was writing to warn the

proud who felt they could presume upon the grace of God (see Rom. 6:1-2; 11:20).

3. God is faithful (10:13).

a. Temptation is the common lot of humanity. Specifically, we might be tempted in different ways, however, in those general areas of lust of the flesh, lust of the eye and pride of life (I Jno. 2:15-17), our temptations are similar.

b. God will not allow his people to be tempted beyond their strength. This does not mean no temptation will ever arise which cannot overcome a disciple (if he yields to it). If it does, the view of sinlessness for every child of God is established. There are tens of thousands of backsliders in our country who prove that such is not the case. No one can argue against a demonstration.

c. God provides a way of escape with every temptation.

(1) Paul was no deist; he taught that God is presently active in the life of each of his people. With every temptation (*i.e.* when the temptation comes), he gives assistance (an activity in addition to his having written the New Testament 1900 years ago).

(2) Way of escape is from "ekbasis" which means "an egress, way out" (Thayer, p. 193). It was used in classical Greek to describe "a way out of the sea" (Vincent, p. 241). Barclay wrote: "The word is vivid (ekbasis). It means 'a way out of a defile, a mountain pass.' The idea is of an army apparently surrounded and suddenly seeing an escape route to safety" (p. 100). Escape from temptation is the way of *victory* rather than *defeat*.

II. Christians Must Not Eat Sacrificial Meat in Idolatrous Worship (10:14-22).

A. Flee or shun idolatry (10:14).

1. "Phuego," from which we get fugitive, translated as flee or shun means "to flee (to shun or avoid by flight)" (Thayer, p. 651). Earlier, Paul commanded the same response to sexual temptation (6:18; see also I Tim. 6:11; II Tim. 2:22).

2. Paul was implying that their best defense against idolatry was not to eat in a heathen temple regardless of the circumstances. "If we go on the verge of what is allowable, we

make it easy for Satan to draw us over the line into what is sinful" (McGarvey, p. 103).

B. An appeal to their wisdom (10:15).

1. Wise is from "phronimos" meaning "prudent, sensible, practically wise" (Vine, vol. IV, p. 222). A different word ("sophos") is used at 1:19-20.

2. Some think Paul was being sarcastic in addressing them as wise ones ("phronimos" is used that way at 4:10; II Cor. 11:19). However, he was probably quite serious as he asked them to judge for themselves what he was saying. They had enough experience with idolatry before becoming Christians to recognize the wisdom of his remarks.

C. Idolatrous worship is fellowship with demons (10:16-21).

1. Meaning of fellowship with demons (10:19-20).

a. Demons (RSV) from "daimonion," is preferred over devils (KJV). There is only one Devil ("Diabolos") but many demons.

b. Greeks employed the word in reference to the spirits of some dead men and to secondary gods, some who were thought to be good and some considered as evil (see Acts 17:18 where "diamonion" is translated as gods or divinities). Jews used the word only to designate evil beings. The best explanations for their *real* identity are the spirits of wicked men or fallen angels. Demons operate under the direction of Satan (Matt. 12:22-30; Eph. 6:12).

c. The Old Testament background for Paul's thought is Deut. 32:17; Ps. 106:37 (for a similar concept, see Rev. 9:20). Only here and I Tim. 4:1 did Paul write of demons.

d. Meaning of fellowship with demons. Idols did not represent gods as Gentiles understood them (10:19; see notes at 8:4). For example, there was no being known as Zeus, regardless of the idols erected in his honor. However, idolatrous Greeks did actually, though unintentionally, pay homage to demons. "The heathen certainly did not intend to worship evil spirits. Nevertheless they did it. Men of the world do not intend to serve Satan, when they break the laws of God in the pursuit of their objects of desire. Still in so doing they are really obeying the will of the great adversary, yielding to his impulses, and fulfilling his designs. He is therefore said to be the god of this world. To him all sin is an offering and a homage. We are shut up to the necessity of worshipping God and Satan; for all refusing or neglecting to worship the true God, or giving to any other the worship which is due to him alone, is the worshipping of Satan and his angels" (Hodge, p. 193).

  2. Illustrations supporting Paul's conclusion (10:16-18).
    a. The Lord's Supper (10:16-17).
      (1) The Supper is participation, fellowship or communion (from "koinonia") with the body and blood of Christ (10:16). In baptism, one initially shares the benefits of the Savior's death (Rom. 6:3). By living the faithful life and regularly partaking of the Supper, one continues to share the benefits of Christ's death (I Jno. 1:7; I Cor. 10:16). Baptism and the Lord's Supper are the *only* two ordinances which specifically relate to the death of Jesus. Why has the modern day religious world given so little attention to their true import?
      (2) One bread and one body (10:17).
        (a) Difference in translations. "It is not difficult to get good sense out of these ambiguous words, but it is not easy to decide how they should be translated. Fortunately, the meaning is much the same, whichever translation is adopted. . . . But, however, we unravel the construction, we have the parallel between many fragments, yet one bread, and many members, yet one body" (S. R. Driver and A. Plummer, *The First Epistle of St. Paul to the Corinthians,* p. 214).
        (b) Meaning of one bread and one body. "The meaning seems to be—We all partake of the loaf, and thereby become qualitatively, as it were, a part of it, as it of us, even as we all become members of Christ's body, which the loaf sacramentally represents" (Farrar, p. 324). "Paul is deducing the mutual communion of believers from the fact of their communion with their common Lord. By each and all receiving a piece of the loaf, which represents Christ's body, they signify that they are all bound in one spiritual body, united to Christ and therefore to each other" (Vincent, vol. III, pp. 242-243).
      (3) The connection with idolatrous worship. As one had communion with Christ and the society of disciples in the Lord's Supper, he also had fellowship with demons and the

brotherhood of demon-worshippers by eating sacrificial meat in an idolatrous service.

b. Eating of the sacrifices by Israel (10:18). A part of the sacrifice was offered to God and part was eaten by the priest (Lev. 8:31) and the people (Deut. 12:18). All who ate the sacrifice were partners in the altar of God (*i.e.* they had communion with God whom the altar represented). Similarly, those who ate sacrificial meat in idolatrous worship had fellowship with demons whom the altars (or images) represented.

c. Why Christians could not take part in idolatrous worship (10:21-22).

(1) It was morally incompatible to partake of the Lord's feast and the feast of demons (10:21). From this principle, it can be inferred that a disciple who lives an ungodly life should not take part in the Lord's Supper.

(2) The Lord is provoked to jealousy by those who partake of his table and the table of demons (10:22). This is an allusion to a woman trying to be faithful to two men at the same time (one of whom is her husband). Any who attempt to serve the Lord and demons must be stronger than he if they intend to escape punishment for their actions.

III. Circumstances in which Sacrificial Meat Might be Eaten (10:23-30).

A. Argument made by some of the Corinthians: "All things are lawful" (10:23).

1. They used that reasoning to justify sexual immorality (6:12) and eating sacrificial meat in an idol's temple (8:10; 10:23).

2. Fallacies in their argument (10:23-24).

a. All things are not expedient or helpful (10:23).

b. All things do not edify or build up (10:23).

c. All things are not good for one's neighbor (10:24; 8:10-11).

B. Circumstances in which sacrificial meat might be eaten (10:25-30).

1. When purchased at the meat market without any knowledge of its former use (10:25). A part of sacrifices offered

to idols went to the pagan priests. They sometimes had more than they could use and sold the rest to the market. Paul discouraged brethren in being overly-scrupulous by telling them not to ask questions about the meat. Regardless of how it had been used, the meat was all right for saints to buy and eat because "the earth is the Lord's and the fullness thereof" (10:26; a quotation from Ps. 24:1 which some Corinthians had probably used to justify eating sacrificial meat even in an idol's temple).

2. When eating with unbelievers who invited them to a social meal (10:27).

3. Exception to the second rule: Do not eat if someone (probably a weak brother) says it has been offered to idols (10:28-30; 8:12-13).

IV. Do Not Give Offense to Jews, Gentiles or the church (10:31-11:1).

A. This section was written in answer to the questions raised at 10:29-30.

1. Why should my liberty be determined by another man's conscience or scruples (10:29)?

2. Why am I evil spoken of or denounced because of that for which I give thanks (10:30; I Tim. 4:4)?

B. Do all to the glory of God (10:31; 6:19-20). It is implied that Christians gave up *all* rights in their acceptance of Jesus as Lord. No longer are they to seek what is rightfully theirs. Love does not seek its own (13:5). Disciples are dominated by the solitary purpose of honoring God in all of life's activities (see Col. 3:17).

C. Give no offense to others (10:32). Offense is from "aproskopos," which appears only two other times in the New Testament (Acts 24:16; Phil. 1:10). "Here in active sense, not tripping others by being a stumbling block" (A. T. Robertson, *Word Pictures in the New Testament,* vol. IV, p. 158).

D. Follow me in striving to please all men (10:33-11:1).

1. God's people were to imitate Paul as he imitated Christ (11:1; Rom. 15:2-3).

2. As pointed out earlier (see notes on 9:19-23), Paul's seeking to please others was limited to matters of indifference. In the realm of faith, he pleased God rather than men (Gal. 1:10).

XII.

CHAPTER ELEVEN

Disorders in Worship

Structure

    I.   11:2-16 — Wearing of the Veil.

   II.   11:17-34 — The Lord's Supper.

I. Wearing of the Veil (11:2-16).

   A. Basis for the discussion (11:2-3).

      1. Traditions (RSV) is preferred over ordinances (KJV). The Greek is "paradosis" defined as "a handing down or on (akin to 'paradidomai,' to hand over, deliver" (Vine, vol. IV, p. 147). Traditions could be transmitted orally or in writing (II Thess. 2:15). They could be bad (*i.e.* in violation of God's will—Matt. 15:2-9; Mk. 7:7-9; Col. 2:8) or good (*i.e.* expressions of God's will—II Thess. 3:6). Paul delivered to the Corinthians precisely what had been given to him by the Lord (11:2, 23; 15:3).

      2. The following instruction is based on the concept of authority. The chain of command is God, Christ, man (husband, RSV), woman (11:3).

   B. Definition of covering.

      1. Veil (11:4-7, 13).

         a. Veil (RSV) or covering (KJV) is from "katakalupto," a combination of two words. They are "kata" meaning "down from, down . . . I Cor. 11:4" and "kalupto" meaning "to cover, to cover up, to hide, veil." "Katakalupto" means "to veil or cover oneself" (Thayer, pp. 327, 323, 331). Of "kata-kalupto," Vine wrote: "to cover up ('kata,' intensive), in the Middle Voice, to cover oneself, is used in I Cor. 11:6-7 (R.V., 'veiled')" (vol. I, p. 252).

b. "The veils worn by Grecian women were of different kinds. One, and perhaps the most common, was the 'peplum,' or mantle, which in public was thrown over the head, and enveloped the whole person. The other was more in fashion of the common eastern veil which covered the face, with the exception of the eyes" (Hodge, p. 209).

2. Hair (11:15).

a. Covering is from "peribolaion" which "literally denotes something thrown around ('peri,' around, 'ballo,' to throw); hence, a veil, covering, I Cor. 11:15" (Vine, vol. I, p. 252).

b. Obviously, a veil is not meant at 11:15 but it has a connection with it. Robertson commented that "anti peribolaion," translated as for a covering, does not mean in place of a veil but answering to it (vol. IV, p. 162). He believed woman's hair as a covering answered to or illustrated the need for her wearing a veil.

c. If the hair covering of 11:15 is the same as the covering of 11:5-6, since men were to pray uncovered (11:4), only bald-headed brethren could have led prayer acceptably when men and women met to worship God!

C. Man was to pray or prophesy with his head uncovered (11:4) or unveiled (11:7 where "katakalupto" appears).

1. First century practice.

a. According to Alford (*Commentary on the Epistles of St. Paul*, p. 201), Vincent (vol. III, p. 246), Farrar (p. 361) and McGarvey (p. 110), *Jewish* and *Roman* men of the first century worshipped with covered heads but Greek men worshipped bareheaded. "Literally, 'having something hanging down from his head.' Referring to the 'tallith,' a four-cornered shawl having fringes consisting of eight threads, each knotted five times, and worn over the head in prayer. It was placed upon the worshipper's head at his entrance into the synagogue. The Romans, like the Jews, prayed with the head veiled. So Aeneas: 'And our heads are shrouded before the altar with a Phrygian vestment' (Virgil, 'Aeneid,' iii., 545). The Greeks remained bareheaded during prayer or sacrifice, as indeed they did in their ordinary outdoor life" (Vincent). Robertson (vol. IV, p. 159), Driver and Plummer (p. 229) were not convinced that Jewish men wore the tallith at this early date. Apparently, none take the position that it was customary for Greek men to wear a covering in worship.

b. Paul was writing to a Greek church. Would he have written the same words to a church where it was the practice for men to wear artificial coverings at worship? Is the custom of the churches of God (11:16) limited to those churches among the Greeks?

2. Reasons why man was to pray and prophesy with uncovered or unveiled head.

a. He is made in the image and glory of God (11:7). So is woman but Paul omitted that point here because he was showing woman's relation to man (11:7-9).

b. To keep from dishonoring his head (11:4). This may refer to his own head or to Christ as his head (11:3).

c. Men worship bareheaded today as an expression of reverence but the practice has no connection with Paul's reasoning.

D. Woman was to pray or prophesy with her head covered or veiled (11:5-6, 13).

1. A woman could prophesy (11:5; Acts 2:18; 21:9).

a. Prophecy was a spiritual gift (12:10) exercised when the Holy Spirit moved a person (II Pet. 1:21) to make known God's revelation (14:30). Such was more than simply teaching; it was inspired teaching.

b. Contextually, there is no reason for taking prayer and prophecy as it is related to woman in a different sense than the way it related to man (11:4). If this refers only to a woman teaching her children at home or teaching a class of ladies or children apart from the church assembled together in one place (14:23), why the teaching about the veil?

c. Syllogism.

(1) Major premise: Some women prophesied (11:5).

(2) Minor premise: One who prophesied edified the church (i.e. assembly) (14:4). In this verse Paul included both

sexes just as he did in 14:24. The women of 14:34-35 were *non-gifted* wives who had been interrupting their prophet husbands as they spoke to the congregation. The instruction in those verses *did not* apply to the prophetesses.

(3) Conclusion: Some women prophesied and edified the church (*i.e.* assembly). Apparently, Huldah (II Kgs. 22:11-20) and Anna (Lk. 2:36-38) exercised the same prerogative under the law.

d. Paul's general rule was that a woman was not to teach over a man (I Tim. 2:12). However, prophetesses (who had to wear a veil, at least in Greek churches) were exceptions to that rule. Prophetesses ceased to exist when prophecy was done away (see remarks at 13:8-10), hence, there are no exceptions to the general rule today. All non-gifted sisters, and there are no other kind living, must abide by the instruction of I Tim. 2:11-15.

2. Reasons why woman was to pray and prophesy with her head covered or veiled.

a. To keep from dishonoring her head (11:5). This may refer to her own head or to man (husband, father or man in general) as her head.

b. As an expression of propriety and decency (11:5-6).

(1) It seems that some of the Greek sisters, upon learning that male and female were one in Christ (Gal. 3:28), had expressed their newly found elevation and equality by laying aside their veils. They may have asked why women were required to wear veils and men were not.

(2) Robertson gave a quotation indicating that morally loose women in Corinth did not wear veils (vol. IV, p. 160). If that is correct, Christian ladies placed themselves on a very low level by abandoning their veils. Such conduct would hardly have won another to Christ.

(3) Paul said woman's failure to wear a veil was the same as though her head were shaved (11:5). There was a time when a lady's shaved head was a sign of mourning (Deut. 21:10-13) but that is not Paul's meaning here for grief would not have been considered as disgraceful (11:6). Likely, the shaved head should be understood as identification with an adulteress. "Among the Jews a woman convicted of adultery had her hair shorn, with the formula: 'Because thou has

departed from the manner of the daughters of Israel, who go with their head covered, therefore that has befallen thee which thou hast chosen.' According to Tacitus, among the Germans [*i.e.* Germanic tribes, J.A.] an adulteress was driven from her husband's house with her head shaved; and the Justinian code prescribed this penalty for an adulteress, whom, at the expiration of two years, her husband refused to receive again. Paul means that a woman praying or prophesying uncovered puts herself in public opinion on a level with a courtesan" (Vincent, vol. III, p. 247).

(4) If a sister would not wear a veil, she was to cut off her hair (11:6). If she was unwilling to act in harmony with the propriety of the times, she was to be consistent by cutting her hair and appearing as one totally disreputable. Two words, shorn and shaven, appear in the verse and can be explained as follows. First, since she had forsaken the veil as a mark of her femininity, she should be shorn (*i.e.* crop her hair short) and even more strongly identify herself with men. Second, since she had laid aside the veil as a mark of decency, she should be shaved (*i.e.* wear the badge of an adulteress) and even more strongly identify with sexually immoral women.

(5) "Among the Jews, in ancient times, both married and unmarried women appeared in public unveiled" (Vincent, vol. III, p. 247). There was a time when a veiled woman was thought to be a harlot (Gen. 38:14-15). The mark of a prostitute then and there became the trait of a decent woman at Corinth in the first century. Obviously, wearing the veil did not originate with Christianity. The teaching of 11:2-16 simply regulated a custom then prevalent among the Greeks.

c. As a sign of authority (11:10; see footnote in RSV).

(1) This is taken by most commentators to mean the veil was a symbol of woman's being under man's authority (Gen. 3:16). However, W. M. Ramsay rejected that view and added, "a preposterous idea which a Greek scholar would laugh at anywhere except in the New Testament. . . . in Oriental lands the veil is the power and the honour and dignity of the woman. With the veil on her head she can go anywhere in security and profound respect. She is not seen; it is a mark of thoroughly bad manners to observe a veiled woman in the street. She is alone. The rest of the people around are non-

existent to her, as she is to them. She is supreme in the crowd. . . . But without the veil the woman is a thing of nought, whom anyone may insult. . . . A woman's authority and dignity vanish along with the all-covering veil that she discards. That is the Oriental view which Paul learned at Tarsus" (as quoted by Driver and Plummer, pp. 232-233). Dods set forth a similar thought: "It was therefore the recognized badge of seclusion; it was the badge which proclaimed that she who wore it was a private, not a public, person, finding her duties at home, not abroad, in one household, not in the city. And a woman's whole life and duties ought to lie so much apart from the public eye, that both sexes looked upon the veil as the truest and most treasured emblem of woman's position" (p. 247).

(2) Meaning of because of the angels.

(a) Because angels covered their faces before God as an expression of reverence (Isa. 6:1-2), women should do the same (J. M. Gettys, *How to Study First Corinthians*, p. 86). If that is correct, why was not the same said to the men?

(b) "Angels, in the presence of their direct and visible Superior, veil their faces (Isa. 6:2); a woman when worshipping in the presence of her direct and visible superior (man), should do the same" (Driver and Plummer, p. 233-234).

(c) Because 6ad angels lusted after unveiled women (Gen. 6:2 where Codex Alexandrinus has angels of God rather than sons of God). Farrar illustrated this possibility by saying, "Thus Khadijah tested that the visitant of her husband Mohammed was really the angel Gabriel, because he disappeared the moment she unveiled her head" (p. 362). Does clothing hide a woman's body from the view of angels? Would they not have been incited to lust as quickly when a woman unveiled or undressed herself at home? The idea that angels can cohabit with women is false. There will be no marriage in the next life because all will be sexless like the angels (Matt. 22:29-30).

(d) Because of church leaders who are angels in the sense of being messengers of God (Rev. 2:1). Veils should be worn out of deference to them.

(e) Because of the guardian angels' of women (Ps. 34:7; Matt. 18:10; Heb. 1:14) who would be appalled if their charges failed to be properly attired.

(f) Angels are mentioned to represent the presence of God (Lk. 15:10). Really, it was God who would have been displeased by the appearance of an unveiled sister at worship.

(g) Because of angels who witness worship (4:9; Ps. 138:1 where LXX has angels rather than gods). If men were shocked by the sight of unveiled sisters, how much greater alarm would be aroused among the angels who observe worship? Alford presented a similar, although slightly different, thought: "Because in the Christian assemblies the holy angels of God are present, and delighting in the due order and subordination of the ranks of God's servants,—and by a violation of that order we should be giving offence to them" (p. 203).

3. Hair was used by Paul as an illustration supporting his teaching concerning veils (11:13-15).

a. The rule of thumb seemed to be—Long hair, wear a veil; short hair, do not wear a veil. As woman had more natural covering (hair) than man, she needed also to have an artificial covering (veil). As man had less natural covering (hair) than woman, there was no need for him to wear an artificial covering (veil).

b. Nature teaches it is degrading or shameful for a man to wear long hair (11:14). Meaning?

(1) Nature, from "phusis," means "native condition, birth (Rom. 2:27; 11:21, 24; Gal. 2:15)" (Harper's, p. 432). It also means "a mood of feeling and acting which by long habit has become nature. . . . Eph. 2:3" (Thayer, p. 660). It is further defined as "the regular law or order of nature, Rom. 1:26, against nature ('para,' against)" (Vine, vol. III, p. 103).

(2) The verse has been interpreted on the basis of all three definitions.

(a) It may mean an inborn perception of what is proper. Robertson said it referred to a "native sense of propriety (cf. Rom. 2:14)," told of a papyrus example of a priest accused of letting his hair grow long and spoke disgustingly of "the long haired man!" (vol. IV, p. 162). What was considered comely or proper (from "prepon"), in light of the custom of that day, had already been mentioned (11:13). Paul may have re-enforced his argument by further appeal to their instinctive sense of what was right. The view of a long-haired Jesus is without support. Hair length evidence from the first century indicates that Hebrew, Greek and Roman men wore their hair short. To the Jews, the only exception was a Nazarite (Num. 6:1-21). The few other exceptions were local and temporary. Since this interpretation may be correct, the safe thing for all Christian men is to keep their hair short. No one believes the wearing of short hair does violence to the word of God.

(b) Nature can be understood as referring to what "by long habit has become nature." If that is correct, when customs change, hair length can also change. However, even then a child of God is not "the first by which the new is tried or the last to lay the old aside." He is so concerned about his influence for Christ, he takes extreme care not to offend the sensibilities of others by engaging in the bizarre and outlandish.

(c) According to Alford, the order of nature is contemplated. "The word does not mean 'sense of natural propriety,' but NATURE—the law of creation" (p. 204). That would mean long hair on a man is as contrary to nature as sexual perversion (see Rom. 1:26-27).

c. Is it sinful for a Christian man to wear long hair today?

(1) If it is sinful "per se" for a man to have long hair, it is also sinful "per se" for a woman to have short hair and for exactly the same reason (11:14-15). Many, who are critical of men wearing hair to their ears, say little or nothing about women cutting their hair. However, seventy-five years ago some preached against "bobbed hair" on the ladies.

(2) It is evident that Paul taught there should be a distinction between the sexes in hair length. How long is long? How short is short? When a Christian man's hair is so long others have difficulty in determining his sex, it is too long. Why should a male dedicated to Jesus want to look womanly? When a Christian woman's hair is so short others have difficulty in determining her sex, it is too short. Why should a female devoted to Christ want to look manly? The present day attempt to produce a unisex in this nation is wrong and it has also given rise to many other evils.

E. Must a Christian woman living in twentieth century America wear a veil to please God?

1. If Paul has bound an artificial covering on Christian ladies for all time and in all cultures (a view held by Roman Catholics and some New Testament Christians).

a. He has also specified that the covering must be a veil. A hat, handkerchief or thread will no more substitute for a veil than sprinkling will substitute for baptism. The covering bound on Greek sisters at Corinth was a veil not a hat. Furthermore, a lady's hat, unlike the Greek veil, has no symbolic value in western civilization at all.

b. The practice cannot be logically limited to church services. Every reason given for wearing the veil aptly applies to any public place whether it is the college campus, marketplace, city office or athletic stadium. Does anyone suppose that Corinthian sisters went everywhere in town unveiled except to the church assembly?

c. Every sister who does not wear a veil must be taught to cut her hair so short she appears to be shorn or shaven (11:5-6). Do those who make an issue of sisters wearing hats to public worship also recommend this procedure? If Christian women refuse to wear veils or cut their hair, should they be held in the fellowship of the church?

2. Reasons why the veil is *not* commanded of Christian women in our country today.

a. When a command is directed to a cultural situation which ceases to exist, the command is no longer binding. The cultural situation that an unveiled woman was the same as one with a shaved head (11:5) no longer exists, hence, the teaching relative to veils cannot be bound.

b. The veil is no longer a sign of authority (11:10).

c. The veil is no longer an expression of propriety and decency (11:5-6).

d. A failure to wear a veil is no longer dishonoring to a woman's head (11:5).

3. Principles from 11:2-16 which still apply today.

a. The sexes are mutually dependent upon one another (11:11-12).

b. Woman is to be in submission to man (11:3; Gen. 3:26; Eph. 5:22-33; I Tim. 2:11-15). Woman is inferior to man only in rank. In many ways, she is his superior. Both are equal before God.

c. From these principles, Paul made specific applications to a culture foreign to our American society. *The principles remain* but the specific applications to the particular scene do not.

F. We recognize no other custom or practice (11:16).

1. Paul was thinking of any person who was contentious about women being unveiled. He did not explain why Corinthian sisters were to be veiled and then refute it by saying no one should be contentious in binding the practice of veil-wearing. If one refused to hear his inspired teaching, he simply said, "This is our practice. Take it or leave it. However, do not be contentious about an opposing viewpoint."

2. The churches recognized no other custom.

a. Did he mean all of the churches? Was the same teaching bound on Jewish and Roman congregations?

b. Was he referring only to the churches in Greece or Achaia? I Corinthians was addressed to those in every place (1:2). II Corinthians was sent to those in the whole of Achaia (1:1, RSV). Is the instruction here limited to the churches of God in every place throughout the whole of Achaia?

II. The Lord's Supper (11:17-34).
   A.   Paul's condemnation (11:17-22, 33-34).

1. In the following instruction conerning the Lord's Supper, he did not praise or commend the Corinthians (11:17, 22).

a. "I praise you not" (KJV) is probably a euphemism for he not only failed to praise but strongly denounced them.

b. Earlier, he had commended them (11:2), however, he could not praise them in this matter since they were not meeting for the better but for the worse (*i.e.* their assemblies did not promote love, harmony, devotion and spirituality but tended to enmity, alienation, division and disorder).

2. Divisions (11:18-19).

a. Paul did not state what was second after *first* dealing with their divisions (11:18). Some think his second admonition was the abuse of the love feast (11:20-22) and others the misuse of spiritual gifts (12:1).

b. Divisions and heresies (factions, RSV) (11:18-19).

(1) Divisions and heresies may be used interchangably in reference to the same evil practice (Hodge, p. 218).

(2) However, heresies or factions (from "hairesis") may be stronger than divisions (from "schisma" and also used at 1:10). According to Vine, "a sect is a division developed and brought to issue" (vol. III, p. 335). The fact that divisions preceded heresies in Paul's writings (see Gal. 5:20) may lend support to this point of view (see also Tit. 3:10; II Pet. 2:1).

c. Factions necessary that the approved or genuine might be recognized (11:19).

(1) The majority of those consulted held the position that the Lord permits factions so those who meet his approval may be manifested or recognized (Matt. 18:7; Lk. 17:1 were the verses most often cited for support). The NEB translates, "for dissensions are necessary if only to show which of your members are sound." This means when appeal is made to the New Testament, those who teach and/or live in harmony with the will of God, having thus been tried and proved, are seen to be genuine in the eyes of the Lord ("dokimos," translated as approved or genuine, is used that way at II Tim. 2:15). If correct, even factions in the church are made to serve a good purpose. Whether it is taught here or not, obviously, there are times when truth essential to salvation must be compromised or a division must take place. In such cases, it is better to be divided by truth than to be united in error.

(2) Some take the verse to be Paul's denunciation of Corinthian practice. Phillips understood it that way and translated 11:18-19 as follows: "For first, when you meet for worship I hear that you split into small groups, and I think there must be truth in what I hear. For there must be cliques among you or your favorite leaders would not be so conspicuous." This means the approved were those whom the Corinthians endorsed as factional leaders ("dokimos" has the meaning of man's approval at 16:3). In support of this interpretation, it can be said that God knows those who are his (II Tim. 2:19) whether factions arise or not.

3. Improper observance of the Lord's Supper (11:20).

a. Although they professed to be meeting to partake of the Lord's Supper, their actions indicated otherwise. Because of their bad attitudes, the Supper had changed its character and was no longer the Lord's.

b. "Kuriakos," translated as Lord's, means "of or belonging to the Lord" (Thayer, p. 365). It appears only in 11:20 (Lord's Supper) and Rev. 1:10 (Lord's day).

c. The verse indicates there was a time when the Corinthians met for the Supper. From 16:2 it appears they met on the first day of the week.

(1) The disciples in Troas broke bread on the first day of the week (Acts 20:7). The command to remember *the* Sabbath Day (Ex. 20:8) meant the Hebrews were to keep *every* Sabbath holy. In like manner, *the* first day means the Christians in Troas broke bread *every* first day. If not, why not? This can also be seen in the following—Major premise: Christians broke bread on the first day of the week. Minor premise: Every week has a first day. Conclusion: Therefore, Christians broke bread on the first day of every week.

(2) Memorial feasts have a stated time of observance (Passover, Feast of Tabernacles, Purim, etc.). The Lord's Supper is a memorial feast (11:25). Therefore, it has a stated time of observance. All the information in the New Testament points toward the keeping of the feast on the first day of the week. The fact that Jesus instituted the Supper Thursday night does not offset this conclusion. "Another may object that Jesus ate the supper on Thursday night and that we therefore have Biblical authority for eating the Lord's Supper on that day. But Jesus and the apostles did not actually observe the supper on the eve of his death, for it would have been impossible to observe a memorial to an event which had not yet occurred. This was simply instruction by demonstration" (Rubel Shelly, "To Young Preachers," *Harding College Lectures,* 1971, pp. 273-274).

(3) Testimony of the early church.

(a) The *Didache* or "Teaching of the Twelve Apostles" (from Syria in the early second century): "But every Lord's day do ye gather yourselves together, and break bread, and give thanksgiving" (14:1).

(b) *Epistle of Barnabas* (from Alexandria ca. 130 A.D.): "Wherefore, also we keep the eighth day with joyfulness, the day also on which Jesus rose again from the dead" (15:9).

(c) Justin Martyr (ca. 150 A.D.): "On the Lord's day all Christians, whether in the city or in the country, meet together because that is the day of the Lord's resurrection and . . . when our prayer is ended, bread and wine and water are brought, and the president in like manner offers prayers and thanksgiving, according to his ability, and the people assent, saying, Amen; and there is distribution to each, and a participation of that over which thanks have been given. . . . But Sunday is the day on which we hold our common assembly, because it is the first day on which God, having wrought a change in darkness and matter, made the world; and Jesus Christ, our Saviour, on the same day rose from the dead" (*First Apology*, 67).

4. Improper observance of the Supper grew out of an abuse of the Love Feast (11:21-22).

a. Information concerning the Love Feast (also known as Agape). Apparently, it was the practice of the early church (Jude 12; II Pet. 2:13 which may be a doubtful reading). Likely, it began in Jerusalem shortly after the establishment of the church (Acts 2:42, 46). "The evidence seems to point to the Apostles, probably because of the precedent of the Last Supper, having combined the Eucharist with a common meal, which before long was called the Agape" (A. J. Maclean, "Agape," *Hastings Encyclopedia of Religion and Ethics*, vol. I, p. 173). The meal had a double purpose. Primarily, it was done to express Christian brotherhood. Secondarily, it satisfied the hunger and thirst of the needy (11:21, 34). Those who were well to do financially provided the food and drink for their poorer brothers and sisters in Christ. "Agape" (a Greek word for love), as the name for the feast, may have been derived from Christ's teaching at Jno. 13:34-35 where the word appears. The evidence indicates that Agape preceded the Lord's Supper and *was distinct from it* because the former was simply a human practice but the latter was divinely ordained. According to the *Didache* (10:1) and the Ignatian Epistle to Smyrna (8:1-2), Agape and Eucharist (*i.e.* Lord's Supper) were combined in the early second century. Tertullian (ca. 200 A.D.) indicated that the Love Feast and the Lord's Supper were

separated in the Western church (*Apology*, 38). The Third
Council of Carthage (398 A.D.) forbade the Love Feast in
church buildings because of the abuses to which it had led and
the Lord's Supper was then conceived as a mysterious priestly
sacrifice which was to be received with fasting.

    b. Abuse of the Love Feast at Corinth.

    (1) The brethren were not waiting for each other
(11:33, 21).

    (2) Intemperance had become common practice (11:
21). It seems that the rich were full and the poor went hungry.

    (3) The needs of some were overlooked (11:21).

    (4) It had become a meal simply to satisfy hunger
(11:34).

    c. Interpretation of 11:22.

    (1) Questions.

    (a) Do you have a kitchen in the church? Church in
the New Testament always means people. Those who ask this
question have confused the people with the building where
they meet.

    (b) Are church buildings sacred (Acts 17:24)? If
so, support the view with biblical book, chapter and verse.

    (c) What meetings can be held in church buildings
with God's approval (funerals, weddings, showers, eating if it
rains, etc.)? Again, support answer with book, chapter and
verse from the New Testament.

    (d) Is it right to eat in the building if a man's
house is also used as a meeting place for the church (Rom.
16:5)?

    (e) Where did the Corinthian church meet (Acts
18:7)? Did eating and meeting occur in the same building?

    (f) Is it right to have a brotherly meal in the
preacher's home built with church money but wrong to have a
brotherly meal in the meeting house erected with church
money? If the answer is yes, why?

    (g) Is it right to have a water fountain in the
church building? If yes, since Paul mentioned *eating* and
drinking in the same verse (11:22), why is it wrong to have a
place to eat in the same building?

    (h) Did Paul sin by eating in the same building
where the church met (Acts 20:7-11)?

(i) Does the Bible *specifically* authorize the building of bathrooms, offices, nurseries, etc. in church buildings? If no, why ask another for specific authority for erecting a fellowship hall (*i.e.* a place where Christians can eat together)? How does one determine what is and is not to be included in a church building?

(j) May Christians eat anywhere other than at home (11:22, 34)? Is it wrong for saints to eat in the home of another Christian family, in a restaurant, in a park or in a rented hall? In the verse cited by some to denounce eating in a church building, Paul specified that the eating was to be done at home. Without proper interpretation, that would mean it is sinful for God's people to eat anywhere else. If not, why not?

(2) At 11:22, Paul was not condemning the *place* of eating but *wrong attitudes* displayed during the meal. He was saying if they intended to make a private or individual meal of Agape, they should do that at home. Through abuse, the purpose of the Love Feast had been undermined. Their practice would have been sinful regardless of where the brethren gathered. This verse does not touch a building top, edge, side or bottom.

B. Meaning of the Lord's Supper (11:23-26).

1. Paul's instruction on the matter came from the Lord (11:23; Gal. 1:11-12).

2. The bread represents Christ's body (11:23-24). Catholics are mistaken in believing the bread, when blessed by a priest, becomes the literal body of Jesus (the view is called transubstantiation). When Jesus said, "This is my body" (Lk. 22:14-22), his body stood in the presence of his disciples. Obviously, he did not mean it was literally or actually his body. He spoke metaphorically (a metaphor is a likeness stated as a reality; a simile is a likeness set forth by using the words like or as) and meant the bread represented his body. For other metaphors, see the Lord's "I am" statements in the Gospel of John (6:51; 10:14; 11:35; 14:6; 15:5; etc).

3. The cup represents Christ's blood (11:25).

a. In saying cup, Jesus used a figure of speech called metonymy (the word literally means to change names) which denotes the use of one word for another it suggests. Cup is really a reference to the contents of the cup (*i.e.* the fruit of the vine—Matt. 26:29).

b. The cup represents the blood of Jesus by which the new covenant is ratified (11:25; see Lk. 22:20 in KJV).

c. Paul gives the solution to the two cups mentioned by Luke (assuming the KJV reading of Lk. 22:19-20 is correct; see footnote there in RSV). The first was the Passover cup (Lk. 22:17) and the second taken after supper (11:25, RSV) was the Lord's Supper cup (Lk. 22:20).

4. The Supper looks to the *past* (proclamation of his death) and to the *future* (until he comes) (11:26).

C. Proper attitude in the Supper (11:27-32).

1. Christians must not partake in an unworthy manner (unworthily, KJV) (11:27).

a. Some have felt unworthy to participate in the communion service because of their imperfections. Paul was not saying saints must live above sin to keep the Lord's Supper. Of course, one living in rebellion to God's will should not partake (10:21).

b. Paul meant one should not engage in the Supper in an unworthy manner (*i.e.* have his mind elsewhere while eating the bread and drinking thě cup), an all too-frequent occurrence among those who profess to be simply Christians.

2. If one participates in the Supper improperly.

a. He profanes (*i.e.* makes common or ordinary) the body and blood of Jesus (11:27, RSV). To say that such a person would have taken part in the Lord's death (see Heb. 6:6) is a little too strong. The individual simply acts irreverently toward the Lord and his death for our sins.

b. He brings judgment upon himself (11:29, 31-32, RSV).

(1) "Krima" is the word translated as judgment. It refers to temporal or eternal judgment. The translators of KJV took the latter view. However, it is likely a reference to temporal judgment since a distinction is made between judgment and condemnation in 11:32.

(2) Many of the Corinthians had experienced God's judgment (11:30).

      (a) Weak and sickly could refer to physical illness or spiritual illness.

      (b) Some had fallen asleep (died in RSV) may refer to physical death (15:6, 20) or spiritual sleep (Eph. 5:14).

   3. The proper way to eat and drink the Lord's Supper.
     a. Each should examine himself (11:28).
     b. Each should discern the Lord's body (11:29).
     c. Each should judge himself (11:31).

XIII.

CHAPTER TWELVE

The Gifts of the Spirit

Structure

I.   12:1-3 — The Confession of the Spirit.
II. 12:4-11 — Nine Gifts of the Spirit.
III. 12:12-26 — The Church Compared to a Body.
IV. 12:27-31 — Nine Positions.

I. The Confession of the Spirit (12:1-3).

A. In their letter, the Corinthians had asked about spiritual gifts (12:1; cf. 7:1; 8:1; 16:1).

B. Their heathen past (12:2).

1. The majority of them had been Gentiles (see Acts 18:4-6).

2. They had been led astray to serve dumb idols.

a. Idols, being lifeless, could not speak (Hab. 2:18-19; Ps. 115:7; 135:16) although pagan priests sometimes made it appear they did (by means of ventriloquism or speaking through tubes which ran from the back of the idol's head to its lips—Rev. 13:15). A message given by an idol was called a revelation. There was a so-called "oracle" at Delphi, not far from Corinth.

b. *Paul's point:* Since idols are dumb, no revelation of spiritual truth had ever been given by them.

3. "However you may have been moved" (RSV).

a. They had been led or moved by Satan, who, in the realm of idolatry, operated by means of demons (10:20; I Tim. 4:1-2) through heathen priests.

b. Possibly, this expression indicates that their acceptance of idolatry had been irrational. Vincent expressed the concept as "blindly hurried" (vol. III, p. 255).

C. No one could say, "Jesus be cursed," by the   Spirit (12:3, RSV).

1. Cursed or accursed is from "anathema" (see 16:22; Rom. 9:3; Gal. 1:8-9). Lenski described its use here as "something that is removed from the possession or use of men and set aside for God as an object of his wrath and devoted to destruction" (p. 494).

2. By the Spirit (or in union with the Spirit) can refer to sphere or instrumentality (Robertson, vol. IV, p. 167). In other words, this may describe any Christian in the sphere ruled by the Spirit (Eph. 6:18) or it may describe only those inspired saints through whom the Spirit spoke (Rev. 1:10). In light of Paul's reference to idols at 12:2, the latter may be correct. However, in light of the contrast between those who said "Jesus be cursed" and those who declared "Jesus is Lord," the former may be the proper interpretation.

3. Who was saying, "Jesus be cursed"?

a. Jews pronounced anathemas upon those they considered as heretics. In their expressions of blasphemy (Acts 13:45; 18:6), they may have used these very words.

b. Weak Christians may have uttered this blasphemous statement in times of persecution to save themselves (Acts 26:11).

c. Some Corinthian brethren may have said it and claimed the Spirit had them in such a frenzied condition they could not control themselves. Later, Paul showed they did not lose self-control under the Spirit's influence (14:32).

d. Contextually, the best interpretation is that the statement was a "revelation" given by an idol.

D. No one could say, "Jesus is Lord," except by the Spirit (12:3, RSV; see I Jno. 4:2).

1. This does not refer simply to words spoken by a person who is not a Christian and has no intention of becoming one. Such a view would violate other plain passages of scripture (Matt. 7:21; Lk. 6:46; Rom. 10:9-10). Obviously, the words convey the sentiment of the heart and are confirmed by a life which demonstrates their sincerity.

2. Lord is from "kurios." In the Septuagint, "Yahweh" (God's name in Hebrew) is translated by "kurios." First century disciples who called Jesus Lord believed he was God (see comments at 10:4).

II. Nine Gifts of the Spirit (12:4-11).

A. Diversities or varieties of gifts (12:4-7).

1. Diversities or varieties is from "diairesis" which "literally signifies to take asunder, from 'dia,' and 'haireo,' to take" (Vine, vol. I, p. 310). It means "in particular, a distinction arising from a different distribution to different persons" (Thayer, p. 137). The word appears only here in the New Testament (12:4, 5, 6, 11).

2. Three points of view (12:4-6).

a. Gifts—emphasis on the Giver.

b. Service or administrations—emphasis on the goal.

c. Working or operations—emphasis on manifestation or means.

3. Each Person in the Godhead had a part in the gifts (12:4-6).

a. Gifts—"the same *Spirit.*"

b. Service—"the same *Lord.*"

c. Working—"the same *God.*"

4. The common good (*i.e.* the good of the spiritual body or church) was the purpose of the gifts (12:7, RSV).

B. Nine gifts of the Spirit (12:8-10).

1. Word or utterance of wisdom.

a. This probably refers to the apostleship.

(1) *Wisdom* is used concerning the gospel or system of truth made known by the apostles (2:6-13).

(2) In the list of positions given at 12:27-31, apostles coincides with the word of wisdom given here (see comparison below).

b. Although a distinction is made between apostles and prophets in this chapter (12:8-10, 27-31), it is true that prophets also revealed the gospel or wisdom of God (2:10; Eph. 3:3-5). In reference to this function, Hodge pointed out the difference between the apostles and prophets as follows: "This gift [*i.e.* word of wisdom, J.A.] in its full measure belonged to the apostles alone; partially, however, also, to the prophets of the New Testament. . . . The characteristic difference between these classes of officers was, the former were endowed with permanent and plenary, and the latter with occasional and partial, inspiration" (p. 246).

2. Word of utterance of knowledge. This refers to miraculously endowed teachers in the first century church. Once the wisdom of God was revealed by the apostles, teachers effectively communicated that knowledge to the disciples.

3. Faith. This is not the faith possessed by all of God's people which comes by hearing the message (Rom. 10:17). It was a wonder working faith or gift which enabled one to perform miracles (13:2; Matt. 17:14-20; 21:21; Lk. 17:6; Acts 3:16).

4. Gifts of healing (Acts 4:30; 5:15-16; Jas. 5:14-15).

5. Working of miracles. This is a larger class than healing since it included acts of punishment (Acts 13:9-11) as well as mercy.

6. Prophecy. Sometimes prophecy included foretelling, however, the predictive element does not inhere in the word. A prophet was primarily a forthteller (*i.e.* one who spoke forth in behalf of God) rather than a foreteller. Since prophecy has been done away (see comments at 13:8-10), God has no prophets living today. Therefore, those who claim to be prophets must be considered as false prophets.

7. Discerning of spirits or ability to distinguish between spirits. This gift enabled some to tell the difference between those who actually spoke by the Holy Spirit and those who did not (see 14:29; I Thess. 5:20-21; I Jno. 4:1). Today the difference between true and false teaching can be discerned by a close study of the New Testament.

8. Tongues.

a. Some scholars believe the tongues of I Corinthians were ecstatic utterances rather than foreign languages. They cite Paul's reference to tongues of angels (13:2) in support of their position. It must be admitted that the statements concerning tongues in I Corinthians could conceivably refer to ecstatic languages. However, in 13:2 Paul did not actually affirm that some spoke the language of angels. He did say that even *if* one had such ability, without love, he could not please God. A similar concept is found in Gal. 1:8 where Paul wrote of an angel preaching another gospel. Obviously, he did not mean angels actually preached to men. He meant even *if* an angel preached a message other than the gospel, it was not to be accepted.

b. Tongues should be interpreted as foreign languages for the following reasons:

(1) The tongues spoken on Pentecost Day were foreign languages (Acts 2:4, 6, 8, 11). Since obscure passages are to be interpreted in light of plain passages, unless there is overpowering evidence to indicate otherwise, the tongues of I Corinthians are the same as the languages of Acts two.

(2) Every reference to tongues in I Corinthians can as easily be applied to foreign languages as to ecstatic utterances.

(3) Paul's quotation of Isa. 28:11-12 in 14:21 is an explicit reference to a foreign language. The only alternative to this conclusion is to contend that the historical setting of Isaiah has no bearing on Paul's use of the quotation.

(4) New tongues (Mk. 16:17).

(a) "Neos" and "kainos" are both translated as new. Although both words may be used in reference to the same thing (*e.g.* new man—"kainos" in Eph. 2:15 and "neos" in Col. 3:10; new covenant—"kainos" in Heb. 8:8, 13; 9:15 and "neos" in Heb. 12:24), they do not have precisely the same meaning. " 'Kainos' denotes new, of that which is unaccustomed or unused, not new in time, recent, but new as to form or quality, of different nature from what is contrasted as old. . . . 'Neos' signifies new in respect of time, that which is recent" (Vine, vol. III, pp. 109-110).

(b) " 'The new tongues,' 'kainos,' of Mark 16:17 are the 'other tongues,' 'heteros,' of Acts 2:4. These languages, however, were 'new' and 'different,' not in the sense that they had never been heard before, or that they were new to the hearers [which would have been the case had they spoken in angelic language, J.A.], for it is plain from v. 8 that this is not the case; they were new languages to the speakers, different from those which they were accustomed to speak" (Vine, vol. III, p. 109).

(c) Since the great commission included all nations (Matt. 28:19), it encompassed both Jerusalem and Corinth. The promised new tongues spoken in Jerusalem were foreign languages. What began at Jerusalem continued at Corinth. Furthermore, the expression "other tongues" of Acts 2:4 and I Cor. 14:21 is the same in Greek. What reason is there for thinking the tongues in the two cities were different?

9. Interpretation of tongues. One could have the gifts of tongues and interpretation (14:13). If a person spoke in a tongue and interpreted his presentation, the result was the same as prophecy (14:30).

C. A comparison of the nine gifts (12:8-10) with the nine positions (12:27-31).

1. Word of wisdom—*Apostles* revealed the divine wisdom.

2. Word of knowledge—*Teachers* communicated the revealed knowledge to others.

3. Faith—*Helps* (KJV) or *helpers* (RSV) had a sympathetic nature and used their miraculous faith to help others.

4. Gifts of healing—*Gifts of healings* (KJV) or *healers* (RSV).

5. Working of miracles—*Miracles* (KJV) or *workers of miracles* (RSV).

6. Prophecy—*Prophets*.

7. Discerning of spirits or ability to distinguish between spirits—*Governments* (KJV) or *administrators* (RSV). It seems that some elders, as overseers (Acts 20:28; I Pet. 5:1-3) in the early church, were granted this gift.

8. Tongues—*Tongues*.

9. Interpretation of tongues—*Do all interpret?*

D. Other passages concerning gifts.

    1. Eph. 4:7-15.

       a. Apostles, prophets and teachers correspond to what is mentioned above.

       b. Pastors. Pastor is from "poimen" and refers to a shepherd who is to care for the flock of God (*i.e.* the church). The verb which describes his work is "poimaino." According to the Greek, that work (translated as feed or tend) is given to the elders (Acts 20:28; I Pet. 5:2). Pastor and elder are two words for the same office (see Acts 20:17, 28). From the viewpoint of work, they are pastors or shepherds. From the viewpoint of age, they are elders or older men. Pastors here is the equivalent of governments or administrators in 12:28.

       c. Evangelists. Evangelist is from "euangelistes" which literally means a messenger of good (Vine, vol. II, p. 44). He is so described because he preaches the "euangelion" which is the good news of the gospel. It is possible that evangelist is an additional gift to those listed in 12:8-10, 27-31. That view has difficulties for the Corinthians were not lacking in any of the gifts (1:7). Perhaps they had this gift and Paul did not mention it. Evangelist is suggested as a possible tenth gift since nothing in I Corinthians twelve corresponds to it.

    2. Rom. 12:4-8. Perhaps supernatural and *natural* gifts are here listed together.

       a. Prophecy—Already given in 12:8-10.

       b. Ministry (KJV) or service (RSV)—Same as helps (KJV) or helpers (RSV)?

       c. Teaching—Already given in 12:8-10.

       d. Exhortation—Evangelists?

       e. Give (KJV) or contribute (RSV)—Helpers?

       f. Rule (KJV) or gives aid (RSV). "Proistemi" can be taken as rule or aid. Vine took it as reference to those who rule the church (vol. III, p. 307). Thayer preferred the concept of giving aid (p. 539). If it is understood as rule, it coincides with governments or administrators in 12:28. If it is taken as giving aid, it could correspond to helpers, healers or workers of miracles.

       g. Show mercy (KJV) or acts of mercy (RSV)—Helpers, healers or workers of miracles?

E. From the questions in 12:29-30, it seems that no one had all of the gifts, however, some had two or more. Obviously, an apostle was also a prophet, teacher, evangelist, worker of miracles and tongue speaker (the apostles spoke in tongues on Pentecost Day—Acts 2:4, 7, 14; Paul also had the power to speak in tongues—14:18). Apparently, a prophet was a teacher and perhaps an evangelist. As pointed out earlier, a tongue speaker might have the ability to interpret (14:13).

III. The Church Compared to a Body (12:12-26).
   A. One body (12:12-13).
      1. There is but one body (12:12, 20).
         a. The body is the church (Eph. 1:22-23). There is but one body. Hence, there is but one church. There is no way to harmonize the divisions of denominationalism with this New Testament teaching.
         b. The one body likely refers to the universal church rather than to a single congregation. If each local church is a body, there is one head (*i.e.* Christ—Col. 1:18) over thousands of bodies and Paul's figure of one head and one body is destroyed.
      2. By one Spirit all were baptized into the one body (12:13). Meaning?
         a. Some scholars think this is a reference to baptism in the Holy Spirit, however, this view is incorrect. There are only two cases of Holy Spirit baptism in the New Testament (Acts 2:1-4; 10:44-46), the last occurring at the house of Cornelius ca. 35 A.D. When Paul wrote Eph. 4:5 ca. 60-62 A.D., there was only one baptism. The one baptism which will abide as long as the world stands is administered by men (Matt. 28:18-20). The only baptism men can administer is baptism in water (the Lord baptized in the Spirit—Matt. 3:11-12). Hence, the one baptism of Eph. 4:5 must be water baptism. Surely, that is the one under consideration here. There is no evidence that any of the Corinthians had been baptized in the Spirit. It is true that some of them could speak in tongues and that those baptized in the Spirit did speak in tongues. However, it is also true that men received the power to speak in tongues by the imposition of apostolic hands (Acts 19:1-5). All things considered, the Corinthians must have received the gift of

tongue speaking (as well as all other spiritual gifts) through the hands of Paul.

b. Some believe that as Christ baptized others through his disciples (Jno. 4:1-2), the Holy Spirit now baptizes through the saints.

c. The Spirit in inspired men taught others to be baptized into the one body.

d. The Spirit operating through God's word teaches men to be baptized into one body.

e. The Spirit operates in God's people (i.e. the body) as they teach others to be baptized into the body in obedience to the gospel.

3. "All were made to drink of one Spirit" (12:13, RSV) is a metaphor in which the Spirit is likened to water (see Jno. 7:37-39). This refers to the indwelling Spirit received when one is baptized (Acts 2:38; 5:32; Rom. 8:15-16; Gal. 4:6).

B. Christians, as members of the body (12:14-26).

1. Reason for this section. There was division among the brethren based on a misunderstanding of the gifts. Apparently, some were arrogant because of the impressionable nature of their gifts. Others were envious of those whom they felt God had more highly favored. They also considered themselves inferior due to the lack of ostentatious display in the exercise of their gifts.

2. Lessons to be learned from the passage.

a. Each member should have been content with the gift he had (12:15-16; Rom. 9:20). Imagine the folly of a foot complaining because it is not a hand or an ear complaining because it is not an eye.

b. Each member fulfills a useful function in the body (12:17-19). If the whole body were an eye, it would be long on vision but short on hearing. If the whole body were an ear, it would be long on hearing but short on smelling. The eye, ear and nose each play a vital part in the human organism.

c. Members are mutually dependent on one another (12:20-24). The eye needs the hand and the head needs the feet. Christians need one another. That "rugged individualist" who thinks he can serve God without the help of his brethren has been deceived. I may go to heaven because of you. You may go to heaven because of me. The church is not composed of independent individuals. It is a body made up of members who must depend upon one another.

d. Those members considered less honorable must be invested with greater honor (12:23-24). A mother instinctively gives more affection to a retarded child than to one who is normal. Dedicated, one-talent disciples must be honored to the point where they can stand on equal footing with five-talent elders and preachers.

e. Members should have the same care for one another (12:25-26).

(1) In suffering—If one members suffers, all suffer. Chrysostom wrote: "For when the heel, as often happens, is pricked by a thorn, the whole body feels it, and is distressed: the back is bent, and the belly and thighs are contracted, and the hands like attendants and servants, approach and draw out the offending substance, and the head leans over, and the eyes look for it with anxious care" (*Homily,* 31).

(2) In honor—If one member is honored, all rejoice with it. Here Chrystom added, "The head is crowned, and all the members have a share in the honor; the eyes laugh when the mouth speaks" (*Homily,* 31).

f. There should be no schism or discord among the members (12:25). It is difficult to imagine one hand deliberately attempting to cut off the other hand. The two hands, under the direction of the head, work together for common goals.

g. The place and function of the members is determined by God (12:18, 28). This thought is similar to the one contained in the parable of the talents (Matt. 25:14-30). Each should use what he has to the glory of God. If one complains about his role in the kingdom, he reflects on the wisdom of the Lord. The issue is not what we would do if we were gifted as others but what we are doing with what we have. "Whatsoever thy hand findeth to do, do it with thy might" (Eccl. 9:10).

IV. Nine Positions (12:27-31).

A. 12:27-30 was considered under the heading of the nine gifts of the Spirit (12:4-11).

B. Conclusion (12:31).

1. Paul's admonition that they should desire the higher gifts (RSV) is an indication they could do something to prepare themselves for the reception of the gifts.

2. The more excellent way of love is treated in the following chapter.

XIV.

CHAPTER THIRTEEN

How Long the Gifts
were to Last

Structure

I. 13:1-3 — Gifts Contrasted with Love.

II. 13:4-7 — Love Defined.

III. 13:8-13 — Gifts were Temporary but Love is Eternal.

I. Gifts Contrasted with Love (13:1-3).

  A. Miraculous (13:1-2).

    1. Tongues (13:1; for definition, see notes at 12:4-11).

      a. Sounding brass (KJV) or noisy gong (RSV)—"The metal is not properly 'brass,' the alloy of copper and zinc, but 'copper,' or 'bronze,' the alloy of copper and tin. . . . Being the metal in common use, it came to be employed as a term for metal in general. . . . The word here does not mean a 'brazen instrument,' but a piece of unwrought metal, which emitted a sound on being struck" (Vincent, vol. III, p. 262).

      b. Tinkling (KJV) or clanging (RSV) cymbal— "Alalazo," translated as tinkling or clanging, is rendered as wailing at Mk. 5:38. Cymbal is from "kumbalon" and "was so called from its shape (akin to 'Kumbos,' a hollow basin, 'kumbe,' a cup)" (Vine, vol. I, p. 264). The cymbal consisted of two half metal globes which were struck together.

      c. Apparently, the Corinthians thought more of tongues than any other gifts. Paul indicated that one with that gift, bereft of love for God and man, was regarded by the Lord as simply a maker of noise (see Ps. 150:5). There is a principle here which preachers should seriously consider. Because of Satan's subtility, man can become so in love with the telling that he loses his love for the One about whom he speaks.

2. Prophecy, knowledge and faith (13:2; for definitions, see comments at 12:4-11).

a. It seems that one could have the miraculous gift of faith without having saving faith (Matt. 7:21-23). Judas had the power to work miracles and may have been devoid of love during their performance.

b. " 'I am nothing' (*outhen eimi*). Not *outheis*, nobody, but an absolute zero" (Robertson, vol. IV, p. 177). "To say that one possessed of such gifts was 'nothing'—a spiritual cipher—was a crushing blow to the pride and vanity of the Corinthians" (McGarvey, p. 128).

B. Non-miraculous (13:3).

1. Generosity—"If I give away all that I have" (RSV). The verb, "psomizo," translated as bestow to feed the poor (KJV) or give away (RSV) is from " 'psomos,' morsel or bit, and so to feed, by putting a morsel into the mouth like an infant (or bird)" (Robertson, vol. IV, p. 177). Several writers saw in this a doling away by mouthfuls (*i.e.* meager amounts given to the poor), however, it likely means no more than "to give a thing to feed someone" (Thayer, p. 678).

2. Martyrdom—"If I deliver my body to be burned" (RSV).

a. The alternate reading of to be burned is "that I may glory" (see footnote in RSV). It is supported by the Alexandrinus, Sinaiticus and Vaticanus. "The reading is extremely uncertain. The change of a letter gives the reading, 'that I may glory' " (Farrar, p. 423).

b. Some have suggested that burning is a reference to branding. That is very unlikely. Hodge felt that martyrdom is not under consideration. He added that "the context requires that the reference should be to a sacrifice made for the good of others" (p. 268).

c. Probably Paul was speaking of improperly motivated martyrdom which became a problem in the early days of the church. In *Lives of the Fathers*, Farrar wrote: "Both at this time and in the persecution of Diocletian, there were Christians who, oppressed by debt, by misery, and sometimes even by a sense of guilt, thrust themselves into the glory and imagined redemptiveness of the baptism of blood. . . . The extravagant estimate formed of the merits of all who were confessors, became, almost immediately, the cause of grave scandals. We are horrified to read in Cyprian's letter that even in prison, even when death was imminent, there were some of the confessors who were puffed up with vanity and pride, and seemed to think that the blood of martyrdom would avail them to wash away the stains of flagrant and even recent immoralities" (as quoted by Vincent, vol. III, p. 264).

II. Love Defined (13:4-7).

A. Longsuffering (KJV) or patient (RSV) is from "makrothumeo," a combination of "makros" (long) and "thumos" (temper, passion, ardor) (Vine, vol. III, p. 12; Robertson, vol. IV, p. 177). Love has the ability to endure evil or persevere in the face of provocation.

B. Kind translates "chresteuomai" which is from "chrestos" (Robertson, vol. IV, p. 177) meaning good, gracious or useful (Vine, vol. II, p. 292). Love is benign, bountiful, gentle, large hearted and open handed in its response to others.

C. Envieth not (KJV) or is not jealous (RSV). Envy or jealous is from "zeloo" which means "to be heated or to boil with envy, hatred or anger" (Thayer, p. 271). In the field of competition, love is generous with others. It can pray God's blessings upon those who are more gifted or talented.

D. Vaunteth not itself (KJV) or is not boastful (RSV). Vaunteth or boastful is from "perpereuomai" (which is from "perperous" meaning vainglorious, braggart, swaggerer) and "means to play the braggart" (Robertson, vol. IV, p. 178). Love does not boast of its real or pretended accomplishments to obtain admiration and applause.

E. Is not puffed up (KJV) or arrogant (RSV). Arrogant is from "phusioo" which means "to puff oneself out like a pair of bellows" (Robertson, vol. IV, p. 178). This word describes one's inward disposition of pride, vanity and egotism and the preceding word (*i.e.* boastful) is simply an outward expression of those feelings. Love does not feel superior to others. It is characterized by humility rather than a bloated self-conceit (a major sin of the Corinthians—4:6, 18, 19; 8:1).

F. Doth not behave itself unseemly (KJV) or is not rude (RSV). Unseemly or rude is from "aschemoneo" (see 7:36) which means indecorus or indecent (Harper's, p. 58). Love does nothing of which to be ashamed. It is well mannered, polite and courteous. A noble heart results in noble manners.

G. Seeketh not her own (KJV) or does not insist on its own way (RSV). This is unselfishness. Love does not seek its own interests (10:24, 33). Instead, it seeks the welfare of others (Rom. 15:1-2; Phil. 2:4).

H. Is not easily provoked (KJV) or is not irritable (RSV). Easily in KJV is not a part of the original language. Provoked or irritable is from "paroxuno" which means "primarily to sharpen, is used metaphorically, signifying to rouse to anger, to provoke" (Vine, vol. III, p. 228). The verb also appears at Acts 17:16 (translated as provoked or stirred). The noun, "paroxusmos" (from which we get paroxysm), appears at Acts 15:39 (sharp contention in RSV) and Heb. 10:24 (translated as stir up or provoke). Love is even-tempered. When perfected, it is not aroused to indignation or exasperation, even though it might have some justification. A violent temper is revealing of a loveless heart.

I. Thinketh no evil (KJV) or is not resentful (RSV). According to KJV, this could be taken as not planning evil, however, it likely means "love keeps no score of wrongs" (NEB) which are done to it. Love has no desire to settle the account by returning evil for evil. Rather than hold to a grudge, it is forgiving.

J. Rejoiceth not in iniquity (KJV) or does not rejoice at wrong (RSV). Love is not made happy by sin nor by the fact that some fall into sin (Rom. 1:32; II Thess. 2:12). What causes us to laugh? Are the actions of one engaged in evil really humorous (*e.g.* a reeling drunkard)?

K. Rejoiceth in the truth (KJV) or the right (RSV). Truth, as it stands in contrast with iniquity, is personified with love (see Ps. 85:10). There are many who resist or oppose the truth (II Tim. 3:8), suppress the truth (Rom. 1:18, RSV) and will not obey the truth (Rom. 2:8). However, love is made happy by truth preached and lived (Acts 11:23; II Jno. 4).

L. Bears all things. Bear is from "stego" which means "primarily to protect, or preserve by covering, hence to keep off something which threatens, to bear up against or hold out against, and so to endure, bear, forbear" (Vine, vol. I, p. 102). "This may either mean, bears in silence all annoyances and troubles, or covers up all things (as 'stego' may have either meaning), in the sense of concealing or excusing the faults of others, instead of gladly disclosing them" (Hodge, p. 271). On the latter view, Vincent wrote: "It keeps out resentment as a ship keeps out the water, or the roof the rain" (vol. III, p. 265). According to Farrar, love "endures wrongs and evils and covers them with a beautiful reticence" (p. 424). In that connection, see Prov. 10:12; I Pet. 4:8. Paul also used "stego" at 9:12; I Thess. 3:1, 5.

M. Believes all things. Love is not suspicious. It does not seek hidden, ulterior motives. It gives others the benefit of the doubt by placing the best interpretation on events, unless compelled to do otherwise. It is opposite to that spirit which paints everything in the darkest colors possible. This does not mean love is naive or gullible (Prov. 14:15).

N. Hopes all things. It sees the bright side of things. Love is optimistic rather than gloomy and despairing. There are times when in hope it will believe against hope (Rom. 4:18).

O. Endures all things. "The word is properly a military word, and means to sustain the assault of the enemy. Hence it is used in the New Testament to express the idea of sustaining the assaults of suffering or persecution, in the sense of bearing up under them, and enduring them patiently (II Tim. 2:10; Heb. 10:32; 12:2)" (Hodge, p. 271).

III. Gifts were Temporary but Love is Eternal (13:8-13).

A. Perfect (13:10) does not refer to Christ. Some, who maintain that the gifts are now being exercised and will continue until the Lord's second coming, contend that Jesus, as the Perfect One, is under consideration. In reply to that view, it should be noted that perfect in Greek is neuter gender ("to teleion") just as imperfect (RSV) or in part (KJV) is neuter ("ek merous"). Apparently, a thing or process rather than a person is contemplated. If this were referring to Jesus, the masculine gender would be used instead of the neuter (*i.e.* "he who" rather than "that which"). Admittedly, the neuter is once used concerning Christ (Matt. 1:20). However, he was still a fetus in Mary's womb at the time. Furthermore, the expression there is "to gar" instead of "to teleion." To my knowledge, there is not a place in the New Testament where "to teleion" is ever used in reference to the Savior after his birth or in connection with his second coming. "Also, since *teleion* is set in contrast to that which is 'in part' (*ek merous*), it must refer to the culmination of a process. The second coming is not a process; it is an instantaneous event" (R. G. Gromacki, *The Modern Tongues Movement,* p. 123).

B. Perfect does not mean the perfect state of heaven which will begin at the second advent of Christ. Some, who believe gifts will last until the consummation of the age, have taken that position. Waymon Miller, in response to such thinking, wrote: "Paul's argument would have been superfluous and meaningless had this been meant, for all understand that in the eternal realm no need for prophecies, tongues, knowledge and the like will exist" (*Modern Divine Healing,* p. 320).

At this point, 13:13 must be considered. The word translated as now in that verse is from "nuni" which may refer to time (Acts 24:13; Rom. 6:22) or to a logical conclusion (Rom. 7:17) (Vine, vol. III, p. 119; Hodge, p. 275). Concerning 13:13, Vincent represented all authorities consulted by writing, "Now is *logical* and not *temporal*" (vol. III, p. 267). It is taken this way in the RSV where "nuni" is rendered as so. Paul did not mean that faith, hope and love are eternal and the gifts are temporal (implying that the gifts would last until the end of the world). Earlier, he had stated that "love never ends" (13:8, RSV). He did not make a similar affirmation for faith and hope. As a matter of fact, faith, in the sense of belief (not in the sense of trust), and hope, in the sense of expectation, will cease to exist (*i.e.* be replaced by absolute knowledge—Heb. 11:1; II Cor. 5:7; Rom. 8:24-25) when time ends. Paul was saying that faith, hope and love will continue after the gifts

have ceased. Since faith and hope continue in time, it necessarily follows that the gifts were to be done away in *time* and
before the second coming of Christ and the end of the world.
According to Phillips translation of 13:13, it is *"In this life"*
(emphasis mine, J.A.) that we have faith, hope and love. Since
it has already been established that love is eternal (13:8), obviously, love will be experienced in the next life too. Here,
then, is Paul's sequence: (1) Cessation of gifts in time. (2)
Cessation of faith and hope when time ends. (3) Continuation
of love forever (which accounts for its being greater than faith
and hope).

C. Perfect likely means the full or complete revelation of
God's word.

1. Meaning of "teleion" (translated as perfect). All
authorities read indicate the word can mean mature or full
grown. However, the following definitions also appear: "Signifies having reached its end (telos), finished, complete, perfect
. . . (II) of things, complete, perfect, Rom. 12:2; I Cor. 13:10
(referring to the complete revelation of God's will and ways,
whether in the completed scriptures or in the hereafter)"
(Vine, vol. III, pp. 173-174). "Brought to its end, finished;
wanting nothing necessary to completeness; perfect" (Thayer,
p. 618). "Complete, entire, as opposed to what is partial and
limited, I Cor. 13:10" (Harper's, p. 400).

2. Context of the passage.

a. They had partial, imperfect or incomplete knowledge
and prophecy at the time (tongues, which also were to cease,
must fit into this category too for when interpreted, the result
was the same as prophecy or knowledge) (13:9). That was true
because only a part of the New Testament had then been
given. The entire new covenant was not revealed at the same
time. It was made known over a period of about fifty years.
Much was yet to be revealed after Paul penned I Corinthians
(ca. 54-55 A.D.). Once God's message was set forth in its
totality, the partial or incomplete was replaced by the full or
completed communication. When Revelation, the last New
Testament book, was finished about 95 A.D., the canon was
completed and the whole existed. This does not mean all New
Testament books had to be placed into one volume before gifts
were done away. It does mean gifts ceased by the time

Revelation was written. If this interpretation is correct, the latter part of Vine's definition for "teleion" concerning the hereafter must be rejected. In response to one who wrote that the view herein maintained is "novel" and "hardly defensible either in the light of the context of the passage or modern scholarship," it should be pointed out that "the prevailing belief" from the time of Chrysostom onward "is that these gifts were destined only for the apostolic period, and have already ceased" (J. P. Lange, *Commentary on the Holy Scriptures—Corinthians*, p. 271).

    b. Paul's illustrations (13:11-12).

    (1) His first illustration is that of a person who had been a child and then became a man. He meant that the church with its gifts and partial revelation was then like a child. However, when the message was completed, the church would be like a mature man in its knowledge and understanding.

    (2) His second illustration is that of a mirror. At first, one can see only dimly but later he can see "face to face." The contrast is between a dim image (representing their partial knowledge) and a full image (representing God's completed revelation). Gary Workman wrote: "To 'see in a mirror' was often a figure of speech which meant 'to receive revelation from God.' " He then cited Num. 12:6 in which vision appears and continued, "The Hebrew word for 'mirror'—*marah*—is the same word that means 'vision' as a means of receiving revelation from God. To see a vision was to figuratively see in a mirror" (*Has "That Which Is Perfect" Come?*, p. 13).

    3. A comparison of I Cor. 13:8-10 with Eph. 4:7-15.

I Cor. 13:8-10	*Eph. 4:7-15*
a. Gifts (13:8).	a. Gifts (4:7-8, 11).
b. To pass away (13:10).	b. To be done away (4:13).
c. Cease when perfect comes (13:10).	c. End when come to the unity of the faith (4:13).
d. Then have completed knowledge (13:10-12).	d. Then have completed knowledge (4:13).

e. Church a child before ful-   e. Church a child before fulfillment (13:11).   fillment (4:14).

f. Church a mature man when   f. Church a mature man when
   gifts ceased (13:11).   gifts ceased (4:13).

The key verse in this comparison is Eph. 4:13 which states that the gifts were to continue "until" (an adverb of time indicating when) the saints attained the unity of the faith. Some have understood this as a reference to the unity of all believers in Christ. They contend that the gifts will last until the sects and denominations become one united church. That view cannot be correct in light of Eph. 4:3 which urged the brethren to keep or maintain the unity of the Spirit in the bond of peace. How could they keep what they did not have? The church was then united. That was a time before sectarianism, as we know it, had arisen. Thus, it is clear that Paul did not mean the gifts were to continue until all man-made churches are united.

Faith is used in at least two ways in the New Testament. Subjectively (Rom. 4:9; 5:1), it refers to the trust in God one has in his heart (Thayer, p. 512). Objectively, it means the message of God, the thing to be believed (Thayer, p. 513; Vine, vol. II, p. 71). Subjective faith is not under consideration at Eph. 4:13. Rather than "the unity of faith" it refers to the "unity of *the* faith." The New Testament message or system of faith is contemplated (see Jude 3; Acts 6:7; 24:24). At Eph. 4:13, Paul was saying God's new revelation reached unity, oneness, completion or perfection when all parts of the faith had been given. He also concluded that the gifts would then cease. If the New Testament is complete, gifts have ended.

D. Argument against the position taken on 13:8-10.

1. Argument: The perfect must refer to heaven since Paul said, "Then I shall understand fully, even as I have been fully understood" (13:12, RSV). Those upholding this viewpoint have interpreted Paul's statement in at least two different ways. Some think he meant Christians in heaven will fully know God as God now fully knows them. Knox translates, "I shall recognize God as he recognizes me." Others think Paul was saying the saints in glory will have full knowledge as God now has full knowledge of them.

2. Reply:

a. J. D. Bales dealt with both concepts as follows: "However, there is no scriptural support for the position that we shall know things with the perfect knowledge that Christ has. In order to know Christ as he knows us we would have to be elevated to the heights to which he has been elevated; but where does the Bible promise that we shall be equal to Christ in knowledge? To have a perfect knowledge of Christ as he has of us would necessitate our being equal with Christ in that point at least. The idea that man can possess knowledge as God possesses it and to the extent that he possesses it, is a form of the lie which was preached by the tempter in the garden of Eden (Gen. 3:5). Man was promised that he would be as God in his knowledge of good and evil. This was a lie by the father of lies. Paul certainly did not teach that lie, or one form of it, which brought the fall of man" (*Miracles or Mirages?*, p. 203).

b. Surely, no one can believe that Christians will have full, complete, unlimited knowledge in the next life (a claim for a share in the omniscience of the Godhead). However, unless the expression, "understand fully," is given some modification, that conclusion must be drawn. Since Paul was discussing the complete revelation of God's will, he likely meant when the message was finished, Christians would fully know God, themselves or the word (in contrast to their then partial knowledge) in light of their capacity as they were fully known by God in light of his capacity. For an illustration, consider how we are to be perfect in light of our capacity as God is perfect in light of his capacity (Matt. 5:48).

E. Additional reasons for believing the gifts have ceased.

1. Gifts were passed on to others only by the imposition of apostolic hands (Acts 8:14-18; 19:6). That means when the last apostle died and the last person on whom the apostles laid hands died, gifts ceased.

a. In an attempt to overthrow this conclusion, some have contended that Saul received the miraculous power of the Spirit through the hands of Ananias (Acts 9:12, 17-18) and Timothy was endowed with a gift by the hands of the elders (I Tim. 4:14).

b. Reply:

(1) The case of Saul. A close reading of Acts 9:12-18 indicates that Saul received *only* his sight by the hands of Ananias prior to being baptized. The passage does not say when the Spirit was given. The expression, "be filled with the Spirit" (9:17, RSV), refers to the ordinary or indwelling measure of the Holy Spirit which is possessed by all of God's children (Acts 6:3, 5; Eph. 5:18). When Saul was baptized by Ananias (9:18), he then received the gift of the Spirit (Acts 2:38; 5:32) or was filled with the Spirit. Only in that sense did Saul receive the Spirit (non-miraculous measure) through the hands of Ananias. He did not receive a spiritual gift.

(2) The case of Timothy. According to II Tim. 1:6, Timothy received his gift by the hands of Paul. How is this to be harmonized with I Tim. 4:14? When Paul imposed his hands to impart the gift, the elders also laid on their hands either to ordain Timothy as an evangelist (I Tim. 5:22) or to ordain him for the work of being Paul's fellow missionary (Acts 13:1-3; 16:1-3).

2. In the days when gifts were exercised, the dead were raised (Acts 9:36-43; 20:9-10). The dead are not now being raised, therefore, the gifts are not now being exercised. The two were part of a miraculous package. What good reason is there for holding to the one while rejecting the other? Where is the person who claims that God performs miracles through him who will attempt to raise the dead?

3. If there are gifted men today, there must also be apostles (I Cor. 12:27-31; Eph. 4:7-11). How can one consistently hold that today's church has tongue speakers but no apostles? If there are twentieth century apostles, God is still giving revelation and the canon of scripture is not closed. The Latter Day Saints claim to have apostles and revelation in addition to the New Testament. Although they are mistaken, they do see the need for consistency. Most charismatic people have completely overlooked this matter.

XV.

CHAPTER FOURTEEN

How the Gifts were to be Regulated

Structure

I. Prophecy Superior to Tongues (14:1-5).
   A. Why prophecy was superior to tongues (14:5).
   1. The tongue speaker did not speak to men but the prophet did (14:2).
      a. This does not mean a tongue speaker, under no circumstances, spoke to men. When he was understood by others or his delivery was interpreted, he did address men. Those present at Jerusalem on the Day of Pentecost understood the tongues spoken by the apostles (Acts 2:4-12). The church (*i.e.* assembly) was edified by tongues which were interpreted (14:5). Paul could have instructed the church with tongues (14:6). Provision was made for the church to hear tongues (14:26-28). When tongues were interpreted, the result was the same as prophecy.
      b. The statement obviously means the tongue speaker did not address men *only* when he was not understood (14:2).

Apparently, speaking in tongues without interpretation had been a common occurrence at Corinth.

2. Tongue speaker edified himself but the prophet edified the church (14:4).

a. As already indicated, the tongue speaker at Corinth did edify the church when followed by an interpretation (14:5).

b. Whether tongues were foreign languages or ecstatic speech, the question of how a tongue speaker edified himself arises. Some have thought he was edified because he had the gift of interpretation. Others were not edified simply because he did not interpret. Hodge suggested that he was edified because he understood his remarks without the gift of interpretation. He then added, "The absence of the gift of interpretation does not prove that the speaker himself in such cases was ignorant of what he had uttered. It only proves he was not inspired to communicate in another language what he had delivered. Had he done so, it would have been on his own authority, and not as an organ of the Spirit" (p. 281). Perhaps he was edified in the knowledge that he was being used as an instrument of the Holy Spirit although he did not understand the words he had spoken.

c. Those who use 14:4, 28 (see comments on verse 28) for a long and complicated theology in behalf of tongue speaking as a private prayer language have taken the verses from their context. How can such great emphasis be given to tongue speaking as private prayer talk when Paul plainly declared that tongues were a sign for unbelievers (14:22)? The statements of 14:4, 28 are in the setting of a church assembly rather than one's private devotional life. Admittedly, a tongue may have been used while communicating with God alone but the same could be said about the gifts of knowledge, faith and prophecy. There may be some truth in the view concerning the private devotional use of the tongue but it does not relate to its primary purpose.

B. The threefold function of prophecy (14:3).

1. Upbuilding (edification, KJV) is from "oikodome" which "denotes the act of building ('oikos,' a home, and 'demo,' to build); this is used figuratively in the N.T. in the sense of edification, the promotion of spiritual growth . . . I Cor. 14:3, 5, 12, 26" (Vine, vol. II, pp. 18-19).

2. Encouragement (exhortation, KJV) is from "para-klesis" which "means a calling to one's side ('para,' beside, 'kaleo,' to call)" (Vine, vol. I, p. 207) for the purpose of exhorting, persuading or encouraging. Discouragement is the common lot of humanity. Children of God are not immune to it. Even the bold and courageous Elijah gave way to despondency and asked the Lord to take his life (I Kgs. 19:4). Barnabas was unusually talented in lifting the downfallen and was known as the "Son of encouragement" (Acts 4:36, RSV). Prophets were placed in the first century church to encourage Christians. Today, the disciples obtain similar help from the word of God personally studied or taught to them by others.

3. Consolation (comfort, KJV) is from "paramuthia," which appears only in this verse and means "primarily a speaking closely to anyone ('para,' near, 'muthos,' speech), hence, denotes consolation, comfort, with a *greater degree of tenderness* [emphasis mine, J.A.] than paraklesis" (Vine, vol. I, p. 207).

II. Necessity for Interpretation of Tongues (14:6-19).

A. Paul's illustrations were the flute, harp and bugle (14:6-8). Unless those instruments gave distinct notes or sound (*i.e.* spoke the language of music), one would have no knowledge of what was being played. In that connection, McGarvey wrote: "Certain notes on a trumpet commanded a charge, others the joining of battle, and yet others the retreat, etc. Now, if the trumpet or trumpeter fails to produce this tone-language intelligibly, the army is thrown into confusion. Spiritual guidance uttered in an unknown tongue was like a blare of the trumpet which gave no order" (p. 137).

B. The results of tongue speaking without interpretation (14:9-12). First, it was a wasted effort like speaking into the air (14:9). Second, the hearers were not benefited (14:6) because they could not understand what was spoken (14:10-11). Third, the speaker and hearers were as foreigners to one another (14:11). Rather than continuing to engage in such useless activity, they were urged to strive to edify the church (14:12).

C. Necessity for interpretation (14:13-19).

1. Pray for the power to interpret (14:13). If the prayer received a positive answer, it came by the laying on of apostolic hands. When Peter and John went to Samaria, they prayed for some of the disciples, laid hands on them and they received the Holy Spirit (Acts 8:15-17). Interpretation, like any other spiritual gift, was passed on to others *only* through the hands of the apostles.

2. Interpretation was essential for others to understand, participate in prayer meaningfully (14:16) and receive edification from the words spoken (14:17).

3. When one prayed in a tongue without interpretation, the spirit prayed but the mind or understanding was unfruitful (14:14).

a. Spirit may be a reference to the Christian's spirit under the miraculous control of the Holy Spirit. On the other hand, it could refer simply to man's spiritual gift. Either conclusion, practically speaking, is the same.

b. Mind (RSV) means the understanding (KJV), thoughts or ideas held by the one praying in a tongue. His mind was unfruitful since his thoughts could produce no fruit in others who did not have the ability to understand the tongue in which he spoke.

4. To pray with the spirit means to pray with a spiritual gift or with one's own spirit under the direction of the Holy Spirit; to pray with the understanding means to pray so that others can understand the thoughts of the prayer's mind (14:15). Obviously, this demanded interpretation of the prayer offered in a tongue. This explanation also applied to singing with the spirit and understanding. Because 14:15 relates to an assembly where spiritual gifts were exercised and there are no such gatherings today, it is a misuse of language for one in a modern church setting to ask God to help brethren worship "with the spirit and with the understanding." It is correct to pray that worship will be sincere and intelligent but scripture is misapplied when this verse is used in that way.

5. Paul spoke in tongues more than any of the Corinthians (14:18), however, he preferred speaking in a few words so that others were instructed by his understanding rather

than many words in a tongue which others could not compre-
hend (14:19). There is a lesson in this for the Romanists who,
until recently, conducted services in Latin. Paul's remarks
must also be taken seriously by any preacher or teacher who
strives to impress his hearers with a display of learned and
technical vocabulary. The profound and difficult things of
scripture must not be evaded but they should be taught as
simply as possible so that everyone can be edified. Even the
common people understood the Master Teacher.

III. Purpose of Tongues (14:20-25).
   A. Tongues were a sign for unbelievers (14:22).
      1. Earlier, 14:21 was used to show that tongues were
foreign languages (see remarks under "Tongues" at 12:8-10).
Here Paul quoted Isaiah 28:11-12 in which the prophet indicated that stubborn, unbelieving Israel would be addressed by
God through the lips of the Assyrians. That prediction was
fulfilled when Assyria invaded the land of Ephraim and, after
a three year siege, destroyed Samaria in 722 B.C.
      2. As the tongues of foreigners were a sign of ancient
Israel's unbelief, the languages spoken at Corinth in the first
century were a sign for unbelievers (14:22). Tongues as signs,
like other miracles, were performed primarily to confirm, cor-
roborate or verify the apostolic message as having come from
God (Jno. 20:30-31; Mk. 16:20; Heb. 2:1-4). Tongues were
evangelistic in the sense of turning the attention of unbelievers to the gospel by which they could be saved.
      3. In reply to the view that the unbelievers of 14:22 were
unbelieving brethren, the following is offered. First, every time
unbelievers are mentioned in the Corinthian correspondence,
nonchristians are contemplated (I Cor. 6:6; 7:12-15; 10:27; II
Cor. 4:4; 6:14-15). Second, it is true that the outsider, un-
learned or ungifted person of 14:16 is a child of God (who else
could properly say "Amen" to a prayer of thanksgiving?).
However, this does not mean the outsiders or unbelievers at
14:23-24 are disciples of Christ. "Idiotes," translated as outsider (14:16, 23-24, RSV), refers to an ungifted person. Some
Christians and all unbelievers were lacking in the gifts. The
ungifted of 14:16 is a brother; the ungifted in 14:23-24 is an

unsaved person. Unbeliever and outsider are used interchangeably in 14:23-24 but this does not mean the unbeliever of 14:23-24 is the same as the outsider in 14:16. To illustrate, all unbelievers were outsiders (*i.e.* ungifted) but not all outsiders were unbelievers. In other words, there was more to being an unbeliever than being an outsider. Tongues were a sign to the unconverted!

4. Tongues were a sign to unbelievers when properly used (14:22-23). Tongue speakers addressing the group one at a time and each being followed by an interpreter (14:27) signified to unbelievers that the message proclaimed by Christians was from above (14:22). Bedlam occurred when all spoke at the same time and to unbelievers such indicated madness (14:23). Surely, the unsaved were turned away from the church by that type of disorder.

B. Prophecy was primarily for believers (14:22). See the notes on 14:3 to learn why this was true.

C. Prophecy was superior to a multitude of tongues (*i.e.* misused tongues) in dealing with unbelievers (14:23-25). After tongues were used to attract the attention of nonchristians, prophecy (*i.e.* inspired teaching) followed. The conversion of the unsaved is set forth in 14:24-25. First, the nonmember was convinced or convicted by all. Likely, that means he was convinced of sin, righteousness, judgment (Jno. 16:8-11), the truth that Jesus was Christ (Acts 9:20-22) and that Jesus could forgive his sins (Acts 10:43; I Tim. 1:15). Second, he was judged or called to account by all. This probably refers to the searching, examining and questioning he experienced due to truth's presentation. Third, the secrets of his heart were made manifest or disclosed. The word of God, as a discerner of the thoughts and intents of the heart (Heb. 4:12), led him to see his true spiritual condition before the Lord (an understanding every lost person must reach to be saved). Fourth, he acknowledged that God was among them, fell on his face and adored the Almighty. By means of Oriental idiom, Paul set forth the culmination of the conversion process. At this point, McGarvey added: "It should be observed that if truth is more potent than signs, much more is it more efficacious in revivals than mere excitement or pumped-up enthusiasm" (p. 141).

IV. All to be Done Decently and in Order (14:26-40).

A. Since many desired to participate in the services (14:25), structure was necessary if Christians were to learn (14:31), be encouraged (14:31) and be edified (14:26).

1. This indicates that unstructured meetings offer little, if any benefit to Christians. Neither a "let happen what will happen" nor a cold, heart-killing formalism was recommended by Paul.

2. The desire of so many to have a part in the assembly programs stands in stark contrast to the unwillingness of today's majority to do anything of a public nature.

3. Explanation of the items in 14:26. Hymn or psalm is a song offered by a gifted person. Singing with the spirit and understanding (14:15) refers to the same type of activity. Apparently, there was solo singing by gifted people in the assembly at Corinth. Lesson or doctrine was a word of knowledge (12:8) presented by one with the gift of teaching (12:28). Revelation was teaching given by a prophet (12:28; 14:30-31). Tongue and interpretation are self explanatory.

B. Paul's instruction concerning procedure (14:27-35).

1. Tongue speakers (14:27-28).

a. Not more than three were to speak at one service (14:27).

b. They were to speak one at a time (14:27).

c. Interpretation was to be given (14:27).

d. If no interpreter was present, they were to be silent (14:28).

e. In the absence of an interpreter, they could speak to themselves and to God (14:28). Speak is from "laleo" and it generally means to speak aloud, however, in this verse it probably means to speak silently. Since keeping silence was to be done in church, it seems logical to conclude that speaking to himself and to God was also done in church. Hence, he was to speak silently to himself and to God in church. Hannah, in her prayer to God for a son, "was speaking ["elalei," a form of "laleo," LXX] in her heart" (I Sam. 1:13). That is obviously a case of silent speaking. The command in 14:28 seems to be another. Chrysostom understood it that way and said the tongue speaker was to speak "in his heart noiselessly" (*Homily*, 36). Hodge wrote: "That is, let him commune silently with

God in the exercise of his gift" (p. 301). Alford quoted Theophylact who thought it meant "softly and quietly to himself" (p. 227).

2. Prophets (14:29-33).

a. Not more than three were to speak at one service (14:29).

b. Other prophets were to weigh or judge what was said. Possibly, this does not refer to the prophets but to those who had the ability to distinguish between spirits (12:10). Or, it could mean the prophets, some of whom also had the gift of discernment. Prophecy had to be judged because there were many false prophets in the world (I Jno. 4:1).

c. They were to speak one at a time (14:30-31). When revelation was made to another, the one speaking was to discontinue his speech (14:30). It was possible for that command to be obeyed since the spirits (*i.e.* their spirits directed by the Holy Spirit or their spiritual gifts) of the prophets were subject to the prophets (an obvious allusion to the false position of those who said they had no control over their gifts) (14:32). Furthermore, Paul's teaching could be followed to the letter because God is not the author of confusion (a situation which would prevail if men could not control their actions while under the influence of the Spirit) but of peace (14:33).

3. Women (14:34-35).

a. Women were to keep silence in the church for two reasons (14:34).

(1) They were not allowed to speak. From 11:5, it has already been seen that prophetesses were permitted to speak in the assembly, hence, they were exceptions to this rule. Furthermore, since it is necessary for women to speak when they sing (Eph. 5:19) and confess Christ (Rom. 10:9-10), it was not intended that they should be excluded from those activities (unless one foolishly concludes that they could sing and confess only outside the assembly!). The meaning is that ungifted women were not allowed to *teach* a group in which men were present. That is the kind of speaking which is excluded.

(2) They were to be in subjection as taught in the law. Subordination of woman to man began in Eden (Gen.

3:16) and will continue until the end of time, regardless of its denial by the Women's Liberation Movement. The prophetess excepted, a woman teaching a group, gathering or assembly of men exercises authority *over* those men and transgresses the will of God (I Tim. 2:11-12). It is possible for a woman to teach a man as Priscilla taught Apollos (Acts 18:26), however, she can never teach *over* a man without doing violence to scripture. The authority of man is not restricted in teaching (Tit. 2:15) as is the woman's.

b. If they desired to know anything, they were to ask their husbands at home (14:35). That statement was not directed to a single woman, a widow, a lady with a nonchristian husband or a woman mature in the faith whose mate was a recent convert. Obviously, it was written to women whose husbands could answer their questions! Paul was referring to ladies married to prophets. Apparently, some prophets' wives were interrupting them as they prophesied to the congregation. Their activity stopped the flow of God's revelation. Remember, they did not have copies of the New Testament as we do now. The apostle corrected their rudeness and commanded them to ask questions at home rather than continue to disrupt the communication of God's spoken word.

c. It is shameful for a woman to speak at church (14:35). As pointed out above, it was no shame for a prophetess to speak or even for an uninspired woman to speak as she sang praises and confessed Jesus as Lord. It would not be shameful for a lady to ask that a song number be repeated in a modern day assembly. It was shameful for a woman to speak in teaching over men and in interrupting prophesying. This does not mean the church has authority for female evangelists. A proper understanding of I Tim. 2:8-15 will forever keep Christian women from occupying the pulpit.

C. Paul's warning (14:36-40).

1. Since the message did not have its origin with you, give heed to what is written (14:36). This language constitutes one of Paul's most sarcastic statements. Lenski paraphrased it as follows: "Are you the only ones in the world who have God's word and are thus able to tell others what it contains?" He then added, "It is ridiculous that any man or any congre-

gation should act in this way. Yet not a few act in this very way. Although throughout all ages of the past God's people have had the Word, these innovators presume to ignore all of them as though they had never existed and now arise to tell us what God's Word contains" (p. 620).

2. The gifted are to acknowledge that Paul's writing is the commandment of the Lord (a clear claim for his inspired authority) (14:37).

3. If any claim to be gifted and do not recognize the authority of this epistle, he is not recognized (14:38, RSV). KJV reads, "If any man be ignorant [*i.e.* fails to accept the inspiration and authority of Paul], let him be ignorant" (since sufficient evidence has already been adduced, waste no effort attempting to correct his willful ignorance). Since the later translations do not use KJV phraseology, perhaps Lenski was right in saying it "loses too much of the force of the original" (p. 622). A failure to be recognized may refer to recognition as a gifted person or to recognition (*i.e.* approval) by God.

4. Desire to prophesy and do not forbid tongue speaking (14:39). Gifts have ceased (see remarks at 13:8-10) and this verse has no application to the twentieth century church.

5. All things should be done decently and in order (14:40).

V. *Concluding Thought.*

When the Sabbath was done away, Sabbath regulations were also done away. Similarly, when spiritual gifts ceased, the teaching concerning their regulation also ceased. It is impossible to regulate what is non-existent. Since this chapter was written to control long-gone phenomena, one might conclude that it has no relevance for present day disciples. However, such is not the case. There are six principles in the chapter (aim for love—14:1; be mature in thought—14:20; all things are to be done for edification—14:26; God is not the author of confusion but of peace—14:33; women are subordinate to men—14:34; all things are to be done decently and in order—14:40) from which Paul made specific applications to spiritual gifts. Although the gifts and their regulations have ceased, *the principles continue to abide.*

XVI.

CHAPTER FIFTEEN

Resurrection of the Dead

Structure

I. Proof for the Resurrection of Christ (15:1-11).

A. Corinthian reception of Paul's preaching of the death, burial and resurrection of Jesus (an appeal to their experience) (15:1-4).

1. The importance of the gospel. It was that which they had *received* (*i.e.* to be initially saved), in which they *stood* and by which they would be eternally *saved* if they kept it in memory or held it fast (obviously, eternal salvation is conditioned upon the saints remaining faithful to the Savior—I Pet. 1:5; II Pet. 1:10) (15:2-3).

2. The death, burial and resurrection of Christ was preached as of first importance by Paul (15:3, RSV). Chris-

tians must study the word, commit much scripture to memory and stand ready to defend the faith, however, in all of the activities, they must continue to be Christ-centered and cross-related. "Jesus keep me near the cross" should be the theme song of every devoted disciple. Christ crucified and risen is to the church what the sun is to the solar system. If God's people move from Calvary, regardless of what else they say or do, they will have left the power of God (1:18, 24; 2:5).

3. Paul's preaching was based upon historical facts. One must believe the facts relating to the life, death and resurrection of Jesus before he can trust him as Savior (Eph. 1:13; Rom. 10:17). Logically, it is impossible to reject the historical material concerning Christ and then blindly leap to a trusting confidence in him. If the story or any part of it is false, how can its conclusion be true? Christianity claims to be a historical religion and it stands or falls on the basis of its historical accuracy. The blind subjectivism (i.e. "Jesus was raised if you think he was raised") of modern theology is not the religion of the New Testament.

B. Appeal to Old Testament prediction (15:3-4). The death (Ps. 22:1, 16; Isa. 53:8), burial (Isa. 53:9) and resurrection (Ps. 16:8-10) of the Messiah were foretold by the prophets. It is worth noting that before appealing to human witnesses in support of the Lord's resurrection, Paul gave the unshakeable testimony of scripture (Jno. 10:35).

C. Witness of Cephas (15:5; Lk. 24:34). In light of Peter's three denials of Jesus the night before his crucifixion, it would be extremely interesting to know what happened at this meeting. Perhaps the scene was so painful for the great apostle, God in his love saw fit to leave the details unrecorded.

D. Witness of the twelve (15:5; Lk. 24:33-53). Really, there were only eleven present since Judas was dead but "the twelve" was their ordinary appellation even when their number was not complete.

E. Witness of the five hundred (15:6). This appearance was likely on a mountain in Galilee where Jesus had promised to meet with his disciples (Matt. 26:32; 28:7, 10, 16). Jerusalem, suggested by Alford as the place where this occurred (p. 230), seems improbable. The fact that most of them were still alive strengthened the evidence for they could have been easily questioned to ascertain their testimony and integrity.

F. Witness of James (15:7). Likely, this does not refer to James, the son of Zebedee, who was killed a few years after the establishment of the church (Acts 12:1-2) or to James Alphaeus who was hardly known to the church in general. Probably, James the brother of the Lord is meant (Gal. 1:19). He was a prominent leader in the Jerusalem church (Gal. 2:9; Acts 12:17; 15:13; 21:18), one who traveled in the interest of Christ's cause (9:5) and the probable author of the book bearing his name. There is no record of this appearance in the gospel accounts, however, according to Farrar, "in the Gospel of the Hebrews was a curious legend that James had made a vow that he would neither eat nor drink till he had seen Jesus risen from the dead, and that Jesus, appearing to him said, 'My brother, eat thy bread, for the Son of man is risen from the dead' " (p. 484).

G. Witness of all the apostles (15:7). Since Paul had already mentioned the twelve (15:5), some think he used apostles here to mean more than the twelve (see comments at 9:6). Chrysostom included the seventy whom Jesus sent on the limited commission (*Homily,* 38).

H. Witness of Paul (15:8-10).
    1. Christ appeared to him last of all (15:8) on the road to Damascus (Acts 9:3-9) to qualify him for the apostleship (Acts 1:22; 26:16-18).
    2. Paul compared himself to an abortion or one untimely born ("ektroma" in Greek) (15:8). Concerning "ektroma," after pointing out that the word appears only here in the New Testament, Vincent continued that "in every case the word means 'an abortion, a still-born embryo.' " A few sentences later he stated that the rendition of KJV "is unsatisfactory, since it introduces the notion of time which is not in the original word, and fails to express the abortive character of the product; leaving it to be inferred that it is merely premature, but living and not dead. The word does not mean an untimely living birth, but a dead abortion, and suggests no notion of lateness of birth, but rather of being born before the time." In

conclusion, he added, "Paul means that when Christ appeared to him and called him, he was—as compared with the disciples who had known and followed Him from the first, and whom he had been persecuting—no better than an unperfected foetus among living men. The comparison emphasizes his condition at the time of his call" (p. 274). Thayer said Paul felt he was "as inferior to the rest of the apostles as an immature birth comes short of a mature one," and that he was "no more worthy of the name of the apostle than an abortion is of the name of a child" (p. 200).

3. Paul used the figure of an abortion to describe himself (15:8), felt least among the apostles (15:9) and said he was "less than the least of all saints" (Eph. 3:8, KJV) because he had persecuted the church of God (15:9; Gal. 1:13). His past haunted him as long as he lived. He knew he had been forgiven (I Tim. 1:13) but he could not erase the memories of violence and bloodshed. Peter may have had similar difficulty in forgetting his denials of Jesus. Perhaps he blushed with shame every time he heard a rooster crow after that fateful night.

4. Paul's apostleship and unflagging zeal were based on the grace of God (15:10; Rom. 15:15). At this point, McGarvey wrote: "But having confessed his crime and consequent inferiority, and knowing that this admission would be most strictly construed by those who disparaged him and contended that he was not an apostle, he rehabilitates himself by showing that his own littleness had been made big by the abounding grace of God, so that he had labored more abundantly than any of the apostles" (p. 148). The key to Christian endeavor today is the motivating power of God's grace in a thankful heart. Although fear has its place in Christianity, it is gratitude for grace which causes saints to wear themselves out in advancing the kingdom of Christ.

I. Concluding thoughts about witnesses.

1. To qualify as a witness, one must be in a position to know the facts, be in possession of a sound mind and be a person of integrity. Everyone given in Paul's list was in a position to know the facts. There is nothing to indicate that they were characterized by insanity. The fact that so many of them were killed for their faith in Christ is proof of their

integrity. Men simply would not die for what they knew to be a lie. Since Christianity is a historical religion, its veracity must be maintained by human testimony. If the witnesses are sound, the system must be accepted as God-given.

2. Some who saw the resurrected Christ (e.g. the women and the two disciples on the road to Emmaus) were left out by Paul probably because they were not well known. The twelve were given because it was understood everywhere that they had been with Jesus during his three year ministry (obviously, their testimony carried considerable weight). Peter and James were included because they were known throughout the brotherhood. Perhaps the 500 were mentioned to rule out the possibility of the resurrection being explained as a hallucination (for they all saw him). Paul added his own word since he had been an enemy of the church. Every sensible person knew that the Savior's appearance to him was totally unexpected.

II. Consequences of Denying the Resurrection (15:12-19).

A. Identity of those who said "there is no resurrection of the dead" (15:12).

1. Jews. Those who did not believe in the resurrection have been called "Corinthian Sadducees" (i.e. the Jewish sect which denied the resurrection—Matt. 22:23-33; Acts 23:8), however, there is no support for that viewpoint. Most of the Hebrews then agreed with the doctrine of the resurrection as taught by the Pharisees (Acts 23:8). The Sadducees were primarily a political group whose power was felt only in Palestine. As far as religious teaching was concerned, they had very little influence in their homeland and none elsewhere (it was the Pharisees who did the proselyting—Matt. 23:15).

2. Gentiles.

a. Epicureans—A Greek philosophical system which taught that one was annihilated at death. Knowing that those who denied the resurrection of the body would be unwilling to accept the Epicurean maxim, "Let us eat and drink for tomorrow we die," Paul cited that very statement (15:32) to show that it was a logical consequence of their doctrine. Hence, the Epicureans were not the ones at Corinth to whom Paul was replying.

　　b. Stoics—A Grecian philosophy which maintained that one lost his identity at death when his spirit was absorbed into the world soul (compared to Hindu thought). Really, that amounted to a denial of personal immortality. Although some Stoics and Epicureans mocked Paul for preaching the resurrection at Athens (Acts 17:32), it is doubtful that he had either group under consideration in this chapter.

　　c. Platonists—They received their name from Plato, a disciple of Socrates. They believed, as did most Greeks, in the immortality of the soul. They held that the soul soared free from the body into salvation at the moment of death. This concept is well-illustrated in Plato's *Phaedo*. Although some accepted the view of re-incarnation, the doctrine of an immortal soul living in an immortal *body* would have been abhorrent as long as they held to Platonism. There is no indication in the entire chapter that those opposing the resurrection denied the immortality of the soul. It is my judgment that Paul's arguments were directed toward Platonists.

　B. Consequences of denying the resurrection (15:13-19).

　　1. Christ has not been raised (15:13). Paul was saying if there is no *universal* resurrection, then Christ *specifically* was not raised. Logically, that conclusion must follow. Obviously, the Lord's resurrection is a part of the total resurrection. For Paul, there was only one resurrection which began with Jesus and will end with all humanity (15:20, 23).

　　2. Our preaching is vain (15:14). The word translated as vain is "kenos" meaning "fruitless" (Thayer, p. 343), "void of effect" (Harper's, p. 228) and "empty" (Vine, vol. IV, p. 181).

　　3. Your faith is vain (15:14, 17, KJV). At 15:14, "kenos" is used (see definitions immediately above). At 15:17, the word translated as vain or futile (RSV) is "mataios" meaning "devoid of force, truth, success, result" (Thayer, p. 399). Vine set forth the difference between the two words as follows: " 'Kenos' stresses the absence of quality, 'mataios,' the absence of useful aim or effect" (vol. II, p. 25).

　　4. We have misrepresented God (15:15, RSV). Obviously, if Christ was not raised, the apostles bore false witness in making the claim that God had raised him (15:15; Acts 2:32; 17:30-31). We are found false witnesses (KJV) is the better

translation. As Farrar said, "Paul does not shrink from the issue. It is not one—it could not be one—between truth and *mistake,* but between truth and *falsehood*" (p. 486).

5. You are still in your sins (15:17). Since Jesus was raised for man's justification (Rom. 4:25), a denial of his resurrection was also a repudiation of their justification. Hence, any taking that position had to conclude they were still under the guilt, power and condemnation of sin. For those who had known the happiness of forgiveness, that conclusion would have been a bitter pill to swallow.

6. Those who have fallen asleep in Christ have perished (15:18). "Apollumi," translated as perished, means "to destroy utterly. . . . The idea is not of extinction but ruin, loss, not of being, but of well being" (Vine, vol. I, p. 302). Thayer concurred by stating that it meant the loss of eternal life and deliverance to eternal misery (p. 64). Also read 1:18; 8:11; II Pet. 3:9; Jno. 3:16; Rom. 2:12 where "apollumi" appears. Do you suppose Corinthians whose loved ones had died in Christ were ready to agree they had gone to hell?

7. We are of all men most to be pitied (15:19). Why? Due to the suffering and hardship which was the common lot of many early saints (15:30-32; II Tim. 3:12) and because they were first-class fools for being misled by such a monstrous falsehood.

III. Necessity for the Resurrection (15:20-28).

A. To fully reap the harvest of the dead (15:20, 23). "On the morrow after the Sabbath of the Passover a sheaf of barley (the earliest grain to ripen) was waved as firstfruits before the Lord (Lev. 23:9-14). The firstfruits had to be thus presented before the harvest could be begun, and its presentation was an earnest of the ingathering. Now on this very day after the Sabbath Christ was raised as the firstfruits from the dead, and became the earnest of the general resurrection" (McGarvey, p. 150). "The apostle does not mean merely that the resurrection of Christ was to precede that of his people; but as the first sheaf of the harvest presented to God as a thank-offering, was the pledge and assurance of the ingathering of the whole harvest, so the resurrection of Christ is pledge and proof of the resurrection of his people" (Hodge, p. 323). See also Acts 26:23; Col. 1:18.

B. To overcome the consequence of sin (15:21-23).

1. Adam and Christ each stand at the head of the human family. All experience physical death as a consequence of Adam's sin. All will be raised from the dead as a consequence of Christ's resurrection. At this point, some have attempted to include spiritual death which Adam experienced in violating God's will (Gen. 2:17). Needless to say, they think all are born under the guilt of Adam's sin. If the death of 15:22 means all are born spiritually dead because of Adam's transgression, since the same verse declares that all are made alive in Christ, the result would be universal salvation (a contradiction of many plain passages—Matt. 7:13-14, 21-23; 25:46; Jno. 5:28-29). What proves too much, proves nothing. The context shows physical death is all that is contemplated.

2. "Each in his own order" (15:22). Order is from "tagma," meaning "a band, troop or cohort. . . . Here in the sense of band, or company, in pursuance of the principle of a descending series of ranks" (Vincent, vol. III, p. 275). From this some have assumed there will be two more resurrections, one for the righteous and after a thousand years, one for the wicked. Two, rather than three, ranks are mentioned. They are Christ, who has already been raised, and Christ's own, who will be raised at this coming. The resurrection of the wicked is not here discussed but it is clear from other passages that the good and evil will be raised at the same hour (*i.e.* simultaneously) (Jno. 5:28-29).

C. That Christ may be victorious over all enemies (15:24-28).

1. The rule, authority and power to be destroyed (15:24) are the anti-christian forces emanating from the kingdom of Satan (Matt. 12:26; Eph. 6:18; Rom. 8:38; Col. 2:15). Like death, which came into the world through the Devil's power, they are considered as enemies of God.

2. The last enemy to be destroyed is death (15:26). The ancient Persians set aside one day each year to kill serpents and venomous creatures. The men spent that entire day in the

fields and forests with their sticks and clubs. God has appointed a day in which Jesus will destroy the serpent of death.

3. The premillennial scheme concerning the end of time is incorrect. Consider the following syllogism—Major premise: Christ will reign at God's right hand (Acts 2:33; 5:31) until the last enemy is destroyed (15:25). Minor premise: The last enemy to be destroyed is death (which will occur when *all* the dead have been raised) (15:26). Conclusion: Therefore, Christ will reign at God's right hand until the last enemy is destroyed or until all the dead have been raised. If this reasoning is true, the premillennial view that Jesus will come again, raise the righteous dead, reign with them on earth a thousand years and then raise the wicked dead is false. Christ will reign with the Father until the last dead person has been made alive!

4. Then the kingdom will be delivered to God and the Son will be subjected to the Father (15:24, 27-28). Frankly, these verses are extremely difficult to understand. Of the explanations read, Alford's seemed best. He wrote: "The kingdom of Christ over this world, in its beginning, its furtherance, and its completion, has one great end,—*the glorification of the Father by the Son*. Therefore, when it shall be fully established, every enemy overcome, everything subjected to Him, He will,—not, reign over it and abide its King, *but deliver it up to the Father*. Hence, His reign will endure, not like that of earthly kings, when he shall have put all enemies under His feet, but only *till* He shall have, etc.,—and then will be absorbed in the all-pervading majesty of Him for whose glory it was from first to last carried onward. It may be observed that the whole of this respects the mediatorial work and kingdom; the work of redemption, and that Lordship over dead and living, for which Christ both died and rose. Consequently nothing is here said which can affect either (1) His coequality and coeternity with the Father in the Godhead, which is prior to and independent of this mediatorial work, and is not limited to the mediatorial kingdom: or (2) the eternity of His Humanity: for that Humanity ever was and is subordinate to the Father; and it by no means follows that when the mediatorial kingdom shall be given up to the Father, the Humanity in which that kingdom was won, shall be put off; nay, the very fact of Christ in the body being the firstfruits of the resurrection, proves that His

body, as ours, will endure forever; as the truth that our humanity, even in glory, can only subsist before God by virtue of His Humanity, makes it plain that He will be *very man* to all eternity" (pp. 235-236).

IV. Questions for Those Who Denied the Resurrection (15:29-34).

A. What do people mean by being baptized for the dead (15:29)? One expositor mentioned a work which has thirty-six explanations of this verse. Another said the interpretations of it were too numerous to catalogue. A few are listed below.

1. Baptized over the graves of the dead. "Huper," translated as for or on behalf of, is understood as over and it is suggested that some had been baptized over the graves of the dead. This view assumes that baptism was administered by affusion which is incorrect (Eph. 4:5; Col. 2:12).

2. Baptized out of respect for the dead. Some saints, then dead, while living had pleaded with others to be baptized. Hence, there were those who had been baptized to fulfill the entreaties of departed disciples.

3. Baptized to fill up the vacant places left in the church by those who had died. This is a military concept of one soldier taking the place of another who has fallen in battle.

4. Baptized for those who are about to die. In other words, why should baptism be administered to those on the brink of death?

5. Baptized on behalf of one who is already dead to the love of sin by repentance. This would make it an allusion to anyone scripturally baptized.

6. Baptism by martyrdom or a baptism of blood (appeal is made to Mk. 10:38; Lk. 12:50). It is thought that Paul's statements in 15:30-31 support this view.

7. Baptism of suffering and persecution. Dead is taken metaphorically as a reference to the hardships experienced by many early Christians. Paul's remarks at 15:30-31 are also used to uphold this concept.

8. Baptism on behalf of the dead Christ. If this is correct, the plural (dead ones) is used for the singular (dead one).

9. Baptized on behalf of their own bodies which were to die.

10. Baptism in the sense of dipping a saint's dead body in water to thoroughly cleanse it prior to burial and in hope of the resurrection.

11. Baptized with a view to joining the dead ones.

12. Baptized with reference to the resurrection of the dead (the view held by most early Greek commentators).

13. Actually being baptized for the benefit of others who had died without baptism.

a. Paul could have used this as an argument for the resurrection without endorsing the practice. When Jesus was accused of casting out demons by Satan's power, he asked, "By whom do your own people drive them out?" (Matt. 12:27, NEB). He did not mean there were some among the Pharisees who really exorcised demons. It was an argument made against their position but with no endorsement of their claim. Today, in contending for the immortality of the soul, one might appeal to the view of the Parsees (or Zoroastrians) for support without giving approval to their peculiar teaching on the point. Perhaps Paul dealt with an unscriptural practice in a similar way. He did not use first person as in verse 30 or second person as in verse 31. He used third person (they or people) in reference to a practice which was neither his nor those to whom he was writing. Alford held this to be correct and expressed it as follows: " 'what shall they do'—There is in these words a tacit reprehension of the practice about to be mentioned, which it is hardly possible to altogether miss. Both by the third person and by the words 'they which are,' he indirectly separates himself and those to whom he is writing from participation or approval of the practice:—the meaning being, 'what will become of'—'what account can they give of their practice?' " (p. 237).

b. There is no evidence for Christians practicing proxy baptism in Paul's day. Later (second century), the Cerinthians and Marcionites, *two heretical sects,* did engage in it. Apparently, it was universally denounced by the church of that time.

c. Mormon practice of baptizing for those who died without baptism is contrary to many plain passages which show the necessity of belief, repentance and baptism in this life (Prov. 11:7; Jno. 8:21; Lk. 13:3; Mk. 16:16; Heb. 9:27). Calling attention to I Pet. 3:18-22; 4:6 will not help their cause. A close study of I Pet. 3:18-22 indicates that Jesus preached to the anti-deluvian world through the Spirit through Noah (in the same way, he preached to the Gentiles through Paul—Eph. 2:17) while the ark was being prepared. The spirits in prison were Noah's contemporaries. They were in prison in the sense of being enslaved to sin when he preached to them (see Jno. 8:34) or they were imprisoned in the Hadean world when Peter wrote his epistle. Those mentioned at I Pet. 4:6 were then dead but they were alive when they heard the gospel.

B. Why am I in peril every hour (15:30-31, RSV)? Paul was never out of jeopardy. His danger was real and constant. According to Moffatt's translation, he said, "Not a day but I am at death's door!" (15:31).

C. What do I gain (15:32)?

1. The questions of this section (15:29-32) are meaningless unless the writer is understood to affirm there will be no eternal reward without a resurrection body. Although the dead *now* exist as disembodied spirits in Hades, they will not live eternally in that condition (II Cor. 5:1-10). In reply to the Sadducees, Jesus showed that the acceptance of immortality implies the resurrection of the dead (Matt. 22:23-33; Lk. 20:27-40).

2. The reference to fighting with wild beasts at Ephesus should be taken metaphorically. As a Roman citizen, it is unlikely that Paul was forced to fight animals in the arena (admittedly, there were some exceptions to that rule). Ignatius, in his epistle to the Romans, used almost exactly the same expression in a figurative way (5:1). Since opponents of God's men are called vipers (Lk. 3:7), dogs (Phil. 3:2) and swine (Matt. 7:6), it would not be unusual for Paul to label them as wild beasts. The Lord's people have always had many animal-like adversaries. Paul's mention of the lion at II Tim. 4:17 could be an allusion to Nero.

D. Let us eat and drink for tomorrow we die (15:32; Isa. 22:13). This is another consequence of denying the resurrection. Paul meant if the body is not raised, there will be no eternal life, therefore, one should live for this life alone (*i.e.* by satisfying his sensual desires).

E. Bad company ruins good morals (15:33, RSV). Some have thought Paul was quoting Meander, however, this does not necessarily follow. The statement was probably a well known proverb. The bad company were those who denied the resurrection from the dead. Paul's declarations in 15:32-33 show the relationship between doctrine and morality. What people believe affects the way they live.

F. Two admonitions (15:34).

1. Come to your right mind (RSV) or awake to righteousness (KJV). The word translated as awake originally meant to become sober after being drunk. Weymouth translates, "Wake from this drunken fit." Apparently, Paul addressed them as though they were drunk or insane.

2. Sin no more (RSV) or sin not (KJV). Perhaps Paul meant they were not to engage in sin through a denial of the resurrection, a fundamental doctrine of the faith. Maybe he was saying a denial of the resurrection would logically lead to a life of sin. If so, he urged them to accept the resurrection knowing that such would result in their living morally rather than sinfully.

3. Why the admonitions (15:34)?

a. Some had no knowledge of God (*i.e.* they did not have a knowledge of God's power to raise bodies from the dead—Matt. 22:29).

b. Their position was one of shame. In an earlier rebuke, he had not intended to shame them (4:14), however, the opposite was true here. A people so inconsistent as to reject the resurrection, while accepting a religion based on the resurrection of its Founder, ought to be ashamed.

V. The Resurrection Body (15:35-50).

A. Question—With what body are the dead raised (15:35)?

1. The question was postulated by those (depicted as one adversary) who denied the resurrection. Likely, it was considered as one of the strongest objections in their arsenal. Even the inspired penman answered by analogy (in reasoning

to the unknown, there is no other approach) and did not give a complete answer. Since it does not yet appear *exactly* what men shall be in the resurrection (I Jno. 3:2), the secret things still belong to God (Deut. 29:29). Paul did supply enough information to meet and overpower his opposition.

2. The questioner is called a fool (15:36). The word does not express a lack of love for the very epitome of love used it in reference to his doubting disciples (Lk. 24:25). Paul did explode the vaunted brilliance of those who rejected the resurrection on such ridiculous grounds. Because there is mystery in the resurrection is no basis for its rejection. This is a concern of Almighty God and nothing is too hard for him!

B. Answer to the question (15:36-50).

1. God gives the body he has chosen (15:36-39).

a. In the vegetable kingdom, each seed has its own body (*i.e.* plant or stalk) (15:36-38). The Lord does not deal with each seed separately. From the beginning, vegetation has reproduced after its kind (Gen. 1:11-12), therefore, God gives bodies to seed according to the fixed laws of nature.

b. In the animal kingdom, each type of animal organism has its own flesh (*i.e.* body) (15:39). It is interesting to note that the ascending scale of creation (fish, fowl, beast and man—Gen. 1:20-27) is here given in descending order.

2. Each body has its own glory (15:40-41).

a. Celestial and terrestrial bodies each have their own glory (15:40). Terrestrial bodies are earthly bodies and include the various kinds just mentioned (15:38-39). By celestial bodies, the writer did not mean inhabitants of other planets. He may have had in mind the sun, moon and stars of the next verse. However, it seems more probable that he was contrasting earthly bodies with the heavenly bodies of angels. Men will be like angels in the resurrection (Matt. 22:30), but men will have bodies in the resurrection, therefore, it appears that angels now have bodies.

b. Each of the heavenly bodies (sun, moon and stars) has its own glory (15:41). Nothing is here said about different levels of glory which Christians may or may not experience in the next life. The illustration deals with the difference between the present and future body.

3. The resurrection body (15:42-50). This section begins with "houtos" (translated as so) which means "in the way described; in this manner" (Thayer, p. 468). "There are illustrations here of the raising of the dead" (15:42, Phillips). Apparently, the meaning is twofold. First, as God has given different kinds of bodies with their different degrees of glory, he will also give man a resurrection body of glory. In answer to "How are the dead raised?" (15:35), Paul said that it will be done by the omnipotent God! For believers, that settles the matter. Second, as bodies and their glories differ, so the resurrection body will differ from the present body. In response to "With what kind of body do they come?" (15:35), Paul showed the false teachers had a groundless objection because the body of the resurrection will be different from the body of humiliation.

a. The resurrection body has a connection with the present body as seed has a connection with the plant which grows from it (15:36-38). That familiar analogy was given to meet the opposition's claim that the body raised had to be made of the same particles as the one put into the ground or there could be no resurrection. Although the two are connected, the seed sown is not the plant (15:37). Similarly, the body which returns to dust will not be raised in precisely the same form with every tooth and nail. Since vegetation reproduces after its kind (Gen. 1:11-12), wheat plant grows from wheat seed. They are not the same except in identity. As seed and plant, the present body has a connection with the future body which preserves identity. Change and identity are not incompatible terms. The river which undergoes constant change remains the same river. Our present bodies are not like the ones we had ten years ago but they are the same as far as identity is concerned. Paul did not affirm sameness nor recreation but identity for the resurrection body. How that identity is maintained is not clearly revealed. Some carry Paul's analogy to the point of saying identity remains because there is a germ of life in the dead body which will be in the future body as the life of the seed emerges in the plant. With a slight variation, Lange set forth that opinion as follows: "Amid this constant change there is something fixed which makes us recognizable as the same from the cradle to the grave—something which gives form, and feature, and organization, to this ever moving current of matter which is momentarily condensed into what we call our bodies. And what is this but the plastic principle of life which is ever shaping the materials which nature gives it for its own uses, and in accordance with an inward law which moulds us after our kind? Here then we have the true substance of the body— that which *stands underneath* the outward phenomenon of a corporeal form and imparts to its sole reality. And if this be so, it is easy to see that when by death the materials of our present structure are all dissolved and scattered abroad, this vital, organific principle, abiding still in connection with the spirit, and in the presence of Christ, may, by the power which He, through His eternal Spirit, worketh in our spirits, at the resurrection gather to itself and assimilate new materials of a wholly different kind, suited to that new condition of things which shall be ushered in at the glorious appearing of our Redeemer" (p. 336).

b. Imperishable (RSV) or incorruptible (KJV). The figure of the seed and plant is retained and Paul spoke of the dead body being sown in corruption (*i.e.* placed in the grave where it would decay). The body of the future will be exalted to a level where it cannot be subjected to decay. Since this present flesh and blood body is perishable, it, in its present form, will not be the body of the future (15:50, 37).

c. Glorious (15:43). The dead body is sown or buried in dishonor. Dishonor is from "atimia," which sometimes means to lose one's rights of citizenship (Robertson, p. 372). Perhaps Paul had that concept in mind. Obviously, a dead body has no rights, unless it would be the right to a decent burial. In contrast to dishonor, it will be raised in glory. Vincent took glory to mean "lustre; beauty of form and color" (vol. III, p. 281). Hodge defined it as "that resplendent brightness which diffuses light and awakens admiration" (p. 347). Lange commented as follows: "By this he means the revelation of the dignity of the children of God in the resplendent brightness of their resurrection bodies, pervaded and glorified by the divine life" (p. 338). Our bodies will be glorious because they will be like Christ's body (Phil. 3:21).

d. Powerful (15:43). The human body while living is weak in comparison to what it will be. When life departs, strength departs too. There is not power to move even a finger. The dead body is literally sown in weakness. The future body will be raised with the energy and vitality to easily fulfill all its purposes.

e. Spiritual (15:44-46).

(1) Natural (KJV) or physical (RSV) (15:44, 46) is from "psuchikos" (see comments at 2:14-16). Rather than describing the material of which the present body is made (i.e. composed of psyche or soul), the word defines it as being suited to the soul or present life. Generally, soul is used in reference to the animal principle of life and spirit describes that immaterial part of a person which is not dissolved in death. Paul cited Gen. 2:7 to show that Adam had a body adapted to the soul or life in this world (15:45). The same is also declared concerning the brute creation (Gen. 1:20, 21, 24). That which distinguished Adam from the animals was not that he became a living being (soul) but that he was made in the image of God (Gen. 1:26) and thus had an eternal spirit. Since Adam is the father of the human family, all of his descendants bear his image or have bodies like his (i.e. designed for the present life) (15:49).

(2) Spiritual (15:44, 46) is from "pneumatikos," which tells nothing about the substance of the future body. D. R. Goodwin wrote: "The spiritual body is body, and not spirit, and therefore must come under the definition of body. If it were spirit, then every man in the future state would have two spirits—the spirit he has here and another spirit received at the resurrection" (as quoted by A. H. Strong, Systematic Theology, p. 1017). The present body is adapted to the soul and the future body will be adapted to the spirit. Adam was given to uphold the first concept, and Jesus, the last Adam, to maintain the second (15:45). Since Christ is head over God's spiritual creation, saints will one day bear his image or have spiritual bodies like his (15:49).

(3) W. J. S. Simpson gave a good summary concerning the difference between the natural and spiritual body in these words: "St. Paul's doctrine is condensed into the two crucial phrases, a 'psychical' body and a 'pneumatical' body.

The psychical body is the organ and instrument of the animal force; the pneumatical body is the organ and instrument whose vitalizing principle is the spiritual personality. The psychical body is that which discharges the functions of animal self-maintenance and reproduction. It is the organ adapted to life under terrestrial conditions. The pneumatical is the organ adapted to life under non-terrestrial conditions" ("Resurrection of Christ," *Hastings Dictionary of Christ and the Gospels,* vol. II, p. 509).

f. Immortal (15:53-54). The redeemed are depicted as putting on garments of immortality at the resurrection (see II Cor. 5:3-4). Hence, the body of the next life will not be subject to death (Rev. 21:4). The immortality which is to be given to God's people in the future pertains only to the body and not to the soul (Rom. 2:7; 8:23-24). The spirit is already immortal.

g. Like Christ's body (15:47-49; Phil. 3:21; I Jno. 3:2). Of course, this raises the question as to when the Savior received his glorified body. Was it at the resurrection or during the ascension?

(1) At the resurrection. Following his resurrection, Christ appeared to the apostles in a room without going through any doors (Jno. 20:19, 26). It is said that he was in "another form" (Mk. 16:12). The word translated as form is "morphe" which deals with essence or nature rather than simply what is seen ("eidos" refers to what is seen and is rendered as form at Lk. 3:22 in connection with the appearance of the Holy Spirit at the Lord's baptism) (Vine, vol. II, pp. 123-124). These two statements seem to indicate that he had already received the glorified body. Further, if Jesus did not receive a body of glorification when raised, the parallel between his resurrection and the saints is not precisely the same at that point. Some conclude that the glorified body is composed of flesh and bones (Lk. 24:39-43). They make a distinction between the flesh and blood body which cannot inherit the kingdom of God (15:50) and the flesh and bones body Christ had after being raised. They contend that since life is in the blood (Lev. 17:11) and since Christ shed his blood on the cross, his body became lifeless. After his resurrection, he was bloodless, therefore, life was no longer imparted to his

body by blood but by the direct power of the Holy Spirit (N. H. Camp, *The Resurrection of the Human Body,* p. 86).

(2) During the ascension. *Prior* to his death, the Lord passed through a mob which was determined to kill him (Lk. 4:30). Perhaps that was done the same way he went into a room without passing through its doors. Since Jesus ate fish after being raised (Lk. 24:43), is it to be assumed that the glorified body is adapted to the eating of physical food? After the resurrection, the Master's body was made of flesh (Lk. 24:40) but flesh cannot enter the kingdom of God (15:50), therefore, the body he then had ceased to be flesh prior to his entrance into the kingdom. If Christ did not use flesh in its ordinary sense, he deceived the apostles. Furthermore, the apostles knew the condition of his resurrection body. They also knew the saints are to be like him in the next life (Rom. 8:29; Phil. 3:21). If the Lord had his glorified body after being raised, in the future existence the redeemed will be like he was then. However, it does not appear what they shall be (I Jno. 3:2). Hence, his pre-ascension body was not exactly the same as his glorified body.

(3) How the information used to support the two views given above can be harmonized. Simpson, in the article already cited, pointed out that the Lord's appearances are commonly classified as being materialistic and immaterial. He continued: "The view given by the Evangelists is independent of both of the above conceptions. It certainly possesses a strongly materialistic side. Yet with equal certainty it is no mere resuscitation of the animal frame. It is anything rather than a return to life under the same conditions. The broadest distinction is drawn by the Evangelists between the revivification of Lazarus and the Resurrection of Christ. Lazarus is obviously represented as granted a re-entrance into earthly life under the same conditions as before, to become again the possessor of a corruptible organism, subject to the same fleshly necessities, and destined again to expire in a second experience of physical death. . . . But the risen body of Christ was spiritual, 'not because it was less than before material, but because in it matter was wholly and finally subjugated to spirit, and not to the exigencies of physical life. Matter no longer restricted him or hindered. It had become the pure and

transparent vehicle of spiritual purpose' (Gore, *Body of Christ,* p. 127). . . . The Evangelists are concerned with the historic manifestations of the Risen Christ; St. Paul with the intrinsic nature of the resurrection body. The former describe the body of Christ during the temporary periods in which its presence was ascertainable by the senses; the latter considers the body as it is in itself. The former say, This is what we touched and saw, and our hands have handled; the latter is concerned with the profound inquiry as to what constitutes the nature of the risen body. Thus the aspects are complementary, not antagonistic. . . . We should suppose that the pneumatical or risen body of Christ, in its normal state, as an ideally perfect utterance of spirit, imperceptible to the human senses as we now possess them. But the capacities of this ideally perfect self-expression are so great that it can manifest itself to persons living under terrestrial conditions. And we believe that this pneumatical body of Christ did temporarily assume such conditions of tangibility and visibility as to bring His 'subtle corporeity,' for evidential and instructive purposes, within range of our 'grosser corporeity' " (p. 509). Simpson believed the body which went into the rich man's tomb *actually came out again* but that it was not limited as it had been prior to the Savior's death.

C. The resurrection of the wicked is not discussed in this chapter. Although the unsaved will have bodies in the hereafter (Matt. 10:28), they are not described as are the bodies of the saved.

IV. The Resurrection Day (15:51-57).

A. Saints living and dead will be changed at the end of time (15:51-54a).

1. Mystery (15:51) is a reference to truth concealed in the past but then revealed by the Holy Spirit (see comments at 2:7).

2. We shall not all sleep (15:51). Some think Paul meant he would be living when time ended. Barclay wrote: "Further Paul insists that that shattering change is going to come in his own lifetime. In this Paul was in error" (p. 179). If Paul's language at 6:14 were pressed in a similar way, he affirmed

that he is to be raised from the dead. How then are the two statements to be harmonized? It is Barclay not Paul who is in error. "But Paul often classes himself with those he is describing without any implication that he actually is one of them (*e.g.* 6:15; 10:22). The plain fact is that Paul did not know when these events would take place, and nowhere does he claim to know. When he says *we* he means 'believers generally,' 'Christians alive at that day' " (L. Morris, *The First Epistle of Paul to the Corinthians,* pp. 232-233).

3. We shall all be changed (15:51). Since flesh and blood cannot inherit the kingdom of God (15:50), those saints living at the last day must be changed before entering their eternal reward.

4. The change will occur in a moment or the twinkling of an eye (15:52). Moment is from "atomos" which "literally means indivisible (from *a*, negative, and *temno,* to cut; English, atom); hence it denotes a moment, I Cor. 15:52" (Vine, vol. III, p. 79). Twinkling is from "rhipe" and appears only here in the New Testament. Vincent defined it as "originally the *swing* or *force* with which a thing is thrown; a *stroke* or *beat.* Used in the classics of the *rush* of a storm, the *flapping* of wings; the *buzz* of a gnat; the *quivering* of a harpstring; the *twinkling* of stars. Generally of any rapid movement, as of the feet in running, or the quick darting of fish" (vol. III, pp. 285-286). Obviously, the change of those living at the end of time will not be a long process but an instantaneous happening.

5. The living will be changed and the dead will be raised at the last trumpet (15:52). The figure of a trumpet is used to announce the end of time. Lange thought the trumpet denoted the "blast accompanying the Theophanies, and resounding over the whole region of their manifestation, arousing and shaking all things there (comp. Ex. 19:16; Isa. 27:13; Zech. 9:14). The last trumpet refers to that great Theophany, or Christophany, by which all the revelations of God in this dispensation will be brought to their close" (p. 346).

6. The nature of the resurrection body (15:53-54a) was dealt with above (see comments at 15:42-50).

B. Victory over death (15:54b-55).

1. Death is swallowed up in victory (15:54) is a quotation from Isa. 25:8. Death will be destroyed (Rev. 20:14) and it will have no place in heaven (Rev. 21:4).

2. The quotation at 15:55 is from Hos. 13:14. KJV, following the LXX reading of "hades," has grave in the second line of the couplet. However, the manuscript evidence favors the use of death in both lines as the better reading. Paul never used "hades" in his writings ("abyss" is employed at Rom. 10:7 rather than "hades").

C. The Sting of death is sin (15:56).

1. Sting is from "kentoo" which means to prick (Vine, vol. II, p. 159). The picture is that of a serpent, hornet or scorpion (Rev. 9:10) stinging men rather than a king with a goad (Acts 26:14) driving his subjects.

2. The sting is not in death but in sin. Death has a sting for those who die under sin's guilt and condemnation. In such cases, there is reason to fear (Heb. 2:14). Sin's power is derived from law. Faithful Christians are not under law (Rom. 6:14; 7:1-7). Since they are not under law, they are not held guilty for having violated law. Therefore, there is no sting in death for faithful Christians. Death for them is personal gain (Phil. 1:21) and precious in God's sight (Ps. 116:15).

D. Victory over death is attained through Jesus Christ (15:57; see also Rom. 7:25; 8:37). Through his death and resurrection, children of God are not under law, the guilt of sin or condemnation (see Rom. 6, 7, 8).

VII. A Practical Admonition (15:58).

A. Steadfast (the word also appears at 7:37). They were to hold to the truth concerning the resurrection of the righteous.

B. Immovable. They had been fickle and prone to change. If they took the posture of steadfastness, they would not be moved by false teachers, temptations or persecution. No more would they be tossed to and fro (Eph. 4:14).

C. Abounding in the work of the Lord. They were not simply to work but abound in the Lord's work. There is so much to do and so little time to do it. All of God's people must become involved in the great task of preaching the gospel to the whole world (Mk. 16:15). One cannot be lazy and dedicated to Jesus. Let us work now for the night is coming when opportunity will have passed (Jno. 9:4).

D. Labor is not in vain in the Lord. Labor is from "kopos" which means wearisome toil (Robertson, p. 380). That kind of toil characterized Paul (II Cor. 6:5; 10:15; 11:23) and every Christian should be known by the same trait. Labor in Christ would be in vain, if there were no resurrection.

XVII.

CHAPTER SIXTEEN

Contribution

Structure

I. Contribution (16:1-4).

A. The collection (KJV) or contribution (RSV) (from "logias," appearing only at 16:1-2 in the New Testament) was for the saints (16:1).

1. The money was to be taken to the poor among the saints in Jerusalem (Rom. 15:26) who were probably impoverished due to their practice of community of goods (Acts 2:44) and persecution from unbelieving Jews who plundered their property (Heb. 10:34).

2. Churches in Macedonia, Galatia and Achaia gave to that good work (16:1; Rom. 15:26).

3. Gentile churches were urged to give because they were spiritually indebted to Jewish Christians (Rom. 15:27; see comments at 9:11).

4. Apparently, the contribution was promoted for the purpose of strengthening the bonds of unity between Jews and Gentiles in Christ (II Cor. 9:11-15).

B. How the Corinthians were to give (16:1-2).

1. In obedience to God's will. Concerning this matter, Paul had ordered (KJV) or given direction (RSV) to the churches of Galatia. Obviously, that is the voice of authority. When, where and how the instruction was given is not revealed. The same order was given to Corinth.

2. To meet a need (16:1). There is little value in urging people to give simply for the sake of giving. When a need is placed before them, sensitive disciples will rally to the call.

3. Individually (16:2). Perhaps the funds could have been obtained by commanding only the rich to give but Paul, under the wisdom of God, intended that everyone participate in the project.

4. On the first day of every week (16:2, RSV). The Greek is "kata mian Sabbatou" (or "Sabbaton"). It literally means "upon one of the Sabbath" (Hodge, p. 363). Sabbath in this instance stands for the seven days which comprise a week (see Lk. 18:12). According to Vincent, "kata has distributive force" and the meaning is "every first day" (vol. III, p. 228). Although the assembly is not mentioned, it is understood (11:20; Acts 20:7; Heb. 10:25) and this accounts for the giving to be done at that time.

5. In harmony with their prosperity (16:2; Acts 11:29). Surely, the brother then making $1,000 a year with only his wife and himself to support was obligated to give more than another Christian earning the same amount who cared for his wife, four children and himself.

6. Into a common fund (16:2).

   a. Some scholars think that each saint laid by at his home.

   b. However, the context seems to deny the validity of that conclusion.

   (1) If it was to be done at home, why did Paul specify the first day of the week? One day would have been as practical as another for a home donation.

(2) If it was to be done at home, why say "that contributions need not be made when I come" (RSV)? Putting aside the money at home would have necessitated contributions when Paul arrived (at least a gathering of the money) and that was the very thing he was seeking to avoid.

c. In reference to a common fund, McGarvey wrote: "The word 'thesaurizoon,' translated 'in store,' means, literally, 'put into the treasury;' and the phrase 'par heuto,' translated 'by him,' may be taken as the neuter reflexive pronoun, and may be rendered with equal correctness as 'by itself.' Macknight thus renders these two words, and this rendering is to be preferred" (p. 161).

7. Additional information about their giving.

a. As they purposed (II Cor. 9:7, KJV). A year in advance, they had planned to give (II Cor. 8:10-11). Paul described their plan as the gift which they had promised (II Cor. 9:5, RSV). Saints ought not to give "left overs" to God. As they plan ahead for the purchase of things needed, they should also plan ahead concerning their donations to the Lord's causes.

b. Willingly or voluntarily (II Cor. 9:7). The gift without the giver is bare. If one gives under compulsion, he misses whatever blessing God has in store for him.

c. Cheerfully (II Cor. 9:7). Let us rejoice in the fact that we are able to share the abundance which God has showered upon us.

d. Bountifully (II Cor. 9:6) or liberally (Rom. 12:8, RSV). One does not have to be wealthy to obey this injunction. It is not what we would do if we had more but what we do with what we have that counts. If we are faithful in a little, we will be faithful in much. Giving less than a tenth was called robbery under the law (Mal. 3:8-10). For a long time, it has been my conviction that every Christian should *start* his giving at a tenth. Such was expected of the Jews under the Mosaic law, a covenant far inferior to ours. An attitude of love and appreciation is under consideration rather than stipulated law. As the faithful child of God grows in the grace and knowledge of Christ, his giving will also increase percentage-wise.

e. Sacrificially. The Macedonians gave from their deep poverty. They had to beg Paul and company to take their offering (II Cor. 8:1-5). The poor widow, by casting two mites into the treasury, gave everything she had, her whole living (Mk. 12:42-44, RSV). Jesus, our supreme example of sacrifice, gave up the riches of heaven, became a poor, peasant carpenter and suffered the shameful death of crucifixion (II Cor. 8:9; Phil. 2:5-11; Heb. 12:2). Christians who give sacrificially will do without or postpone obtaining some things which they deeply desire.

f. Confidently (II Cor. 9:8-10; Matt. 6:33). God will provide for his people. As long as he has a purpose for them in this life, they will not die of starvation or exposure. This does not mean it is wrong to plan for one's financial future, however, it does suggest a type of abandon rarely seen in the Christian community.

g. At the home congregation (16:2). This should be done when one is absent or the gift ought to be doubled the following Lord's day. What is to be thought of the man who fails to provide for his family while he is away? Is it any less evil for one to fail to carry his honorable share of the financial burden in the local church because of absence? The congregation cannot depend on visitors for financial support (Christians visiting from elsewhere are obligated at home and the unsaved cannot be expected to be generous). The local members must carry the load.

c. How the money was to be handled (16:3-4).

1. The funds were to be taken to Jerusalem by those whom the Corinthians appointed. They and those selected by brethren elsewhere were messengers of the churches (II Cor. 8:23). Paul wanted the messengers because he was desirous of placing himself above suspicion in handling money for others (II Cor. 8:19-20). However, false teachers accused him of pocketing the money for his own use in spite of his precautions (II Cor. 12:16-18). Nothing short of absolute honesty should be countenanced in those who handle monies donated for good works (II Cor. 8:20-21).

2. The messengers of the churches were to be approved by letter. Apparently, that letter was written by Paul to the Jerusalem brethren (RSV; all scholars read accepted this

view). There is a remote possibility that the letters were written by the churches for their messengers (KJV).

3. Paul would go to Jerusalem with the messengers if it seemed advisable. Apparently he meant he would accompany the gift if it was large enough to justify his changing plans to take charge of distributing the funds. "If the gift be sufficiently large to warrant an apostolic journey to Jerusalem," was the wording used by Vincent (vol. III, p. 289). The apostle did make the trip (Acts 19:21; 21:18; II Cor. 8:19-20). He was accompanied by Sopater, Aristarchus, Secundus, Gaius, Timothy, Tychicus and Trophimus (Acts 20:4), men chosen as messengers of the churches.

4. The funds were administered by Paul and his party (II Cor. 8:19-20; Acts 20:1-4). In an earlier contribution, money sent from the disciples at Antioch to a church (perhaps Jerusalem—Acts 12:25) or churches in Judea was received and administered by elders (Acts 11:27-30). Since the two collections were not handled in the same way, there is no unalterable pattern to be followed in such matters.

II. Paul's Plans for the Future (16:5-9).

A. A visit to Corinth (16:5-6).

1. Only one trip is proposed here. He intended to arrive in Corinth after passing through Macedonia (16:5-6).

2. However, he later indicated the Corinthians were expecting two visits (from Ephesus across the Aegean to Corinth and then by land to Macedonia and back to Corinth) (II Cor. 1:15-16). Apparently, they had been informed of his new schedule between the writing of I and II Corinthians. Because he changed his plans from one visit to two, some (probably the false apostles of II Cor. 11:13-15) accused him of vacillation (II Cor. 1:17).

3. Yet, Paul eventually reverted to his original itinerary of going to Macedonia and then to Corinth (Acts 20:1-3).

4. Why he went back to his former plan of one rather than two visits.

a. After writing I Corinthians, a rebellion arose against him in the Corinthian congregation. He went to Corinth to deal with the trouble and returned to Ephesus. As far as an immediate resolution of the problem was concerned, his voyage was a failure.

b. He then canceled his proposed first visit (the trip over in an attempt to quell the rebellion was not considered as part of the two pleasant stays, benefits or pleasures he had earlier envisioned—II Cor. 1:15) to spare them the pain it would have been necessary for him to inflict had he gone while they stood in defiance against him as Christ's apostle (II Cor. 1:23-2:1; 10:1-13:14). Instead of that visit, he sent the severe letter or Corinthians C (see introduction).

c. Paul wanted time for them to repent (after receiving the severe letter). He also needed time to contact Titus in Troas or Macedonia to learn if the letter had produced the desired results (see introduction).

B. Why the apostle did not go to Corinth at that time (16:6-9).

1. Had he gone, he could not have stayed long. He desired to spend more time with them than his schedule would then allow (if the Lord permitted—Jas. 4:13-17) (16:6-7).

2. He had opportunity to do a great work at Ephesus (16:8-9). Since the door is a metaphor for opportunity (Acts 14:27; II Cor. 2:12; Col. 4:3; Rev. 3:8), a wide door (RSV) indicates he had a great opportunity. For his success at Ephesus, read Acts 19:1-20. For more information about his adversaries, read Acts 19:21-40; II Cor. 1:8-10.

III. *Timothy and Apollos* (16:10-12).

A. Timothy (16:10-11).

1. Paul had sent Timothy and Erastus from Ephesus to Corinth by way of Macedonia (Acts 19:21-22). Timothy was to remind them of Paul's ways (4:17). When the apostle wrote II Corinthians from Macedonia (II Cor. 2:12-13), Timothy was with him (II Cor. 1:1). Timothy probably went to Corinth and returned to Macedonia where he met Paul. However, Paul may have overtaken Timothy while he was still working in Macedonia and before he arrived at Corinth.

2. When Timothy comes (16:10, RSV).

a. Put him at ease among you for he is doing the work of the Lord (15:58) as I am (16:10). Maybe that was written because of Timothy's timidity.

b. Let no one depise him (16:11). Perhaps that was said because of Timothy's youth (I Tim. 4:12).

c. Speed him on his way in peace back to me (16:11). Paul did not want his son in the faith involved in strife and contention. The brethren he expected to be with Timothy were probably Erastus and other unnamed men who made the trip with him (Acts 19:22).

B. Apollos (16:12). He had worked in Corinth earlier (Acts 18:27-19:1).

1. The apostle had strongly urged him to go to Corinth with the other brethren (*i.e.* Timothy, Erastus and those who traveled with them—Acts 19:22).

2. It was not Apollos' will to then go. His unwillingness is not explained. Some have suggested he felt it improper to go because his name was involved in the party strife at Corinth (1:10-13).

3. He will come when he has opportunity.

IV. Closing Admonitions (16:13-18).

A. Be watchful (16:13). Christians must be on the alert constantly lest they be destroyed by Satan who seeks the ruination of their souls (Matt. 26:41).

B. Stand firm in your faith (16:13).

1. In this connection, Hodge wrote: "Do not consider every point of doctrine an open question. Matters of faith, doctrines for which you have a clear revelation of God, such for example as the doctrine of the resurrection, are to be considered settled, and, as among Christians, no longer matters of dispute" (p. 369). In light of the fact that we are to contend earnestly for the faith once delivered (Jude 3), Hodge's advice is eminently correct.

2. However, in bold contrast to the foregoing, consider the following written by a member of the New Testament church for Christian scholars and teachers: "*Because no knowledge is then final* [emphasis mine, J.A.], all areas are open to question. . . . If truth is an illusive goal, then one has an imperative to question, not only in areas involving disagreement but also in areas involving agreement—perhaps

especially in areas involving agreement" (J. L. Atteberry, *The Freedom of Scholarship*, pp. 5-6).

C. Be courageous (16:13). One of the greatest needs of our time is courage. Saints must have it to live righteously, to teach the truth without fear or favor and to withstand slander, ridicule and persecution from within and without the church. There is no way to stand for the Lord and his cause without making enemies. Jesus, the only perfect man who ever lived, was despised, hated and finally killed by his enemies. If we live and die without ever having made adversaries, many times we will have allowed the banner of Immanuel to be dragged through the dust without raising a voice in its defense. A true child of God will never deliberately court conflict but he simply cannot live without it. The poem below illustrates this truth.

NO ENEMIES?

> You have no enemies, you say?
> Alas! My friend, the boast is poor—
> He who has mingled in the fray
> Of duty, that the brave endure,
> Must have made foes!
> If you have none,
> Small is the work that you have done;
> You've hit no traitor on the hip;
> You've dashed no cup from perjured lip;
> You've never turned wrong to right—
> You've been a coward in the fight.
>
> —*Charles Mackay.*

D. Be strong (16:13). Bravery without strength will accomplish very little in time of battle. The Christian's strength is in his Lord (Eph. 6:10; 3:16).

E. Let all be done in love (16:14). The Christian religion is based on love for God and one's fellows (Matt. 22:35-40). For love's traits, study 13:4-7 again. Of the five admonitions appearing in 16:13-14, Chrysostom wrote: "He says, watch, as though they were sleeping; stand, as though they were wavering; quit you like men, be strong, as though they were showing themselves cowards; let all you do be done in love, as though they were in strife" (*Homily,* 44).

F. Be subject to such men (16:16). He was referring to the household of Stephanas, the first converts of Achaia (16:15), whom he had baptized (1:16). Stephanas and his family were devoted to the service of the saints (16:15).

G. Give recognition to such men (16:18). He was then referring to Stephanas, Fortunatus and Achaicus (16:17), the men who likely carried a letter from the Corinthians to Paul (see introduction). "Honor to whom honor is due" (Rom. 13:7).

V. Greeting and Benediction (16:19-24).

A. Greetings from.

1. The churches of Asia (16:19). Ephesus, where Paul wrote I Corinthians (16:8), was in Asia. As a result of his teaching in the school of Tyrannus at Ephesus, God's word had sounded throughout the province of Asia (Acts 19:10). It was likely at that time the churches began in Smyrna, Pergamum, Thyatira, Sardis, Philadelphia, Laodicea, Colosse and Hierapolis. Perhaps Paul was representing all of those churches in sending greetings to the Corinthians.

2. Aquila and Priscilla and the church in their house (16:19). Paul had first met that man and wife at Corinth on the second missionary journey (Acts 18:1-2). Later they went with him to Ephesus and remained there while he returned to Syrian Antioch (Acts 18:19-22). Their statement of greeting indicates he worked with them again when he returned to Ephesus on the third journey. When Paul wrote his epistle to Rome, Aquila and Priscilla were in that community (they had earlier been driven out by Claudius Caesar—Acts 18:2) and, again, they had a church in their house (Rom. 16:3-5). Surely, this indicates their great zeal for sharing the gospel. May their number become legion among undenominational Christians today!

3. All the brethren (16:20). This is probably a reference to the brethren who were working in Ephesus with Paul as his missionary companions (see Acts 19:29).

B. Greet one another with a holy kiss (16:20; Rom. 16:16; II Cor. 13:12; I Thess. 5:26). For a discussion of the holy kiss, see my *Survey of Romans,* pp. 118-119.

C. Greetings were written by Paul's own hand (16:21). Most of his letters were written by a stenographer (likely Sosthenes wrote this epistle—1:1). Customarily, Paul wrote the concluding sentences with his own hand to indicate their authenticity (Col. 4:18; II Thess. 3:17).

D. If one has no love for the Lord (16:22).

1. Let him be accursed (16:22) or anathema (Greek).

2. Our Lord, come (16:22). In Greek, the expression is "marantha."

3. *The point:* Paul was saying that brethren who had quit loving the Lord (Rev. 2:4; II Tim. 4:10) will be devoted to destruction at the coming of Christ. Of "anathema" and "marantha," McGarvey wrote: "They were the words with which the Jews began their greatest excommunication" (p. 166).

E. Benediction (16:23-24).

1. The grace of the Lord Jesus be with you (16:23).

2. My love be with you all in Christ Jesus (16:24).

AMEN!

THEY SHALL ALL BE TAUGHT OF GOD

Allen,
Charles Coil,
and
Jerry Jones.

Bob Helsten teaching Bible on front lawn.

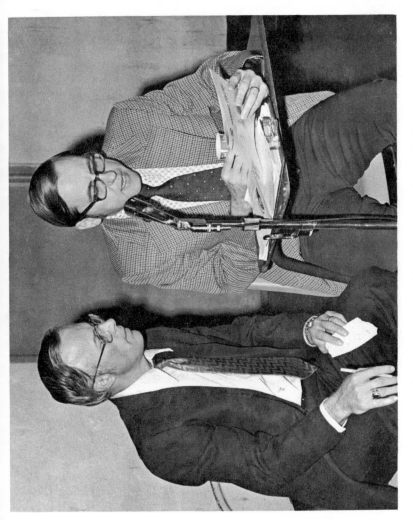

Allen and Jerry Jones working a Harding basketball game.

Amarillo Campaign

in which Allen preached.

Preaching the Word.

Preaching the Word.

Devotional on the lawn (Jimmy Carr in foreground).

"Brother Allen, please run that by again."

45 and still love that flag football!

SWAN POINT

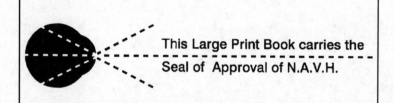

This Large Print Book carries the
Seal of Approval of N.A.V.H.

THE SWEET MAGNOLIAS

SWAN POINT

SHERRYL WOODS

THORNDIKE PRESS
A part of Gale, Cengage Learning

GALE
CENGAGE Learning·

Farmington Hills, Mich • San Francisco • New York • Waterville, Maine
Meriden, Conn • Mason, Ohio • Chicago

GALE
CENGAGE Learning®

LIBRARY OF CONGRESS CATALOGING-IN-PUBLICATION DATA

Woods, Sherryl.
    Swan Point / by Sherryl Woods. — Large print edition.
        pages ; cm. — (The sweet magnolias) (Thorndike Press large print romance)
        ISBN 978-1-4104-7480-3 (hardcover) — ISBN 1-4104-7480-1 (hardcover)
    1. Divorced mothers—Fiction. 2. Large type books. I. Title.
PS3573.O6418S593 2014
813'.54—dc23   2014031918

Published in 2014 by arrangement with Harlequin Books S.A.

Printed in the United States of America
1 2 3 4 5 6 7 18 17 16 15 14

Swan Point

CHAPTER ONE

Adelia watched with her heart in her throat as the moving van pulled away from the crumbling curb in Swan Point, one of the oldest and, at one time, finest neighborhoods in Serenity, South Carolina. With moss-draped oaks in perfectly maintained yards backing up to a small, man-made lake, which was home to several swans, the houses had been large and stately by early standards.

Now, though, most of the homes, like this one, were showing signs of age. She found something fitting about the prospect of filling this historic old house with laughter and giving it a new lease on life. It would be as if the house and her family were moving into the future together.

Letting go of the old life, however, was proving more difficult than she'd anticipated. Drawing in a deep breath, she turned to deal with the accusing looks of her four children, who weren't nearly as convinced as she was that they were about to have an exciting fresh start.

Her youngest, Tomas, named for his grandfather on her ex-husband's side of the family, turned to her with tears streaming down his cheeks. "Mommy, I don't like it here. I want to go home. This house is old. It smells funny. And there's no pool."

She knelt down in front of the eight-year-old and gathered him close, gathered all of them close, even her oldest, Selena.

It was Selena who understood better than any of them why this move had been necessary. While they all knew that Adelia and their father had divorced, Selena had seen Ernesto more than once with one of his mistresses. In a move that defied logic or compassion, he'd even had the audacity to introduce the most recent woman to Selena while he and Adelia were still making a pretense at least of trying to keep their marriage intact. His action had devastated Selena and it had been the final straw for Adelia. She'd seen at last that tolerating such disrespect was the wrong example to set for her three girls and even for her son.

"I know you'd rather be in our old house," she comforted them with a hitch in her voice. "But it's just not possible. This is

8

home now. I really think you're going to love it once we get settled in."

She ruffled Tomas's hair. "And don't worry about the funny smell. It's just been shut up for a few months. It'll smell fine once we air it out and put fresh paint on the walls." She injected a deliberately cheerful note into her voice. "We can all sit down and decide how we want to fix it up. Then you can go with me to the hardware store to pick out the paint colors for your rooms."

The girls expressed enthusiasm for the idea, but Tomas remained visibly skeptical.

"What about the pool?" he asked sullenly.

"We can use the town pool," Selena said staunchly, even though there were tears in her eyes, too. "It's even bigger than the one at home, and our friends will be there. And since we're living so close to downtown now, we can walk to the bakery after school for cupcakes, then stop in and see Mom at work. Or go across the green to Wharton's for ice cream."

Natalia sniffed, but Adelia saw a spark of interest in her eyes.

"I like ice cream," eleven-year-old Natalia whispered, then nudged Tomas. "You do, too."

"Me, too," Juanita chimed in. Until the divorce Adelia's nine-year-old had been boundlessly enthusiastic about everything, but this was the first sign in weeks that her high spirits were returning.

Tomas continued to look unconvinced. "Will *Abuela* be able to find us here?" he asked doubtfully.

"Of course," Adelia assured him. Tomas adored her mother, who'd been babysitting him practically from infancy because of all the school committees on which Adelia had found herself and, more recently, because she was working at a boutique on Main Street. "She helped me to find this house."

Amazingly, for once, her mother had kept her lectures on divorce to herself and professed to see all the positives in the new life Adelia was fashioning for her children. She'd told stories about the days when the elite in town had lived in Swan Point. There had been lavish parties in this very house, she'd reported to Adelia. She'd stuck to focusing on the possibilities in the house and the quiet, tree-shaded neighborhood, not the negatives.

Her mother's support had actually given Adelia the courage to move forward. To her surprise, Adelia had recognized that even in her early forties, she still craved her mother's approval. It was one of the many reasons she'd waited so long to end her travesty of a marriage.

"Can we still go to *Abuela*'s house for cookies?" her son pressed.

"Absolutely," Adelia said. "You can go every day after school if you like, the same as always."

Though he was starting to look relieved, a sudden frown crossed his face. "What about Papa? Is he going to live here, too? He won't like it, I'll bet. He likes our real house, same as me."

Selena whirled on him. "You know perfectly well he doesn't live with us anymore. He's not coming here. Not ever! He's going to live in our old house with somebody else."

Adelia winced at the disdain and hurt in her oldest's voice. Ever since she'd realized that her father had been openly cheating on Adelia, Selena had claimed she wanted no part of him. Her attitude had hardened even more when she'd overheard Ernesto describing her as her mother's child in a tone that made clear he wasn't complimenting either one of them.

Adelia had even spoken to a psychologist about this rift between father and daughter, but the woman had assured her that it wasn't unusual for an impressionable teenager — Selena had just turned thirteen — to react so strongly to a divorce, especially

11

when Ernesto's cheating had been so public and when he'd shown no remorse at all once he'd been caught. In fact, he'd remained defiant to the bitter end, so much so that even the judge had lost patience with him.

At Selena's angry words, Tomas's eyes once again filled with tears.

"Enough," Adelia warned her daughter. To Tomas and the younger girls, she said, "You'll still be able to see your father whenever you want to." Like Tomas, Natalia and Juanita looked relieved, though they carefully avoided looking at their big sister, clearly fearing her disapproval. That was yet another rift she'd have to work on healing, Adelia concluded with a sigh. Ernesto certainly wouldn't make any effort to do it.

As hurt as she'd been and as much as she'd wanted to banish Ernesto from her life forever, she'd accepted that her kids deserved to have a relationship with their dad. It would be selfish of her to deny them that.

Besides, she'd had enough explaining to do to the rest of her rigidly Catholic family when she'd opted for divorce. Then, to top it off, she'd insisted on moving out of the huge house on the outskirts of town that Ernesto had apparently thought was reasonable compensation for his infidelity. Her sisters had been appalled by all of it — the scandal of Ernesto's cheating, the divorce and the move. Keeping her children away from their father — however distasteful his behavior — would have caused even more of an uproar.

Not that Adelia cared what any of them thought at this point. She'd made the only decision she could make. Her only goal now was to make this transition as easy for the children as possible. She'd do it with as much cheerfulness as she could possibly muster. She might not even have to fake it, since on some level she was actually eager for this fresh start.

For now, though, she forced a smile and looked each of them in the eye. "I have an idea," she announced, hoping to turn this difficult day around.

"What?" Tomas asked suspiciously.

"I think we all deserve a treat after such a long day."

"Pizza?" Natalia asked hopefully.

Adelia laughed. Natalia would eat pizza three times a day if she were allowed to.

"Yes, pizza," she confirmed.

"Not here, though," Tomas pleaded, wrinkling his nose in distaste.

"No, not here. The dishes aren't unpacked," she said. "We'll go to Rosalina's. I'll call your uncle Elliott and see if he and Aunt Karen would like to join us with Daisy, Mack and the baby."

This last was offered especially for Selena, who adored her uncle and who'd become especially close to his adopted daughter, Daisy. Adelia might not intend to keep Ernesto away from his children, but Elliott was the male role model she really wanted in their lives. Her younger brother was loving, rock solid and dependable. She'd be proud to see Tomas grow up to be just like him. And she desperately hoped her girls would eventually find men like him, too.

Once the decision to divorce had been made, Elliott had overcome all his own strong objections to offer her the support she'd desperately needed. She owed Karen for bringing him — and even her mother — around. Her own sisters continued to treat her as if she'd committed a mortal sin.

The prospect of pizza at Rosalina's with Uncle Elliott and his family wiped away the last of the tears, and Adelia took a truly relieved breath for what seemed like the first time all day. Her family was going to be all right. There might be a few bumps along the way, thanks to her determination to shed any of her own ties to Ernesto, but they

14

would settle into this new house.

And, she concluded with new resolve, they would turn it into a real home, one filled with love and respect, something that had been in short supply with her ex-husband.

Gabe Franklin had claimed a booth in the back corner of Rosalina's for the fourth night in a row. Back in Serenity for less than a week and living at the Serenity Inn, he'd figured this was better than the bar across town for a man who'd determined to sober up and live life on the straight and narrow. That was the whole point of coming home, after all, to prove he'd changed and deserved a second chance. Once he'd accomplished that and made peace with his past, well, he'd decide whether to move on yet again. He wasn't sure he was the kind of man who'd ever put down roots.

Thank heaven for his cousin, Mitch Franklin, who'd offered him a job starting on Monday without a moment's hesitation. Recently remarried, Mitch claimed he needed a partner who knew construction so he could focus on his new family. He'd taken on a second family just as he'd started developing a series of dilapidated properties on Main Street in an attempt to revitalize downtown Serenity.

Gabe had listened in astonishment to Mitch's ambitious plans as he'd laid them out. Despite his cousin's enthusiasm, Gabe wasn't convinced revitalization was possible in an economy still struggling to rebound, but he was more than willing to jump in and give it a shot. Maybe there would be something cathartic about giving those old storefronts the same kind of second chance he was hoping to grab for himself.

"You're turning into a real regular in here," his waitress, a middle-aged woman who'd introduced herself a few nights ago as Debbie, said. "Are you new in town?"

"Not exactly," he said, returning her smile but adding no details. "I'll have —"

"A large diet soda and a large pepperoni pizza," she filled in before he could complete his order.

Gabe winced. "I'm obviously in a rut."

"That's okay. Most of our regulars order the same thing every time," she said. "And I pay attention. Friendly service and a good memory get me bigger tips."

"I'll remember that," he said, then sat back and looked around the restaurant while waiting for his food.

Suddenly he sat up a little straighter as a dark-haired woman came in with four children. Even though she looked a little harried and a whole lot weary, she was stunning with her olive complexion and high cheekbones. She was also vaguely familiar, though he couldn't put a name to the face.

There hadn't been a lot of Mexican-American families in Serenity back when he'd lived here as a kid, though there had been plenty of transient farmworkers during the summer months. For a minute he cursed the way he'd blown off school way more often than he should have. Surely if he'd gone regularly, this woman would have been on his radar. If there had been declared majors in high school, his would have been girls. He'd studied them the way the academic overachievers had absorbed the information in textbooks.

Instead, he'd been kicked out midway through his junior year for one too many fights, every one of them justified to his juvenile way of thinking. He'd eventually wised up and gotten his GED. He'd even attended college for a couple of years, but that had been later, when he'd stopped hating the world for the way it had treated his troubled single mom and started putting the pieces of his life back together.

He watched now as the intriguing woman asked for several tables to be pushed together. He noted with disappointment when a man with two children came in to join them. So, he thought, she was married with six kids. An unfamiliar twinge of envy left him feeling vaguely unsettled. Since when had he been interested in having a family of any size? Still, he couldn't seem to tear his gaze away from the picture of domestic bliss they presented. The teasing and laughter seemed to settle in his heart and make it just a little lighter.

When his waitress returned with his drink, he nodded in the woman's direction. "Quite a family," he commented. "I can't imagine having six kids. They look like quite a handful."

Debbie laughed. "Oh, they're a handful, all right, but they're not all Adelia's. That's her brother, Elliott Cruz, who just came in with two of his. He has a baby, too, but I guess she was getting a cold, so his wife stayed home with her."

Gabe hid a grin. Thank heaven for chatty waitresses and a town known for gossiping. It hadn't been so great when he was a boy and his promiscuous mother had been the talk of the town, but now he could appreciate it.

"Where's her husband?"

The waitress leaned down and confided, "Sadly, not in hell where he belongs. The

18

man cheated on her repeatedly and the whole town knew about it. She finally kicked his sorry butt to the curb. Too bad the whole town couldn't follow suit and divorce him." She flushed, and her expression immediately filled with guilt. "Sorry. I shouldn't have said that, but Adelia's a great woman and she didn't deserve the way Ernesto Hernandez treated her."

Gabe nodded. "Sounds like a real gem," he said.

In fact, he sounded like a lot of the men who'd passed through his mom's life over the years. Gabe felt a sudden surge of empathy for Adelia. And he liked the fact that his waitress was firmly in her corner. He suspected the rest of the town was, too, just the way they'd always stood up for the wronged wives when his mom had been the other woman in way too many relationships.

Funny what a few years could do to give a man a new perspective. Back then all he'd cared about was the gossip, the taunts he'd suffered at school and his mom's tears each time the relationships inevitably ended. He'd witnessed her hope whenever a new man came into her life and then the slow realization that this time would be no different. His heart had broken almost as many times as hers.

Still, he couldn't help thinking about all the complications that came with a woman in Adelia's situation. He had enough on his own plate without getting mixed up in her drama. Much as he might enjoy sitting right here and staring, it would be far better to slip away right now and avoid the powerful temptation to reach out to her. Heaven knew, he had nothing to offer a woman, not yet, anyway.

"Darlin', could you make that pizza of mine to go?" he asked his waitress.

"Sure thing," Debbie said readily.

She brought it out within minutes. As Gabe paid the check, she grinned. "I imagine I'll see you again tomorrow. Maybe you'll try something different."

"Maybe so," he agreed, then winked. "But don't count on it. I'm comfortable in this rut I'm in."

She shook her head, then glanced pointedly in Adelia's direction. "Seems to me that's just when you need to shake things up."

Gabe followed the direction of her gaze and found the very woman in question glancing his way. His heart, which hadn't been engaged in much more than keeping him alive these past few years, did a fascinating little stutter step.

20

No way, he told himself determinedly as he headed for the door and the safety of his comfortable, if uninviting, room at the Serenity Inn. He'd never been much good at multitasking. Right now his only goal was to prove himself to Mitch and to himself. Complications were out of the question. And the beautiful Adelia Hernandez and her four kids had complication written all over them.

"Looks as if somebody has an admirer," Elliott commented to Adelia. Though his tone was light, there was a frown on his face as he watched the stranger leaving Rosalina's.

"Hush!" Adelia said, though she was blushing. She leaned closer to her brother. "That is not the sort of thing you should be saying in front of the kids. The ink's barely dry on my divorce papers."

Elliott laughed. "The kids are clear across the restaurant playing video games. You're only flustered because you know I'm right. That guy was attracted to you, Adelia. I recognize that thunderstruck expression on a man's face. I wore it a lot when I first met Karen. I saw it in the mirror when I shaved. It happened every time she crossed my mind."

Adelia smiled at the memory of her little brother falling hard for a woman no one in the family had approved of at first simply because she'd divorced a deadbeat husband. Elliott had fought hard to ensure that they all came to accept Karen and her kids and love them as much as he did. After her own marital troubles, Adelia had come to admire her sister-in-law's strength.

"You were a goner from the moment you laid eyes on her, weren't you?" she said.

"No question about it," he said. "I still am, and I don't see that ever changing. I want that happily-ever-after kind of love for you."

"Maybe someday," she said, not really able to imagine a time when she'd be willing to risk her heart again.

Elliott nodded in the direction of the door. "So, any idea who your admirer is?"

"Stop calling him that," she ordered, blushing again.

"Just calling it like I see it," he teased. "And it's nice to see some color in your cheeks."

She gave him a mock frown. "Don't make me sorry I called you tonight," she scolded. "There are some aggravations I can't avoid, but you're not one of them."

He grinned. "You needed me here to help

22

you corral those kids. And don't even try to pretend that you didn't enjoy the way that man was looking at you. You're not just a mom. You're a woman. You've seen far too little of that sort of appreciation in recent years."

"That may be so, but I'm not even remotely interested in dating anytime soon," she repeated emphatically, though she knew she was wasting her breath. Her brother loved getting under her skin and he'd just found a new way to do exactly that.

"You didn't recognize him?" he persisted, proving her point that he didn't intend to let this drop. "You work right downtown. You're involved in every activity in the school system. You see people all day long."

She shook her head. "I've never seen him before. He must be new in town."

"And Grace Wharton hasn't sent out a news bulletin?" he asked, only partially in jest. Grace, who ran the soda fountain at the local drugstore, prided herself on knowing all the comings and goings in town and being the first to spread the word. "Or are you just pretending that you missed the latest edition?"

Adelia tried a stern look that on rare occasions worked with her kids. "Drop this, please. There's been enough turmoil in my life these past months to last a lifetime. These days I'm a mom first and foremost. I need to get the kids settled in our new house and on an emotional even keel. That's my only focus for now."

"You're still a vibrant, attractive woman," Elliott reminded her, clearly undeterred by her expression or her words. "You deserve to find a man, the right man, who'll appreciate and respect you in a way that Ernesto never did." His expression darkened. "I still wish you'd let me teach him a lesson about mistreating my big sister."

She almost smiled at his zealous desire to stand up for her but didn't because she didn't want to encourage him. "I dealt with Ernesto. Thanks to Helen Decatur-Whitney, he'll be paying for his misdeeds with those generous support payments for the kids for years to come. Every penny is going in the bank. They'll have enough money tucked away to attend any college they choose when the time comes."

"I still don't get why you refused any alimony," Elliott told her, his frustration plain. "The man owed you, Adelia. You have a business degree, but you never used it so you could concentrate on being the perfect wife and mother. Who knows what you might have achieved by now if you'd started

24

a career after college?"

"Being a wife and mother was the career I chose," she told him. "I don't regret that for a second. Now that I'm a single mom, I'll put just as much energy into working and being a good parent. Being independent is important to me, Elliott. I need to know I'm in control of my life."

"I'm just saying that Ernesto's money might have made it easier," he argued.

"Don't forget that Helen got enough money in a lump sum to pay for the new house and to keep our heads above water for a year, longer if I'm careful. I'm making decent money at the boutique, especially since Raylene made me the manager. I want to show my girls they can grow up to take care of themselves."

"I guess that's an admirable goal," he said, though his tone was doubtful.

She smiled at him. "Isn't that what your wife did after her husband left her with a mountain of debt? Karen made a life for herself and her kids. It was a struggle, but she persevered. That's one of the reasons you fell for her, because she was strong in the face of adversity."

"I suppose." He grinned. "But then she found me and now it's my mission to take care of her and our family."

25

"Funny," she said. "Karen seems to think you have a partnership."

Her brother winced at the reminder. "Sorry. Apparently the Cruz macho tendencies die hard."

"As long as they die," she told him. "But I'll leave it to Karen to teach you that lesson."

Elliott frowned. "How did we get off track and start talking about my marriage? We were talking about you and that man who just walked out of here after giving you a thorough once-over."

"While the idea of any man staring at me appreciatively is a welcome change," she conceded, "I'm not looking for a relationship now. Maybe never. How many times do I need to say that before you believe me?"

Elliott looked dismayed rather than convinced by her response. "Don't let what Ernesto did shape the rest of your life, Adelia," he said fiercely. "Not all men are like that."

"You're certainly not," she agreed. "And for that I am eternally grateful." She touched his cheek. "I imagine Karen feels the same way. She must count her blessings every night."

"*Most* nights," her brother corrected with a grin. "At least when she's not exasperated with me for one thing or another, like forgetting about that whole partnership thing, for instance."

"Yes, I can see how you might test a woman's patience," she told him. "As a boy you were certainly a pest."

"Gee, thanks."

She patted his cheek again. "Don't fret, *mi hermano*. We all wind up loving you just the same. Even though this conversation is making me a little crazy, I know you mean well and I love you for caring."

Elliott's expression suddenly sobered. "Adelia, promise me something, okay?"

"Anything."

"If a man comes along, you'll leave yourself open to the possibilities. I'm not talking about the man who just left here, but any man."

"Any man?" she echoed, amused.

"After I've checked him out thoroughly," he amended.

"Now *that* sounds much more like the overly protective brother I know and love," Adelia said.

"Promise," he repeated.

Though she couldn't imagine it would be a promise she'd have to keep, at least not anytime soon, Adelia nodded. "Promise."

Just then the pizza and the kids arrived at

the table simultaneously and, thankfully, further conversation was impossible.

Time and time again, though, she found herself glancing toward the door and thinking about the man who'd cast a lingering look in her direction. Whether it was the openly appreciative way he'd studied her or her brother's teasing, she felt the oddest sensation stirring deep inside. It was a sensation she hadn't anticipated and didn't especially want, but it felt a whole lot as if she might be coming alive again.

CHAPTER TWO

If Rosalina's had become his restaurant of choice in the evening, the bakery was the place where Gabe satisfied his sweet tooth every single morning. Not only was Sweet Things owned by his cousin's new wife, Lynn, but he'd quickly discovered that the woman made the best cookies, pies, pastries and cupcakes he'd ever put in his mouth. If Mitch hadn't beaten him to it, he'd have courted Lynn himself, not that he'd mentioned that to his cousin. He needed Mitch as an ally, not an enemy.

Thank goodness, though, ever since Gabe had arrived in town, Mitch had insisted on starting their mornings here over coffee and pastry warm from the oven as they planned how Gabe was going to fit into the company. His cousin filled him in on the work needed on the neighboring properties. Lynn joined them from time to time, but she was usually far too busy baking to take a break just past the crack of dawn.

At full daylight and after getting his fill of coffee and pastries, Gabe walked the length of Main Street with Mitch, trying to get a feel not only for downtown Serenity as it currently existed, but for his cousin's vision.

The historic brick town hall at one end of the large, tree-lined green housed the city's offices. Wharton's, which had been in business as far back as Gabe could remember as a combination pharmacy and soda fountain, anchored one side of Main Street. A hardware store revitalized by Ronnie Sullivan anchored the other side.

Sweet Things was in that block, along with Chic, the stylish women's boutique next door. The remaining storefronts were empty and mostly boarded up, victims of the economic downturn and of the tendency in too many small communities for business to flee to the outskirts of town and more modern strip malls. The one exception in the next block was the relatively new and apparently wildly successful country radio station with its studio window facing the green so the on-air hosts could report on Serenity's many holiday festivals and everyday happenings.

Gabe had been able to view the recent progress with appreciation, but he was still

30

mindful that a lot more was needed before downtown Serenity could be described as thriving.

This morning — his first official day on the job — he studied Mitch over his mug of coffee. "You really think turning this town around is possible?"

"I'm counting on it," Mitch said. "Our town manager, Tom McDonald, believes it's possible and is doing everything he can to lure new business to town. I want to be sure there are up-to-date properties available to rent when the prospective business owners come to look things over. I want downtown to be irresistible. I want them to see it immediately as a better bet than one of those strip malls that have started popping up along the highway outside of town."

Gabe smiled. "Were you always this idealistic and ambitious?"

"I don't see it as ambition. I see it as a chance to do something for a town I love, the town where I've built my life. I don't want to see downtown die the way it has in so many towns." Mitch shrugged. "Maybe that is idealistic."

"I hate to tell you, pal, but that ship has sailed. Right now, this downtown is on life support at best."

"I know a few people, my wife among

31

them, who'd tell you otherwise," Mitch retorted. "And Dana Sue Sullivan, whose restaurant lures people from all over the state, would pick a major fight with you if she heard you say that. Sullivan's may not be right on Main Street, but her success speaks for itself."

Gabe laughed. "Well, I'm not about to take on Dana Sue. I've heard too many stories about her temper. But Lynn is what they call a pie-eyed optimist. She married you, didn't she? What does that say about her judgment?"

Mitch didn't take offense at his teasing. He laughed with him.

"She took a chance on me, all right," Mitch said. "I thank my lucky stars for it. After Amy died and the boys were away at college, I was a lost soul for a while." His expression sobered. "I wish you'd come over for dinner one night, instead of existing on pizza. You know you're welcome anytime."

"I know that," Gabe said. "But you're still a newlywed. I don't want to intrude."

"We're past the honeymoon stage," Mitch said, though the appreciative glance he cast in his wife's direction as she came out of the back to wait on a customer said other-wise. So did the touches he couldn't resist making every time she was in close proximity. "We've been together almost a year now. And with Lynn's two kids underfoot, it's not as if we have a lot of privacy, anyway."

"In my book a year still makes you a newlywed."

Mitch gave him a knowing look. "And in my book, you're just making excuses. You're family, Gabe. You're not an outsider. I know you didn't feel that way as a kid and I'm as sorry as I can be about the way the rest of the family treated your mother."

Gabe waved off the apology. "You were just a kid yourself. You had no control over what the adults did and thought. Besides, I get where they were coming from. My mom had her share of problems. Drinking was the least of it."

Mitch winced. "I came way too close to relying on alcohol myself after I lost Amy," he revealed quietly, startling Gabe. "I'd like to think I wouldn't have judged your mother for that weakness."

Gabe wondered if there was some hereditary inclination that seemed to steer Franklins toward booze. "I took a brush with it myself after Mom died," he said. "Even though I knew firsthand where that path could lead. Now that I've got my feet back under me and can see what dangerous decisions I was making, I feel a lot more sympathy for her myself than I did when I was living with it. I can also see a lot more clearly that she sure as heck had an addiction to the wrong sort of men. It was a bad combination."

"But those shouldn't have become your problems, too," Mitch said. "You took them on when the family should have been there to support both of you, instead of passing judgment. It wasn't right that you got labeled a troublemaker for trying to protect your mom."

"Water under the bridge," Gabe insisted. "Can we stop talking about this, please? You've more than made up for the past by giving me this job."

Mitch dismissed the sentiment. "I have to admit that I'm still a little surprised that you wanted to come back to Serenity. You were awfully eager to put the town and your family behind you when you took off after your mom died."

Gabe shrugged. "Seemed to me like the best place to get a second chance would be in the same place where you blew the first one. I guess I was finally ready to face the past, instead of running from it. Maybe I can shake those ghosts that seem to go with me wherever I am."

"A very mature outlook."

Gabe laughed. "Yeah, well, I imagine that's a surprise for you, too. It sure is to me. Maybe hitting forty somehow turned me into a grown-up." He set out determinedly to change the subject once and for all. "Now, what's on the agenda for today? You've given me enough time to get settled in. I'm anxious to get started and prove you didn't make the wrong decision by taking me on. I filled you in on my experience, but you haven't seen my work firsthand. I meant what I told you — if it doesn't measure up, you can tell me that straight-out, okay?"

"That's not likely," Mitch said. "Your job history speaks for itself. I know some of those men you worked for around the state."

"Did you speak to them? That's why I gave you their names."

"No need. I trust you," Mitch claimed, giving Gabe's sometimes shaky self-esteem a needed boost.

Just then, the door opened and Adelia Hernandez stepped into the bakery. If anything, Gabe thought she was even prettier with her long hair tousled by the wind and wearing a dress that showed off her shapely legs. That crazy pulse of his skipped a couple of beats.

Apparently the reaction wasn't entirely one-sided. When she spotted him, her cheeks flushed and her step faltered.

Naturally Mitch noticed Adelia's discomfort and Gabe's fascination. His eyes narrowed.

"You two know each other?" he asked Gabe. Adelia hesitated as if she was torn between whatever she'd come in to get and getting away from Gabe as quickly as possible.

"She was at Rosalina's when I was there last night," Gabe replied carefully.

"And?"

"That's it. She was there with her family. I was there by myself. Nothing more to it."

Mitch regarded him doubtfully. "Looked like a little more than nothing just now," he said as Adelia hurried to the counter and placed her order with Lynn.

"I've never even spoken to the woman," Gabe assured him. "And if that gleam in your eyes has anything to do with matchmaking, you can forget about it. I'm here to work. Period."

Despite his very firm disclaimer, he couldn't seem to keep his gaze from straying to Adelia, whose hand appeared to be shaking as she accepted a container of coffee from Lynn. As soon as she'd paid, she whirled around and practically ran out the door.

"Adelia!" Lynn called after her, then glanced toward Mitch. "I don't know what in the world is wrong with her this morning. She's jumpy as a june bug and she ran off without her pastry."

Gabe was instantly on his feet. He held out his hand. "I'll take it to her."

He saw the startled expression on Lynn's face and heard his cousin's chuckle as he took off. So much for any pretense that he wasn't interested, he thought ruefully. Oh, well. He figured that had pretty much been doomed from the instant he'd laid eyes on her, anyway. It was a darn good thing he'd had a ton of practice at controlling most of his craziest impulses.

This is ridiculous, Adelia thought as she struggled to get her key to work in the lock at Chic, the boutique next door to the bakery. How could a man to whom she'd never even spoken rattle her so badly? She'd been squeezing the Styrofoam cup so tightly since leaving Lynn's, it was a wonder there was a drop of coffee left in there. It was all her brother's fault for planting that crazy idea in her head, for suggesting that the stranger was a potential admirer.

She'd barely set the coffee down by the cash register when the bell over the front

37

door tinkled merrily and she realized she hadn't locked the door behind her. More startling was the sight of the man entering.

"You!" she exclaimed.

She must have sounded alarmed, because he stopped in his tracks and held out a small pastry bag. "I come in peace," he teased, seemingly fighting a smile. "You left this behind at the bakery. Lynn was worried, so I said I'd deliver it."

She sucked in a deep breath and closed her eyes for an instant. "Sorry. You just caught me off guard. I usually lock the door behind me since we don't open for another half hour. I come in early. Well, I guess that's obvious, isn't it? I like to get started before any customers walk in. I want to make sure the displays are neat and the cash register is set to go, that sort of thing. I'm a little obsessive about it."

She realized she was rambling. She clamped her mouth shut. He held out the pastry bag, and when she didn't immediately reach for it, he set it on the counter, amusement written all over his face.

"I'm Gabe Franklin," he told her. "Mitch's cousin."

Adelia felt herself relaxing ever so slightly at that. Mitch was a good guy. One of the best, in fact. Any cousin of his would surely be okay, even if this man seemed to have the power to rattle her in ways no man had for years. Any rattling Ernesto had done had been to her temper.

"Mitch is great," she said.

"That seems to be the consensus," he responded.

She frowned at the edge she thought she heard in his voice. "You don't agree?"

He winced. "Sorry. It's an old habit. In the interest of full disclosure, I was the black sheep Franklin growing up. Old resentments die hard. He *is* a good man. I can appreciate that now."

"I imagine it can be hard growing up in someone else's shadow," she said. "I know Mitch is a local. We knew each other in school, but what about you? Are you from Serenity?"

He nodded. "Born and bred here."

"Then I'm surprised we haven't crossed paths before. We must be about the same age. I imagine we were in school around the same time. I'm Adelia Hernandez, by the way. I was Adelia Cruz before I married."

"And I spent more time suspended from school than I did in classes," he admitted. "I left town for a lot of years after that. I just got back a week ago. Fortunately I got my act together during that time and picked up a diploma, then went on to college. I suppose I should say I took classes, since I never graduated. I was in too much of a hurry to get on with life."

"Did you regret that later?"

He shook his head. "No point in regrets. It was the decision I made. I try not to look back, just focus on the here and now."

"I'm trying to work on that," she told him. "And I've recently had to face the fact that human beings are an imperfect lot. What matters is how we deal with our mistakes. Sounds as if you've made up for yours."

"Not entirely, but I'm working on it."

She watched as he glanced around the very feminine shop, which was currently displaying summer dresses and a new line of lacy lingerie. His gaze landed on the lingerie. Color bloomed in his cheeks. His nerves definitely showing, he shoved his hands in his pockets and backed toward the door.

"I'd better get back to the bakery. Mitch has a long list of projects he wants to go over with me. It's officially my first day on the job."

Adelia nodded and held up the pastry bag. "Thanks for bringing this."

"Not a problem."

She watched him leave, admired the way

his jeans fit snugly over a very excellent backside and felt heat climb up her neck. She thought of Elliott's advice just the night before to keep her heart open and her own very adamant declaration that she was a long, long way from being interested in another relationship. She suddenly couldn't help wondering if Gabe Franklin with the wicked gleam in his eyes and his flirtatious ways was about to make a liar out of her.

It was midmorning before Adelia was able to push all thoughts of Gabe Franklin aside and concentrate on work. Just as she was about to reorganize a display to show off a new shipment of colorful scarves, her cell phone rang. To her dismay it was the principal of Selena's middle school.

"Adelia, I'm so sorry to bother you at work, but we have a problem. Selena's not in her physical education class. The teacher didn't notice it until they were choosing sides for soccer. She'd taken attendance earlier and Selena was there, but she disappeared sometime between that and when they went outside."

"Are you sure she didn't just stay in the locker room?" Adelia asked, trying to tamp down the panic that was already rising. "She hates soccer. Skipping it to sit in the locker room and read a book is something she might do."

"She's not on the school grounds," Margaret Towson told her. "I've had several people checking for the past twenty minutes or so. Do you want me to call Carter Rollins?"

"The police chief? Do you really think that's necessary?"

"It's standard procedure if a child disappears during the school day and the parents don't know where they are, either. Do you have any idea where we might find Selena?"

Adelia felt tears gathering in her eyes. "No."

"Perhaps I should check with her father then," Margaret ventured, her tone tentative.

"No," Adelia said quickly. "I'll handle this. I'll call Carter and start looking myself," she said. "Thank you for letting me know so quickly, Margaret."

"Adelia, I know Selena has been going through a difficult time. Her teachers are aware of it, as well. If there's anything we can do to help, just ask."

"Thanks."

She disconnected the call and immediately called her boss, Raylene Rollins, rather than Raylene's husband, Carter. The minute she explained the situation, Raylene said, "Lock up the store and go. I'll be there in a few minutes to take over, but don't wait for me. I'll call Carter and tell him what's going on. Try not to worry. Selena can't have gone far. She might even be at home. Have you tried her cell phone or the phone at the house?"

"No. I wasn't thinking," Adelia admitted, completely shaken by the oversight. "I'll do that now. Thanks for understanding, Raylene."

"Don't thank me. Just go. And call me the minute you find her."

Adelia grabbed her purse from the office, put a closed sign on the door, then locked up the boutique. She opened the door to Sweet Things, drawing a startled look from Lynn.

"Is everything okay?" Lynn asked. "You're white as a ghost."

"The school just called. Selena's missing."

Lynn had her own cell phone out before Adelia could finish the sentence. "Mitch will start looking, too," she reported. "What can I do?"

"Just call me if she shows up here or if your daughter has any idea where she might have gone. I know Lexie's older, but kids hear things. I'm hoping this was just an impulsive decision, but with everything that's happened lately, I can't help worrying that she might have been planning to run away."

"I'll check with Lexie right now," Lynn promised just as Mitch and Gabe came rushing into the bakery.

Mitch put steadying hands on her shoulders. "Stay calm," he said quietly. "We're going to find her. Gabe, why don't you go with Adelia. I'll start driving around town. Any place you think I ought to check first?" he asked.

"I don't know," she said, fresh tears gathering in her eyes.

She'd been so sure that Selena was handling the divorce okay. She was angry at her father, of course, but beyond that she seemed to be taking the move and all the rest in stride. The rebellion of a few months ago had seemingly vanished, replaced by resignation. Adelia should have seen through that. Apparently her mom-radar wasn't as sharp as she'd thought.

"I've got this," Gabe told Mitch. "You start looking."

Mitch nodded. "I'll start by the school and fan out from there. I'll check with Carter, too, so we're not duplicating our efforts."

44

Gabe turned to Lynn. "How about a cup of tea? Something herbal, maybe?"

Adelia regarded him as if he were nuts. "I don't have time to sit here and sip tea," she said, starting toward the door.

Gabe blocked her path. "We'll get it to go. It'll help to calm your nerves so you can tell me where you want to start looking."

"He's right," Lynn said, already handing her the to-go container. "I've put plenty of sugar in there for you. That'll help, too."

Adelia told herself she only accepted the cup so she could get out of the bakery, but in some part of her brain, she knew they were both right. The tea might help to settle her nerves so she could think straight.

With Gabe watching her closely, she took several sips, then met his gaze. "Satisfied?"

"It's a start," he said lightly. "Now let's go find your daughter."

Something in the way he said it, with full confidence that they'd be successful, reassured her, even though nothing had really changed in the past few minutes.

"I want to go by the house first. I've called and there was no answer, but that doesn't mean she's not there."

"Where's the house?"

"Swan Point."

He nodded and turned in that direction.

"Just tell me where to turn once we're there," he said.

The drive through the neighborhood of fewer than a dozen homes took only minutes, as did the search of the house. There was no sign of Selena, no bookbag tossed on the sofa or remnants of a snack in the kitchen.

"What about her father? Would she go to him?" Gabe asked.

"Not likely," Adelia said, unable to keep a note of bitterness from her voice. "She's very angry at him these days."

"Anybody she's especially close to?"

Adelia immediately brightened. "Her uncle. Elliott runs that new men's gym just off Palmetto. You know the place?"

Gabe nodded. "I just joined."

As they made the drive to Fit for Anything, Adelia's mind started racing. "What if — ?"

The words were no sooner out of her mouth than Gabe cut her off. "No what-ifs," he declared firmly. "She hasn't been missing long. If she's upset, she'll go someplace where she feels safe."

"But she might not be thinking clearly," Adelia protested, her panic returning. "She's only thirteen, Gabe. I'm afraid I've been forgetting that myself. I should have been paying more attention. Instead, I was so worried about my younger kids, I missed all the signs that Selena was in real trouble. I was just grateful that she was no longer rebelling against the world."

In front of the gym, she bolted from the car practically before it could come to a stop. Inside, she scanned the room until her gaze landed on her brother. He regarded her with alarm, which grew visibly when Gabe came in right on her heels.

Misreading the situation, Elliott stepped between them. "Is this guy bothering you, Adelia?"

She held up a hand. "No, it's nothing like that. Selena's missing. Gabe is helping me look for her. I thought maybe she'd come here to see you."

Elliott shook his head. "I haven't seen her. Let me check with Karen. She's not working today. She's at the house with the baby."

Adelia felt herself starting to shake as her brother made the call to his wife. Then she felt Gabe's steadying hand on her shoulder. He didn't say a word, just kept his hand there until the moment passed.

Elliott listened intently to whatever Karen was saying, his expression brightening. "Thanks, *querida*. Adelia will be there in a few minutes." Smiling, he turned to her. "Selena's at my house playing with the baby.

Karen didn't think to call anyone because Selena told her she only had a half day at school and swore you knew where she was."

Adelia finally let out the breath she felt like she'd been holding for hours. "Of course Karen believed her," she said wryly. "Selena's very convincing when she wants to be."

"Want me to drive you over there?" Elliott offered. "I can get one of the other trainers to take my next client."

"I can take her," Gabe said. He looked at her. "Unless you'd prefer to have your brother go with you."

Adelia hesitated, then shook her head. "If you don't mind making the drive, that would be great," she told him. "Elliott, there's no reason for you to miss an appointment. I can handle this."

Elliott looked worried but eventually nodded. "You'll be there when I get home? I want to have a talk with my niece about skipping school and worrying you."

She smiled. "Believe me, she'll get more than enough talking from me tonight. You can save your lecture for another day."

Elliott nodded with unmistakable reluctance. "Whatever you think, but I will have a word with her. You can be sure of that."

"Not a doubt in my mind," she said, then

turned to Gabe. "Let's go. That is, if you're really sure you have the time."

"I have the time," he said without hesitation.

On the way to her brother's, Gabe called Mitch and told him they'd located Selena and were on the way to get her. After the call ended, he told her, "Mitch will speak to Carter and let him know to call off the search."

Adelia sighed. "I should have thought to do that."

"You have plenty of other things on your mind," he said, excusing her. "I imagine you're pondering a dozen different things you can say to drive home the point that what your daughter did was wrong."

Surprised by his understanding, she nodded. "How'd you know?"

"Not because I got my share of lectures, that's for sure," he said. "My mom was pretty oblivious to the trouble I was getting into." He glanced her way. "Word of advice?"

"Sure."

"Whatever punishment you decide to dole out, and there should be one, be sure you hug the daylights out of her first."

Adelia felt her heart tumble just a little. "You didn't get the hugs, either?"

"Nope, which is why I know exactly how important they are," he said as he pulled to a stop in front of Elliott's house in a new subdivision outside town.

Adelia turned to him then. "Thank you."

"For chauffeuring you around town for an hour? Don't mention it. I'm just glad there's a happy ending."

"Not just for that," she corrected him. "For reminding me that discipline always needs to come with a hug."

He winked at her. "I saw you with your kids at Rosalina's, remember? Something tells me you already knew that."

Adelia stood in the driveway and watched him leave. She'd seen a different side of Gabe Franklin just now, one that was even more appealing than the flirtatious man she'd encountered before. Something told her this thoughtful, more vulnerable side made him even more dangerous.

CHAPTER THREE

"Thanks for helping out just now," Lynn said when Gabe stopped by the bakery for a large cup of coffee before heading back to the construction site. "Adelia would never admit it, but she had to be scared out of her wits. I know I would have been if it had been one of my kids missing. I'm sure having you around kept her calm."

"I don't know how much help I was," Gabe said. "All I did was drive the car in whatever direction she asked me to."

Lynn smiled at the self-deprecating comment. "And you didn't say one single word in all that time? Didn't offer any support? Maybe insist she drink some tea?"

"The tea made sense," he grumbled.

Lynn's smile spread. He was obviously self-conscious about accepting praise for what he apparently considered to be nothing more than a neighborly gesture. She considered that very telling. Mitch had told her about Gabe's past and how determined he was to fight his old reputation as a troublemaker. This humility was definite evidence that he was well on his way.

"Don't make a big deal about that, or about anything I did, for that matter," he said. "It was nothing anyone else wouldn't have done."

"Whatever you say," she said, laughing. "Something tells me things are about to get real interesting here on Main Street."

Gabe frowned at her. "Just because you and my cousin still have stars in your eyes doesn't mean the whole world is just waiting for romance."

"Adelia would probably say the same thing," Lynn said agreeably. "She just got a divorce. She's not interested in meeting anyone right now. Yada yada yada. I've heard it all before. Said it myself, in fact, when Mitch came along. Doesn't mean I believe a word she says." She regarded him pointedly, then added, "You, either. My theory is that neither of you has a clue what you really need in your lives."

"Well, whether you buy it or not, could you stay out of it?" Gabe pleaded. "I've got problems enough up and down this block without adding your meddling into the mix."

"What problems?" she asked at once, her mood sobering. "Does Mitch know?"

"Of course he knows. I haven't been on the job long enough to make decisions without running them by him. Now, if you'll get that cup of coffee I asked for when I first walked through the door, and maybe a few of those chocolate chip cookies, I'll get back to work, so he doesn't fire me for hanging out too long with his wife."

She quickly poured the coffee and bagged his cookies, choosing a few from a tray still warm from the oven, but she waved off payment. "Just a reward for helping Adelia," she said. "Where will you be if Mitch stops by here looking for you?"

"In the old supermarket space on the corner trying to figure out how we're going to replace those old beams without the roof tumbling down on our heads. The termites have been living it up in there for ten years at least."

Lynn looked alarmed. "That can't be good. What about Chic? It's right next door to that space. Is their ceiling okay?"

"I'll check with Mitch, but I imagine he did a thorough job fixing up that place and this one. If there was damage, I doubt he missed it."

Relieved, she nodded. "You're right, of

course. Mitch pays attention to details. It's one of his best traits."

Gabe grinned at her. "I imagine that comes in handy in more ways than one," he said with a wink, then took off, brushing past Maddie Maddox, Helen Decatur-Whitney and Dana Sue Sullivan in his hurry.

Their arrival wasn't particularly unexpected. Once word of a crisis spread through town, the original Sweet Magnolias were always among the first to respond. The loosely formed group of friends had grown to include many other women now, including Lynn, but these three were still its heart and soul.

"What's his hurry?" Helen asked, her eyes narrowed. The town's — maybe even the state's — most prominent divorce attorney was by nature cynical and suspicious, even after several years now of being deliriously happy in her own marriage.

Lynn chuckled. "I made him nervous."

Maddie regarded her with surprise. "How?"

"By suggesting that his willingness to jump in to help Adelia was something more than a neighborly gesture," Lynn said.

"I knew it!" Dana Sue said, her expression smug. "All day long I was hearing gossip that Adelia and Gabe had crossed paths at Rosalina's the other night and fireworks went off. It was Grace spreading the story, and you know how she is. She can spin a romance out of a passing glance."

Helen held up her hands. "Hold on a minute! The latest Serenity romance alert is fascinating, but shouldn't we be focusing on what we can do to help in the search for Adelia's daughter? That's why we rushed over here."

Maddie and Dana Sue immediately looked guilt-stricken.

"Of course we should," Maddie said.

"It's okay," Lynn soothed. "Selena's safe and sound. Adelia and Gabe found her at Elliott and Karen's house. He stopped in just now to fill me in." She glanced at the three women, who'd been best friends since childhood. "Now who needs coffee and maybe a slice of pie while you fill me in on what you've heard about Gabe and Adelia?"

"I wouldn't turn down a slice of lemon meringue," Maddie said at once.

"Coconut cream for me," Helen said as Lynn poured the coffee.

Dana Sue stared at the display case longingly. As she did, Lynn remembered hearing that she was at high risk for diabetes. That would be a tough diagnosis for anyone, but Dana Sue owned a restaurant and was around food constantly. She sighed now.

"I'll pass on the pie," Dana Sue said with unmistakable disappointment, "but I will take the coffee."

"How about a couple of sugar-free oatmeal cookies?" Lynn suggested. "They have cranberries and walnuts. I promise they don't taste like sawdust."

Helen's eyes lit up. "Ooh, those sound fabulous. Maybe I'll have those, too."

"Instead of pie?" Lynn asked.

"Absolutely not," Helen replied, then hesitated. "But maybe you'd better put them in a bag. I'll pretend I'm taking them home for my daughter."

Maddie and Dana Sue exchanged a look.

"Want to bet they're gone before she gets to the corner?" Maddie asked.

Dana Sue shook her head. "Why would I want to bet against a sure thing?" She grinned at Lynn. "Bring on the cookies and don't waste a bag, okay?"

Helen patted the chair next to her. "And sit right here next to me. I want to know everything you can tell me about Gabe and Adelia."

Lynn chuckled as she imagined how Gabe would react to being linked with Adelia all over town. He'd been grumpy enough when

56

she'd merely hinted at a potential romantic pairing. Now that the Sweet Magnolias and Grace Wharton were alert and watching for every sighting, it was going to make him crazy. In Lynn's opinion, a little craziness was just what he needed.

Gabe found Mitch standing on scaffolding in the middle of the construction site on the corner. Mitch was regarding the damage-riddled support beam with disgust. When he caught sight of Gabe, he climbed down.

"What's your plan?" he asked at once, surprising Gabe.

"You don't have one?" Gabe asked.

Mitch chuckled. "Of course I do, but I put you in charge. I want to hear yours."

Startled by the confidence his cousin was placing in him, Gabe pulled a rough sketch from his back pocket and spread it out on a rickety old table that comprised his office space for now.

"Here's what I was thinking," he said, going over the drawing. "I had Ronnie Sullivan in here earlier for some cost estimates on the lumber. He says if we want a couple of steel beams, he can get prices for those, too, but we're talking big money."

Mitch's expression was thoughtful as

Gabe talked. He glanced up at the existing beams, then at the figures Gabe had jotted down, then nodded. "Let's do it right," he said eventually. "If we're going to fix this building up, we need it to be built to last."

"I'll have the prices for you tomorrow," Gabe said, relieved. He'd been cautious, but he, too, believed in getting it right, not cheap. "By the way, your wife's expecting you. I stopped in to grab a cup of coffee just now. She might need a little reassuring about the state of the ceiling over the bakery."

Mitch frowned. "Why?"

"It's possible I planted a few seeds of doubt talking about all the termites," Gabe admitted, then shrugged at Mitch's incredulous expression. "Hey, I had to say something to get her off the topic of me and Adelia Hernandez."

"And all you could come up with was termite damage?" Mitch said with mock exasperation. "She's going to want to go up there and check out those beams herself."

Gabe laughed. "I suspected as much. Where's the trust? That's what I want to know. You did renovate that space for her."

Mitch shook his head. "Which just means we probably should add contractors to the list of people who need to avoid doing business with family." He sighed heavily. "Thanks for that, by the way."

"Anytime," Gabe said.

Let his cousin deal with Lynn's inquisitive nature. That was a whole lot easier on Gabe than having her pecking away at his personal life.

Adelia stood outside the nursery at Elliott and Karen's house trying to calm her temper before she confronted her daughter about scaring her and everyone else. She needed to remember what Gabe had said about doling out hugs before discipline. She thought she'd always been pretty good at that, but today had been a real test. What she wanted more than anything was to give her daughter a good shake and ground her for at least the remainder of her school years. Fortunately, she was wise enough to know none of that was the answer to what had happened today.

When she opened the door, she found Selena sitting in a rocker with the baby in her arms and sunlight spilling over them. Even at only thirteen, she had the serenity of the Madonna about her. It was a terrifying reminder of how quickly she was growing up.

When Selena glanced up and caught sight

59

of Adelia, though, wariness filled her eyes and she was a nervous teenager who knew she was in trouble. "What are you doing here?" she asked, her voice unsteady.

"I think the better question is what are *you* doing here in the middle of a school day?" Adelia responded, careful to keep the fear and temper out of her voice. "You've had half the town running around trying to find you, including the police chief."

Selena had the grace to look shocked by that. "I'm sorry. I didn't think anyone would miss me. I just skipped out on soccer. I'm no good at that, anyway."

"And what about the classes you have after physical education? Were you planning to go back for those? If so, you're already late."

Selena winced. "I lost track of time," she whispered, clearly aware that Adelia wasn't likely to buy it.

"Seriously? You expect me to believe that?"

"I was hoping," Selena said, her expression guilty.

"Afraid not. Put the baby down and come outside so we can talk," Adelia said, pausing to brush gentle fingers over the baby's soft-as-silk curls. With black hair and big brown eyes, she was all Cruz, that's for sure.

Maybe because she knew it was inevitable,

Selena did as she'd been told to do, then followed Adelia from the room. As they passed Karen in the living room, Adelia asked, "Mind if we sit on your deck for a little while? We need to talk."

"It's fine," Karen said. "Would you like something cool to drink? I've just made fresh lemonade."

"I'd like some, please," Selena said at once, clearly relieved by any delay she could seize. "I can get it."

She scampered off to the kitchen before Adelia could protest. Karen smiled. "She's awfully eager to make amends, isn't she?"

"Seems so," Adelia said, then released a sigh. "I've never been so terrified in my life."

Karen, who'd been reserved with her for a long time, stepped forward and pulled her into an awkward embrace. "But she's okay. That's what counts, Adelia. She came here, to a safe place. She didn't run away."

"I know and I'm more grateful than I can express for that. Did she talk at all?"

"No. I think she just wanted some space on neutral turf. She asked if she could hold the baby. She's been in the nursery ever since." She gave Adelia an apologetic look. "If I'd had any idea you didn't know where she was, I would have called you immediately."

"I know that," Adelia assured her. "Thanks for being so kind to her."

"She's my niece," Karen said simply.

Selena returned from the kitchen with three glasses of lemonade and looked at Karen hopefully. "Are you coming outside to talk, too?"

"No, sweetheart. This is between you and your mom." She looked at Adelia. "If you need anything, let me know. I can give you all a lift home whenever you're ready, unless you'd like to stay for dinner."

"We'll see," Adelia said. It depended on how this conversation went and whether she thought she needed some backup from her brother to drive her points home with Selena. Her mom would keep the younger kids for the night, if need be.

Adelia led the way outside. She sat on a cushioned bench on the shady side of the deck, then patted the seat next to her. With unmistakable reluctance, Selena sat beside her. Adelia reached for her hand.

"Do you have any idea how precious you are to me?" she asked softly. "You're my firstborn, Selena."

Rather than looked reassured, Selena looked sad. "But if it weren't for me, you might never have married Dad."

Adelia frowned at what seemed to be an

entirely out-of-the-blue comment. "What do you mean?"

"Come on, Mom. I can count. You and Dad got married because you were already pregnant with me. If that hadn't happened, then you wouldn't have been trapped with a man who cheated on you every chance he got."

Adelia closed her eyes, trying to gather her composure. She'd hoped this conversation would never be necessary, but Selena had clearly overheard way too many arguments with Ernesto and the accusations that had been flung about.

"It's true that I was pregnant when your Dad and I got married," she confessed, then forced Selena to meet her gaze. "But you need to believe me, sweetheart. I don't regret that decision, not for a single minute."

"How can you not regret it?" Selena asked angrily. "Dad did."

"No, he didn't. Not really."

"I heard him, Mom."

"People say things in the heat of the moment that they don't really mean, even your dad. But let's focus on how *I* feel for now. How can I regret marrying your dad when I have you and your sisters and your brother because of that decision? The four of you mean everything to me. I may hate what's been happening, I may be really angry at him right now, but I can't regret being married to him, sweetheart. One of these days you'll discover that things are never as black-and-white as we might like them to be. There's a lot of gray in the middle. Good just happens to come with bad sometimes."

Tears streamed down Selena's cheeks. "I'm never getting married," she declared.

Her determined words were as painful for Adelia to hear as her own had probably been for Elliott on Sunday night. She didn't want her daughter's future to be shaped by the divorce. She pulled Selena close and Selena actually allowed it, resting her head on Adelia's shoulder as she had when she was younger.

"That's not a decision you need to be making now," she told her daughter. "And it certainly isn't one you should base on what happened between your father and me. Look at your uncle Elliott and Karen and how happy they are."

"But Karen's first husband was a real jerk," Selena reminded her. "So was Raylene's. I heard all about how he abused her and then came here and tried to kill her."

"But Raylene has Carter now and they're expecting a baby," Adelia reminded her. "She found real happiness this time, the kind that will last."

"But there's no way to know for sure," Selena protested. "I'll bet you thought Dad was great at first or you wouldn't have fallen in love with him. The same with Karen and Raylene. They're smart, too, and look what happened to them."

"Okay, here's what I know," Adelia said, brushing a lock of hair back from Selena's damp cheek. "People make mistakes. And sometimes people change. Human beings are flawed, but that doesn't mean you should never take a risk. The important thing is that it be an informed risk, one you only take after very careful thought. And even then, if you get it wrong, you pick up the pieces and move on."

Even as she said the words meant to re-assure her daughter, Adelia realized they were very similar to the sentiment that Elliott had expressed to her. She wondered if she was any more capable of hearing them right now than Selena was.

"How do you do that, though?" Selena asked. "Move on, I mean? You make it sound easy, but it's not."

"No, it's not," Adelia said. "But you do it because you must and you do it one day at a time. Some days will be easier than others."

"I made today harder, didn't I?" Selena asked, real regret in her voice.

"You did," Adelia said, unwilling to gloss over the effect her behavior had. "But I understand why you came here. Sometimes I forget that you're not a grown-up and that all these decisions your dad and I have made affect you in ways I might not even realize. But, baby, you need to talk to me about it, not take off." She tucked a finger under Selena's chin and forced her to look into her eyes. "Deal?"

Selena nodded slowly. "Deal." Her expression turned worried. "How much trouble am I in? Grounded is a given, huh?"

"Grounded is a given," Adelia agreed. "But I imagine we can smooth things over at school, even though they have a very low tolerance for skipping classes. You'll need to apologize to your teacher and to the principal for worrying them."

Selena didn't look happy, but she nodded. "Anybody else?"

"Raylene and Carter for inconveniencing them," Adelia said. "Mitch Franklin, who dropped everything to help look for you, and his cousin Gabe, who drove me around to all the places I thought you might be, then brought me here."

"I don't even know him," Selena protested. "Why did he help?"

"Because that's what people do in Serenity," Adelia told her. "I know you think this town is way too small and old-fashioned and that you can't wait to get away, but the positive side of living here is that we look out for each other. We pitch in when anyone's in trouble."

It was something she was just coming to realize for herself, and in the past few months, when her world had been turned upside down, she'd been grateful for all the support, sometimes from the most unexpected people. Gabe Franklin, she was forced to concede, fell into that category.

Gabe stayed on the job until after eight, running the numbers Ronnie Sullivan had given him for new steel support beams until he had a proposal ready to pass along to Mitch first thing in the morning. While he'd told himself it was the responsible thing to do, he knew the real reason he was still at the construction site was to keep himself from heading over to Swan Point to check on Adelia and her daughter.

"She's not your responsibility," he muttered to himself on more than one occasion when he found his thoughts straying to her panicked expression when she'd first found out her daughter was missing.

For the entire hour he'd been with her, though, she'd lost control only once when *what-if* calamities had crept into her head. He thought he'd done an okay job of diverting her attention before she could sink into real despair. Other than that moment, she'd shown admirable strength. After his own childhood, it had been eye-opening to see how a good mother handled things.

He was about to turn out the lights, lock up and head for Rosalina's, when the door opened and Elliott Cruz walked in. Gabe stilled at the sight of him. He'd seen the protectiveness in the other man's eyes earlier and couldn't help wondering what had brought him here now. A warning to stay away, perhaps? Gabe was ready to reassure him on that point. He intended to steer clear of Adelia as much as possible for his own peace of mind.

"Elliott, right?" he asked, seizing the initiative and holding out his hand. "We didn't really meet earlier."

Adelia's brother looked startled, but he shook his hand.

"What brings you by?" Gabe asked.

"I came to apologize," Elliott told him.

The statement took Gabe by surprise. "Why?"

68

"Because you pitched in to help this afternoon and I came on too strong and all but attacked you when you came into the gym with my sister."

Gabe shrugged. "You didn't have all the facts."

"No, I certainly didn't," Elliott said. "Adelia would be the first to tell you, jumping to conclusions is a bad habit of mine. In my family I was the only son with three sisters. They were all older, but I took on the role of protecting them when our father died. Sometimes I've been known to get carried away."

"Seems to me they're lucky to have someone looking out for them," Gabe said.

"Tell *them* that," Elliott replied, his expression rueful. "I don't get half the gratitude you might expect, especially from Adelia. She's the oldest and always thought *she* should be protecting *me.*"

"That whole dynamic is a mystery to me," Gabe admitted. "I was an only child."

"But you had cousins, right? I thought I heard you and Mitch are related. And there are other Franklins around town."

"Mitch and I are cousins, but we weren't that close growing up. I might as well tell you straight-out that I was the black sheep of the family and my mom was a pariah in

69

the family and around town. You won't hear a lot good said about either of us."

Elliott frowned at that. "Black sheep?" he repeated, worry back in his expression.

"Reformed," Gabe assured him. "I haven't gotten into a brawl in years. Haven't really needed to since my mom died and I stopped needing to stand up for her."

Unhappy with himself for revealing far more about his past than he was in the habit of doing, he held Elliott's gaze. "You've apologized. I've accepted. Anything else?"

Though Elliott looked faintly taken aback by his direct words, he didn't look away. "Just one more thing," he said. "I saw you at Rosalina's the other night. I saw the way you were looking at Adelia. Saw it again earlier today, in fact."

"Look, I don't know what you think you saw —"

Elliott smiled. "I *know* what I saw," he corrected. "I saw a man who's hungry for a woman. It's a look I recognize, so a word of warning. Don't start something with my sister that you have no intention of finishing. She's feeling overwhelmed and vulnerable these days. I don't want her hurt again."

"Not my intention, believe me," Gabe said, respecting the directness, even if it made him uncomfortable to be having this

70

conversation with a man he'd barely met. "I have plenty on my plate these days. I'm not looking for a fling and I'm certainly not in the market for anything more serious."

"If that's the case, then steer clear of Adelia," Elliott said. "That's the best way I know to avoid any misunderstandings."

Even though it was advice he'd already been telling himself to heed, Gabe took exception to being warned off. "Look, I respect the fact that you're only looking out for your sister, but she strikes me as a woman who's smart enough to know her own mind. I doubt she'd appreciate you running interference for her."

To his surprise, Elliott laughed at that. "No question about it," he conceded. "She'd be furious, so maybe it would be best if we kept this conversation just between us."

Gabe relaxed. Despite Elliott's tendency to come on too strong, he had to respect his intentions. "I can do that. No reason at all for us to be crossing paths except casually. I can't imagine the topic coming up."

Elliott looked relieved. He hesitated, then said, "I missed dinner at home to come by here. Since you've obviously been working late, I'm guessing you haven't eaten, either. Feel like grabbing a pizza at Rosalina's?"

Since he'd been planning to head over there anyway, Gabe saw no reason to refuse the overture. He figured the cross-examination and warnings were out of the way. It might be nice to have some guy talk instead of eating all alone. Eating with Elliott would sure as heck keep his thoughts from straying to Adelia, and that had to be a good thing.

"Sure," he said.

He finished locking up, then followed Elliott to the Italian restaurant. To ensure that the conversation stayed on less disquieting topics, he asked about Fit for Anything and Elliott's role there.

"I'm just one of the partners," Adelia's brother explained, describing the agreement he'd made with several of the men in town to run the place in exchange for a share. "I'm a personal trainer there and at The Corner Spa, too."

"Sounds like a demanding schedule," Gabe said.

Elliott nodded. "You have no idea, especially with two stepchildren and a new baby at home. Fortunately, I'm blessed with an understanding wife who has her own career. Karen's just been promoted to sous-chef at Sullivan's. Between her cooking and my mother's, believe me, I need to work out even harder than most of my clients do."

Gabe laughed. "If I keep existing on pizza, I'll need to add a few extra workouts into my routine, too. I tell myself I'd eat healthier if I were in my own place, but the Serenity Inn will have to do for now."

"That's where you're living?" Elliott asked, sounding shocked.

"I know its reputation as a place the locals go for trysts," Gabe said. He'd known all about that when he'd been a kid, thanks to his mom, who'd been a frequent visitor. "But it's clean and not too expensive."

"Are you planning to look for your own place?"

"Sooner or later," Gabe hedged. It all depended on how long it took for him to get antsy. The instant he sensed he might be starting to put down roots, it would be time to go. That was the pattern he'd established in a half-dozen other towns across the state. His motives for coming back to Serenity might be different, but there was no reason for that particular pattern to change.

"Well, if you decide you want to look at some houses or apartments, I know a couple of good Realtors. Mary Vaughn Lewis or her daughter can probably hook you up."

"Mary Vaughn's still around?" Gabe

asked, not sure why he was so surprised. She'd been just a little ahead of him in school. It had always seemed to him that she was ambitious enough to take off at the first opportunity. She'd had her own family demons to battle back then, though she'd handled them better than he had.

"Wait a second," he said. "Did you say Lewis? As in Sonny Lewis, the mayor's son? That's who she married?"

Elliott nodded. "They divorced, but they're back together now and have a new baby, a boy."

Gabe shook his head. The longer he stuck around, it seemed the more surprises awaited him. It was a little worrisome that he found that intriguing.

CHAPTER FOUR

Even though she desperately wanted a morning caffeine fix, Adelia found herself avoiding Sweet Things for the next few mornings, determined to steer clear of Gabe. Involving him in her drama with Selena was one thing. She'd had little choice about that. But the attraction that was starting to simmer, for her, anyway, was a little too disconcerting for a woman who'd declared herself to be single-mindedly independent for now. She wasn't ready to cede that stance. She might never be.

Her determination lasted quite nicely through the weekend. After a busy Saturday at the boutique, she devoted herself to spending time with the children on Sunday, finally caving in to Tomas's pleas to go to the usual family dinner at her mother's.

Just as she'd anticipated, it was awkward and tense from the moment they arrived. Her sisters scowled at her and looked relieved when she finally abandoned the kitchen in favor of going outside to watch the kids. Her brothers-in-law regarded her as if she were deliberately trying to shake up their orderly worlds. Only the determined cheerfulness of her mother, Elliott and Karen made the afternoon tolerable. None of the others would have dared to voice their opinions aloud in front of her mother especially. The risk of alienating the family matriarch was too great.

The children, thankfully, were unaware of most of the undercurrents as they ran boisterously through the house and played in the yard with their cousins. Watching them, she was almost able to believe life would eventually return to normal, or whatever the new normal might be.

By three, though, Adelia had had more than enough. She excused herself to go home and work on the list of repairs needed at her new house. Surrounded by welcome silence, she'd made good progress on her list by the time Elliott and Karen dropped the children off on their way home.

"I'm sorry about today. It won't always be like that," her brother reassured her, regarding her with worry. "Everyone will eventually get past this."

"And stop judging me?" she asked wryly.

Her annoyance kicked up a notch. "What right do they have? They know what Ernesto was doing. In fact, I suspect our sisters knew all along and never said a word."

Elliott frowned at that. "You can't really believe that. Why would they do such a thing? What about family loyalty?"

Adelia voiced her theory. "I'm very much afraid because they've been brainwashed to believe that sort of behavior is expected, just the price a woman has to pay for a certain lifestyle."

When her brother's expression immediately darkened, Adelia realized she'd revealed too much about her possibly unfounded suspicions. "Wipe that look right off your face," she ordered. "And don't go roaring over to their houses tossing around accusations. I don't know anything. I just have a feeling in my gut."

"Your gut feelings are usually right on the money," he said.

"Really? I never had a single one about Ernesto, not until the end when he grew careless."

"Only because you didn't want to believe he'd ever treat you that way," Elliott said. "Love sometimes makes people blind. Do you think that's the case with —"

Adelia cut him off and tried to stare him

77

down. "Promise me you're not going to get in the middle of this, not between me and them nor in their marriages," she commanded. "I mean it, Elliott. Our sisters are living their lives as they see fit. I just wish they'd show me the same courtesy."

He sighed deeply. "I hope you're wrong," he said.

"I hope so, too."

But she didn't think she was. Of all people, she knew only too well what it was like to live with delusions just to keep the peace and hold on to a familiar lifestyle.

Adelia was well aware of Mitch's habit of starting his day in his wife's bakery. She also knew she couldn't avoid the place forever, even if steering clear was the best way to give Gabe a wide berth. From the moment the bakery had opened, she'd gotten into the habit of pausing to share a cup of coffee with Mitch and Lynn before heading next door to the boutique. They'd probably make way too much of it if she stayed away too long, especially after Gabe and Mitch had pitched in to help with the search for Selena. The last thing she wanted was for any of them to think she was ungrateful.

But even as she'd reminded herself of that, she let another week pass before she mustered up the courage to return to her old routine. She had work to discuss with Mitch, she reminded herself. That alone was the perfect excuse, if she needed one, to stop by the bakery.

She'd stayed up late the night before fine-tuning the list of projects needed to fix up the house. She needed to get cost estimates and then prioritize those that were essential and those that could wait. The list was a whole lot longer than she'd anticipated. It seemed that history and architectural character came with a host of problems.

Thankfully, when Raylene had promoted her to manager of the boutique she'd given her a nice raise to go along with it. That extra money would allow her to do at least some of these improvements without dipping into her nest egg from the divorce. Adelia was still a little shocked by her promotion. Sure, she'd gotten a business degree in college, but for years the only "jobs" she'd held outside her home had been on the numerous school committees she'd chaired. Raylene had taken a chance on her, and she claimed she'd more than proved herself. Adelia seemed to have an innate sense of fashion and an ability to help customers make choices that flattered them. Sales had skyrocketed in the months after she was first hired.

"To be honest, I'm a little nervous about how I'll handle the whole parenthood thing," Raylene had claimed after the first trimester of her pregnancy when she'd offered Adelia the promotion.

"But you've been raising Carter's sisters with him, practically since their parents died in the car crash," Adelia had protested. "You've been great with them and they adore you."

"They're teenagers," Raylene had replied, as if that had made her role easier. "I have no idea what to expect with a baby. You're practically running this place for me already, so you deserve the title and the raise that goes with it. You'll still get your commission, too, since you're the best saleswoman I've ever seen. All those lookers who used to leave without buying now can't get out the door without being loaded down with bags."

Adelia had hardly been in a position to turn her down, even though the responsibility had been a little terrifying. Now she was more than grateful for yet another chance to prove to Raylene, but even more importantly to herself, just how capable she was.

It was ironic, really, she thought on her walk into downtown bright and early on

Saturday morning. She was a mature woman with an increasingly responsible job. She had a head full of ideas to prove that Raylene's faith in her hadn't been misplaced. She was a good mother, at least according to most assessments. If those things were true, how ridiculous was it that she was scared of a man she'd just met simply because she found him attractive?

Mitch was attractive, for heaven's sake, and he didn't scare her. Neither did any of the other men she knew in Serenity.

Because they were all safely married, she concluded with a sigh. Gabe, it appeared, was not.

Outside Sweet Things, she sucked in a deep breath and wiped her sweaty palms on a tissue. Today was as good a day as any to get back into her preferred routine. That it was a Saturday, a day she was less likely to encounter Gabe, was *not* the reason for her sudden bravery, she assured herself.

As she entered the bakery, she reminded herself that she was here to have a business discussion with a man she'd known for years. Mitch wasn't the terrifying Franklin, after all. That was Gabe, and he frightened her only because of how easily he disconcerted her.

After the pep talk she'd been giving

herself, she was actually stunned and a little disappointed to find Mitch all alone at his usual table, sipping a cup of coffee and studying a blueprint. He glanced up and smiled.

"There you are. Lynn and I have been wondering where you've been. You've been MIA for a while now."

"Just getting settled in the new house," she claimed. "I'm glad you're here, though." She reached in her purse and withdrew several yellow sheets torn from a legal pad. "I have a list of renovation projects I wanted to discuss with you, that is, if you're not too swamped with your Main Street redevelopment these days."

"I'm never too swamped to tackle a job for a friend," he said. "Have a seat. I'll get you some coffee. Lynn's in the back cussing away at some pie dough or something. The woman may make the best pastry in two states on a bad day, but she's a perfectionist."

"Ah, but that's why she has such an incredible reputation," Adelia said, joining him at the table, which had been covered with a blue-checked cloth. He'd pushed aside a Mason jar filled with fresh daisies that added a cheerful, homey touch. "This place has been a success since the day she opened. Thank goodness, Raylene and all those Sweet Magnolias ganged up on her and convinced her this was something she could do."

Mitch laughed as he poured her a cup of coffee. "They're a sneaky bunch, all right."

Adelia regarded him with amusement. "You did your own share of fast-talking, the way I understand it. Isn't that how you wound up buying up all these vacant storefronts with Raylene? Wasn't this downtown revitalization actually part of your plot to lure Lynn into opening a bakery and becoming a tenant?" She laughed at his guilty expression. "Just as I thought."

"It was a sound business decision," Mitch declared, setting the coffee in front of her. "That's my story and I'm sticking to it."

Just then the door opened and Gabe walked in. He was halfway through apologizing to Mitch for his tardiness when he noticed Adelia. A smile broke across his face, one that revealed dimples. They only added to his allure as a bit of a scoundrel.

"Hey, darlin'. Where have you been hiding?" he asked her.

Adelia blushed, flustered not only by his teasing, but because he'd taken note of her absence. "I've been right next door," she told him. "Every day, same as usual."

Mitch apparently noticed her reaction because he stepped in. "Adelia just bought one of those old houses in Swan Point," he told Gabe.

"I saw it," Gabe reminded him. "When we were looking for her daughter."

"Of course," Mitch said. "I doubt you had much of a chance to take a look around that day. She's brought me a list of a few things she wants to have done."

Gabe caught sight of the pages of notes and sketches and chuckled. "From the looks of that list, you sure you wouldn't be better off tearing it down and starting over? It might be cheaper."

"But then it wouldn't have any character," she protested defensively. "I love the house. It just has a few age-related flaws, the same as most people." She studied him with narrowed eyes. "Or are you one of those who thinks anything past a certain age should be tossed away?"

Gabe held up both hands. "Hey, that was a comment based on financial considerations, not age."

His glance skimmed over her, deliberately lingering until she flushed. "Some things improve with age," he commented appreciatively.

Adelia wished she could grab her coffee

and run, but she knew that would be far too revealing. She concluded the really courageous thing to do would be to stay put. She took a sip of coffee, instead, to steady her nerves.

"Let me see," Gabe said, taking her list from his cousin. He got to page two and frowned. "Didn't you have the roof inspected?"

"Of course I did," she said impatiently.

"And you knew it was leaking?"

"Yes, and I got a very nice credit for that, thank you very much. Now, though, I need to get it repaired. I've run out of pots and pans to put under the leaks." She turned to Mitch. "That probably should be at the top of the list."

"No doubt about it," Mitch agreed, then unexpectedly stood up. "Gabe, you can handle this, right? I want to check on those reinforcing beams going in down the block."

Adelia stared at him. "But I thought you'd be doing this," she said, then winced. "Sorry, Gabe. No offense."

He grinned, clearly aware of exactly why she looked so rattled. "None taken."

Mitch gave her shoulder a squeeze. "You're in good hands. Gabe has plenty of experience, some of it in historic renovations, as a matter of fact. He knows what he's doing, probably even better than I do. If you have any questions after he gives you an estimate, we'll talk about them. How's that?"

"Fine," she said, though she couldn't seem to hide her reluctance.

After Mitch had gone, she glanced warily toward Gabe. He was leaning back in his seat, the chair on two legs. His own denim-clad legs were stretched out in front of him. While the posture was relaxed, she sensed a coiled tension just beneath the surface.

"If you're not okay with this, just say the word," he said quietly.

"Of course I'm okay with it," she said irritably. "Mitch says you're more than qualified and I trust his judgment."

A wicked gleam sparked in his eyes. "Then it's me personally you're not so sure about. I promise you I'm harmless."

Adelia didn't believe that for a single second, not with her heart pounding like a jackhammer. But maybe that was her problem, not his. It wasn't as if he'd made a blatant pass at her. And despite her impression that he was single, maybe she'd been wrong about that. Maybe he was happily married. Married would be good.

"Are you married, Gabe?"

As if he'd followed her train of thought,

he laughed. "Nope. Free as a bird. You?"

"Divorced," she admitted. "*Recently* divorced."

"As in not interested in taking another chance on love anytime soon," he concluded. "Duly warned."

Though his tone was solemn, the wicked spark in his eyes was anything but reassuring. He was going to be trouble, she concluded with a sigh. No question about it.

"How'd things go with Adelia this morning?" Mitch asked Gabe at the end of the day.

"I make her nervous," Gabe admitted.

Mitch frowned at that. "How so?"

"She's a beautiful woman. I can't seem to stop myself from a little harmless flirting. I get the impression she's not used to that."

"She's just getting out of a bad marriage," Mitch told him.

"So I've heard. The guy was a cheater. I imagine that left her with some issues."

"The cheating was certainly bad enough," Mitch confirmed. "But he paraded his mistresses openly around town. The last one lived right in his neighborhood. Even his daughter knew about her. I think that's what nobody in town will ever be able to excuse, the way he disrespected Adelia so openly in front of one of his kids."

Gabe frowned at that. "You've got to be kidding me. What kind of lowlife does something like that?"

"Ernesto apparently thought his marriage vows only extended to providing well for his family, not to fidelity. The way I hear it, he thought he was entitled to play around, that it was part of the deal in exchange for the nice house and lots of spending money."

"That explains why she's now living in a house with a leaking roof," Gabe guessed.

"More than likely. She's a smart woman. She's just discovering that she can make it on her own. Independence is real important to her right now." His expression turned thoughtful. "She reminds me of Lynn in that way. I wanted to rush in about a million times to make things easier for her while she was divorcing Ed Morrow, but she needed to figure things out for herself, to prove that she was strong enough to do right by her kids. Much as it killed me to sit idly by while she struggled, letting her get back on her feet on her own was the right thing to do. She didn't need a knight in shining armor. She needed a partner, someone who'd treat her like a woman with a lot to offer."

"I suppose you think that's the strategy for winning Adelia, too," Gabe said.

Mitch leveled a long look at him. "Do you need a strategy?"

Gabe thought about the question. It was fraught with all sorts of implications. "No way," he said candidly. "I only came here with the intention of getting back on my feet, maybe making amends."

Mitch frowned. "You did nothing wrong, Gabe. You don't owe anybody in this town a thing."

"But my mother was a piece of work. In my zeal to defend her, I made my share of mistakes."

"Okay, let's say you make amends. Then what?"

Gabe hesitated, pondering the question, then shrugged. "I'll probably move on. I can't see myself putting down roots, here or any place else."

"Then a word of advice. Be careful with Adelia, my friend. We all recognize how strong she is, but she doesn't see it just yet. Give her time to get there and don't do anything that might lead her to believe you're staying. And if you think that word of warning is coming just from me, think again. You ever heard of the Sweet Magnolias?"

Gabe shook his head. "Who are they?"

"It's not an official organization or anything, but a lot of the women in town have formed this deep bond. They look out for each other, and heaven help anyone who messes with them. You probably remember Maddie Maddox?"

"Doesn't sound familiar."

"She would have been Maddie Vreeland in school. Then she married and became a Townsend. When that ended in divorce, she married the high school baseball coach. Anyway, she, Dana Sue Sullivan and Helen Decatur-Whitney started calling themselves Sweet Magnolias way back in high school."

Gabe held up a hand. "Slow down." He described the three women who'd been entering the bakery as he'd fled to get away from Lynn's teasing on the afternoon Selena had gone missing.

"They're the women who started it," Mitch confirmed. "Over the years, they've included a bunch of other women, Lynn among them. I'm not sure what they do beyond the occasional margarita night get-together, but they sure do stick up for one another. I wouldn't want to tangle with them or get their backs up, that's for sure. I'm not sure I'd be married to Lynn right now if they'd objected to it."

Mitch grinned. "Fortunately, Maddie, Helen and Dana Sue and I go way back. They jumped on my side. In addition to any wooing I did, Lynn got the full-court press from the Sweet Magnolias, too." His expression sobered. "I'm just saying, if you do anything to hurt Adelia, they'll be all over you. I have a hunch her recovery's going to be their next project."

The advice was perfectly reasonable, but Gabe took offense just the same. "Whatever my flaws might be, Mitch, they don't include a trail of brokenhearted women. Listening to my mom cry her eyes out at night taught me to be honest and never offer something I don't intend to deliver."

His cousin nodded. "Good to know." A grin spread across his face. "Something tells me, though, that battling wits with you could be just what Adelia needs to get her confidence back."

Gabe waved those yellow pages in his cousin's face. "So, I was right. Despite all those warnings you just uttered, you do have some crazy idea about pushing the two of us together for more than fixing up that house of hers."

Mitch shrugged, his expression innocent. "The work needs to be done. You're good at what you do. If a few sparks fly in the process, all the better." He gave Gabe an amused look. "For both of you. Just keep in mind those boundaries I warned you about."

Gabe scowled at his cousin, suddenly wondering if coming back to Serenity had been as smart a move as he'd once thought it was. "I'm not likely to forget."

Chic closed promptly at six on Saturday, though it was usually closer to seven by the time Adelia wrapped up all the chores she felt were necessary before locking up for the night. When she stepped outside, she was stunned to find Gabe leaning casually against the building. He straightened at the sight of her.

Adelia regarded him with confusion. "Were you waiting for me?"

He grinned. "What was your first clue? You know any other pretty women in the neighborhood?"

"Gabe!" she protested. "You have to stop doing that."

"Doing what?"

What was he doing exactly, other than rattling her, that is? Was he flirting? It had been so long since any man had teased and flattered her, she couldn't be entirely sure.

"Saying things like that," she told him

finally, then started striding down the block with the crazy idea that she might be able to shake him if she walked away quickly enough.

He easily fell into step beside her. "Hasn't anybody ever told you how beautiful you are?" he inquired curiously.

"Not in a long time," she admitted wistfully before she could stop herself.

He stared at her incredulously. "Then the men of Serenity are idiots," he declared.

She smiled at his vehemence. "Or maybe they just had good instincts for self-preservation," she suggested. "Until recently I was married, remember?"

"So compliments were reserved for your husband?"

"Something like that."

"And did he lavish you with a lot of them?"

She frowned. She had a hunch he already knew the answer to that. "We're divorced. What do you think?"

"Then I get to lump him in with all the other idiots," he said.

Adelia stopped in her tracks and turned to face him. "Gabe, why were you waiting for me? And why are you walking home with me? If we were sixteen, I'd say you were angling to carry my schoolbooks."

93

He laughed at that. "If I'd known you back then, I probably would have been." He pulled the now-rumpled yellow pages from his back pocket. "I thought I could look over these projects of yours and try to get a handle on what needs doing first."

For a few minutes, Adelia had forgotten all about the renovations and his assignment to take them on.

Gabe was studying her with unmistakable amusement. "Did you forget about these?"

"Temporary lapse," she assured him.

"Is this a bad time? If you have a date or something . . ." His voice trailed off as he studied her speculatively.

"No date," she responded tersely. "And this is as good a time as any. I should warn you, though, that my mother's at the house with the kids. That might ensure that you'll get an invitation to a good meal, but it will also come with a lengthy interrogation."

"I made it through your brother's. I imagine I can handle whatever your mother asks."

Adelia regarded him with alarm. "Elliott interrogated you? When?"

"On the day we were looking for Selena. He came by the construction site that evening. He told me he was there to apologize for the way he'd reacted when we stopped by the gym, but it was evident he wanted to clarify a few things for me."

"Such as?"

"My intentions. His concerns. That sort of protective guy stuff."

Adelia groaned. "He didn't! I may have to kill him. He had no business getting in your face like that."

"Oh, he thought he was being subtle about it, but men are rarely as subtle as they'd like to think when they're warning people off. I got the message." He shrugged. "Then we went out for pizza."

"Men!" she said, shaking her head.

"He just wanted me to know you have someone looking out for you. I don't imagine he realizes he's not the only one."

"Who else?" she asked before she could stop herself.

"Mitch chimed in just a couple of hours ago. He also said there's some group of women in town, the Sweet Magnolias I think he called them. He said they'd have my hide if I hurt you."

Adelia actually laughed at that. Though she wasn't an actual member of that unofficial group of women, she certainly knew them all. She also knew their reputation for protecting their own with a ferocity that was a little terrifying to any rational man in town.

"And yet here you are," she said. "Risking life and limb by walking through town with me."

"Darlin', there are some things worth taking an occasional risk for," he said.

Then he very deliberately added a wink that rocked her nice, safe world. Adelia actually thought her heart might have come to a complete standstill for a few seconds.

And that, she concluded, should be sufficient warning to send her right back to where her day had started, knowing that she needed to avoid this man at all costs.

CHAPTER FIVE

Gabe got one whiff of the aromas coming from Adelia's kitchen and decided that any interrogation that might lie ahead would be well worth it, as long as he was invited to stick around for dinner. Adelia must have noticed that he was practically drooling, because she chuckled.

"Let me put you out of your misery," she said. "Would you like to join us for dinner?"

"Yes," he said so quickly that it immediately brought a deepening smile to her lips.

"You haven't even met my mother yet," she reminded him. "Are you sure?"

"Not a doubt in my mind."

"Either you're sick of pizza or you're a very brave man."

Gabe laughed. "Probably a little of both with some curiosity thrown in."

"Curiosity?"

He nodded. "I find myself wanting to meet the woman who can fill this house with such incredible aromas and yet make grown men cower. That's an impressive combination. It'll be interesting to discover if you two are anything alike."

Just then the very woman in question, diminutive in size but with the regal bearing of a matriarch used to respect, came out of the kitchen.

"I thought I heard voices," she said, regarding Gabe speculatively. "I don't believe we've met."

"Mother, I'd like you to meet Gabe Franklin," Adelia said.

Mrs. Cruz's eyes narrowed. "I believe my son has mentioned you."

"Uh-oh," Adelia murmured under her breath.

"He probably has," Gabe said easily. "Elliott and I had dinner just the other night."

Mrs. Cruz's eyes lit with amusement at his interpretation of the encounter. "I hardly think my son's choice of a dinner companion would have stuck in my mind. I believe it was his comment that we needed to keep an eye on you around Adelia. Do we?"

"Mother!" Adelia said, blushing furiously. She turned to him. "I warned you. There's still time to make a run for it."

"Not a chance," he replied. Since Mrs.

Cruz didn't seem to harbor any particular biases toward him, Gabe figured he'd passed some sort of test with Elliott, if not yet with her. He was eager to see how the evening might play out. He couldn't help it. Challenges always caught his interest.

"Gabe is here to check out the work I want to have done on the house," Adelia explained quickly. "I've invited him to join us for dinner."

"If it's not an imposition," Gabe told the older woman, drawing on manners he'd picked up from watching the way civilized people behaved, rather than any examples that had been set in his home.

"It's not an imposition at all," Mrs. Cruz said. "I have a large family. I cook accordingly. There's always more than enough for company. Dinner will be ready in a half hour, if that will give you time to look around at the renovations my daughter has in mind."

"Absolutely," Gabe said, relieved to have passed the initial screening at least.

Somehow, though, he wouldn't be one bit surprised to find Elliott and heaven knew how many other members of the Cruz family joining them at the table.

Adelia took one look at her mother's face

99

and decided that giving Gabe a personal tour to go over her notes would be preferable to the cross-examination she was likely to receive if she joined her mother in the kitchen, even long enough to apologize for bringing home a last-minute guest. She realized there was a certain irony in the fact that she was more intimidated by the thought of answering her mother's penetrating questions than Gabe was. Of course, she'd had experience that he didn't share.

"Let's start outside," she suggested to Gabe. "I think I saw a ladder in the shed, if you want to check out the roof. Mother, you don't need my help, do you?"

Her mother gave her a knowing look. "Of course not. The girls are helping. It's time they learned their way around a kitchen. I left Selena stirring the sauce for the enchiladas. Knowing how distracted she gets by those text messages she receives every couple of minutes, I'd better check on it before it burns."

Adelia frowned. "She's not supposed to be using her cell phone these days."

Her mother looked startled. "I see. She didn't mention that."

"I'd better go in there and deal with this," Adelia said.

Her mother waved her off. "I can handle it."

"Thanks," Adelia said, relieved not to have to force yet another confrontation with her daughter or get caught in her mother's crosshairs.

Adelia avoided Gabe's gaze as she led the way to the backyard. When she finally risked a glance, she found his eyes sparkling with barely concealed mirth.

"When did I become the lesser of two evils?" he asked.

"In the past five minutes," she said, not even trying to pretend he hadn't hit the target with his observation. "If I'd had any idea she and Elliott had been chatting about you and me, you wouldn't have gotten within a hundred yards of this place while she was here. I don't need the aggravation."

A smile spread across his face. "You're scared of your mother," he taunted.

"Terrified," Adelia admitted, seeing little reason to deny it. "Why do you find that so amusing?"

"Because you're a pretty formidable presence in your own right."

"Formidable? Me?" she said, laughing. "Hardly. As you just heard, not even my own daughter takes my rules seriously."

"Maybe you need to see yourself from

where I'm standing," Gabe said, his expression turning serious. "Seems to me you could hold your own with anybody, even Selena. She's just testing the limits."

Adelia wished she could see herself that way. After years of Ernesto's criticism and neglect, she had a very low opinion of her own worth. She was determined to get past that, but she wasn't there yet.

"So, what is it about your mother that intimidates you?" Gabe asked.

Adelia gave the question a moment's thought before responding. "She has some very rigid and old-fashioned ideas about the role of women, the sanctity of marriage and in general about the relationships between men and women. I've been a disappointment."

He looked skeptical. "I didn't hear even a hint of judgment in her voice, just concern."

"You haven't had the practice I've had at reading between the lines," Adelia told him. "It's ironic really, because on many levels, I don't even disagree with her."

"So you're an old-fashioned woman at heart?"

She considered the label. It actually fit better than she'd realized. She might chafe at it, but she'd done nothing in her life that would indicate she'd broken that particular mold. Until very recently she hadn't even been sure she wanted to. It was only lately that she'd come to appreciate the value of independence and self-sufficiency.

"In some ways, I suppose I am old-fashioned," she said. "I liked being a stay-at-home mom and wife. I thought marriage vows meant forever." She shrugged. "I've just come to accept that some marriages can't be saved."

She shuddered at the memory of the day she'd broken the news of her intention to divorce Ernesto. "You have no idea how much courage it took for me to tell my devoutly Catholic mother that I was leaving my husband. That brought on a huge family intervention that entailed quite a bit of yelling and a host of recriminations about how I'd failed the test as a dutiful wife."

Gabe regarded her with surprise. "She disapproved, even under the circumstances?"

"At first I was too humiliated to admit the reason, so she vehemently disapproved. When I was finally persuaded to tell her everything, it took some adjustment on her part, but she actually turned out to be surprisingly supportive."

"And the rest of the family?"

"Elliott and his wife have been incredible,"

she said. "The others, not so much." She held up a hand. "Could we drop this? It's more than you ever really wanted or needed to know about my personal life, I'm sure."

Gabe looked as if he wanted to argue about that, but he nodded and gestured toward the shed. "The ladder's in there? Is it locked?"

"No, it's open."

She took a deep breath and fought for composure while he got the extension ladder and put it against the side of the house. No sooner had he started up to the roof, than Tomas spotted him and came running across the yard.

"Who's that?" he asked, staring after Gabe. "Can I go up on the roof with him?"

He already had one foot on the bottom rung when Adelia clamped a hand on his shoulder. "Not now," she said firmly. "Let Gabe do his job."

Tomas stared up at the roof, his disappointment plain. "But what's he doing?"

"Looking to see what kind of shape the roof is in and what it will take to fix it," she said.

Tomas frowned. "Do we know him?"

"I do," she said. "You remember Mitch Franklin?"

"The man who's fixing all those stores on

Main Street," Tomas said. "He's married to the cupcake lady."

Adelia smiled at the characterization. Clearly baking cupcakes was more memorable to Tomas than Lynn's name. "Exactly. Gabe is his cousin. He works for Mitch."

"Is he gonna do anything else here?" he asked, his curious gaze still fixed on Gabe, who was scrambling over the steep roof with the agility of a mountain goat.

"Lots of things," Adelia said. "He or the people who work for him are going to do all those things on that list we made."

"Like paint my room?"

She smiled at his sudden eagerness. "That's definitely on the list," she agreed.

"Will he let me help? Mitch let Jeremy help when he was working at Raylene's."

"I'm sure he'll try to find some things you can do," Adelia said, hoping that would be the case. She was sure Tomas would start to feel better about this new home if he had even a tiny role to play in making the necessary improvements. "You have to promise, though, to do exactly what Gabe or any of the other professionals tell you to do and never to do anything involving tools without supervision."

"Promise," Tomas said, his attention already wandering as he saw Gabe descend-

ing the ladder. He scampered over to wait
for him.

"Hi," he said, startling Gabe so badly he
almost missed his footing. "I'm Tomas."

Gabe steadied himself, then held out a
hand. "I'm Gabe," he said. "Are you the
man of the house?"

Tomas looked surprised by the question,
but Adelia saw his chest swell just a little as
he realized that was exactly what he was.
"Since my dad's not here, I am."

"Then I'll be sure to talk things over with
you when I start working around here,"
Gabe promised him, winking at Adelia over
his head.

"I don't imagine he'll give you much
choice," she told Gabe. "Tomas wants to be
part of your crew, that is, if you can find
anything for him to do that isn't too dangerous."

"Mom! I'm not a baby," her son protested.

"Of course not," Gabe was quick to say.
"But you are inexperienced, or am I wrong
about that? Have you built a house before?"

Tomas giggled. "No."

Gabe nodded solemnly. "Then in that
case, you'll learn on the job."

"I can do that," her son said with enthusiasm. "I'm a quick learner. I get really good
grades in school and I hardly have to study

at all." He made a face. "Except spelling. I'm bad at spelling."

"We've all struggled with that on occasion," Gabe said.

Tomas looked surprised. "Even you?"

"Even me," Gabe said. "Why don't you show me these things that are on your mom's list? This is man's work, after all."

Adelia might have taken offense at that if Tomas hadn't looked so excited at being included among the men on this particular job.

Smiling, she said, "I'll leave you to it, then. Make sure you're in the dining room for dinner in fifteen minutes," she told them both. "*Abuela* doesn't like dinner getting cold."

Tomas nodded at once, then confided to Gabe. "*Abuela* makes the best food ever!"

"I'll bet she does," Gabe said. "I'm looking forward to it." He glanced at the list, found the next item — painting the bedrooms — and suggested that Tomas lead the way.

As they went into the house, she heard her son chattering away, sounding happier than she'd heard him in weeks.

Left with no other alternative, she went into the kitchen and found all three of her girls dealing with various assignments while her mother watched over them. Natalia was putting rice into a bowl almost as big as she was. Juanita, her tongue caught between her teeth and a frown of concentration on her forehead, was carefully pouring steaming, fragrant black beans into another bowl.

"Sounds to me as if you just made Tomas's day," her mother said, regarding her approvingly. "What do you know about this man? Is he a good role model?"

"I can't really say," Adelia admitted. "But he was very kind to Tomas just now. If he hadn't been, if he'd shown any hint of impatience, I wouldn't have left them alone."

"And is he equally kind to you?" her mother asked quietly, the question spoken low enough that she wouldn't be heard over the girls' squabbling.

"He doesn't need to be kind to me. He just needs to get the work done," Adelia replied.

"I spoke to your brother just now and mentioned that Gabe was here."

"Thanks for that," Adelia said dryly. She should probably expect a visit or call from her protective brother no later than tomorrow.

Her mother ignored the hint of sarcasm in her voice and told her, "Elliott still seems to think there might be more to his interest than any work he might do around here."

"My brother has stars in his eyes these days," Adelia said in a tone that made light of Elliott's opinion. "Karen has made him very happy with their life as a family."

"One thing has nothing to do with the other," her mother insisted. "He's concerned for your happiness. We all are."

"I'm happier than I have been in years," Adelia said. Even as the words tumbled out just to divert unwanted attention, she realized they were actually true. Her life might not be perfect, but it was a whole lot better than the lie she'd been forced to live with Ernesto. Better yet, her happiness was within herself and not tied to any man.

Gabe couldn't ever recall having a meal that came with quite as much commotion as the one he was sharing with Adelia and her family. The good news was that it was impossible for them to share a single private word. That was the bad news, as well.

Still, he liked seeing her up close like this with her family. Her daughters, well, the younger two, anyway, had plenty to say, talking over each other in an attempt to get not only their mother's attention, but his. To do that, though, they had to compete with

Tomas, who'd managed to sit beside Gabe and asked more questions than Alex Trebek in a year's worth of *Jeopardy* episodes. Gabe noted that Adelia seemed amused and showed not the slightest inclination to rescue him.

Mrs. Cruz, however, did chime in from time to time to remind her grandson to give Mr. Franklin time to breathe.

Tomas regarded her blankly. "He is breathing," he said, looking puzzled. "Wouldn't he die if he wasn't?"

Adelia laughed, and the light sound echoed in the room in a way that drew the attention of even Selena, who looked as if she hadn't heard that laugh in a while. The teen stared at her mother with evident surprise, then turned a scowl on Gabe, as if she didn't like him being even indirectly responsible for her mom's brighter mood.

Selena started to push back from the table, but at a pointed glance from her grandmother, she hesitated. "May I be excused?" she asked.

Adelia frowned at the request. "You haven't finished your meal."

"I'm not hungry. Please."

"Let her go," Mrs. Cruz said.

After Selena had run upstairs, Adelia turned to her mother. "Any idea what that

110

was about?"

Mrs. Cruz looked in his direction. "I have some idea."

As her implication registered, shock settled on Adelia's face. "But there's nothing . . ." She regarded him with dismay. "Gabe, I'm sorry."

"Maybe I should go," he said, not wanting to be the cause of dissension between Adelia and her daughter, even inadvertently. Maybe it was time for him to go, anyway. He'd been enjoying the whole meal — and the company — a little too much. It would be easy to get comfortable here, a little too alluring to experience how real families interacted. With his cousin's recent warning still echoing in his head, he knew what a bad idea that would be.

"Not before you've had dessert," Mrs. Cruz said adamantly.

"*Abuela* made flan," Natalia said excitedly. "She hardly ever makes it anymore. It's the best. And she let us help."

Gabe could see how proud she was of herself. "Do you think it'll be as good as if she made it herself?" he teased.

"It'll be even better," Juanita said firmly. "We made it with love."

Gabe had to hide his desire to chuckle at her repetition of something she'd obviously heard often.

"And do you think I haven't always made it with love?" Mrs. Cruz inquired with feigned indignation.

"Uh-oh," Adelia said. "Do you think you might have hurt your grandmother's feelings?"

Juanita studied her grandmother closely, then shook her head. "No, she's just teasing," she declared.

"I think so, too," Natalia chimed in.

Gabe laughed at their solemn expressions. "Then I think I definitely have to try this flan you've made with such love," he said. He turned to Adelia with what he hoped was a believably quizzical expression, then whispered, "What is flan?"

Mrs. Cruz and Adelia both chuckled at the question. Even the girls giggled.

"Girls, clear the table and let *Abuela* bring in the flan, so Mr. Franklin can find out for himself why it's your favorite dessert," Adelia said. "The best way to learn about flan is to experience it."

Tomas pulled on Gabe's sleeve until he leaned down.

"It's like custard with caramel," Tomas confided. "You're gonna love it."

"I'll bet you're right," Gabe said, glancing across the table at Adelia. "There's been

112

nothing about this meal so far that I haven't loved."

And that just about scared him to death.

It was late on Monday afternoon before Gabe had time to sit down with Mitch and go over his estimates for the work Adelia wanted done. There'd been one crisis after another all day long on the Main Street job. Add in his cousin's distraction thanks to some other job he was handling across town and they hadn't exchanged more than a couple of words all day.

He was sitting at his makeshift desk on the construction site when Mitch wandered in after six.

"You look beat," Gabe said, frowning. "Why don't you go on home? This can wait."

"I need to unwind a little before I head home," Mitch said. "Going over those figures with you should do the trick."

"Are you sure? I don't want your wife on my case for making you late for dinner."

"It'll be at least another hour before we eat. Lynn's gotten in the habit of taking a nap once she closes the bakery and gets home. Being up at the crack of dawn is wearing on her more than she wants to admit." He managed a weary grin. "She

113

doesn't think I know about the naps, but I've caught her a time or two."

"She doesn't know that?"

Mitch shook his head. "I slip right back out the door. She wants to believe it's her little secret. If I say something, then we'll wind up fighting over whether the bakery's too much for her or when she needs to think about hiring some help. It's her business and her decision. Anything I say is bound to come off as interference."

Gabe regarded his cousin with surprise. "How'd you learn so much about women? It's not as if you dated a ton of them. You went from that secret crush you had on Lynn in high school —"

"It can't have been much of a secret if you knew about it," Mitch grumbled.

"Please, you started wearing your heart on your sleeve in junior high," Gabe said. "Then you married Amy. Where did all this profound knowledge of yours come from?"

Mitch laughed. "Observation and self-preservation. Any man intent on staying married has to figure out all the clues to keeping his wife happy. Unfortunately, a whole lot of them are left unsaid. It complicates things."

Gabe could believe that. He'd failed to understand a whole lot of women over the

114

years. He'd never had the will to work on getting it right with a single one of them. He had a feeling Adelia could be an exception.

Mitch beckoned for Gabe's notes on Adelia's renovations. "Looks as if you've got everything covered," he said.

"Except labor," Gabe pointed out. "I didn't know if you were figuring on bringing in one of your crews, assigning a single guy for most of it or what?"

"It'll be cheaper if it's done by one person," Mitch said.

"But it'll take longer," Gabe replied.

"Has she said anything about being in a hurry?"

"No, but people usually are," Gabe said.

"Maybe that's something you should discuss with her before we finalize this," Mitch said, then gave him an innocent look. "Of course, with the exception of the roof, a lot of this could be handled in your spare time. Not that you wouldn't get paid," he added hurriedly. "I'm just saying, it might be a project you wouldn't mind tackling."

Gabe knew exactly what Mitch was up to. "Don't you think I have my hands full keeping up with this Main Street project?"

"Sure you do," Mitch said at once. "Especially since I've seen the way you throw yourself into your work. I'm just saying that this primary job doesn't have the same perks."

"Perks?"

"Adelia," Mitch said, unsuccessfully fighting a smile. "Meals with the family."

Gabe stared at him incredulously. "How did you know about my staying for dinner the other night?"

"Tomas told Jeremy all about it," Mitch said, laughing.

"Who knew little boys could spread gossip that fast," Gabe complained. "I thought that particular trait was reserved for the adults in town."

"Tomas already has a bad case of hero worship," Mitch said. "I remember what that was like. Jeremy followed me around more than once when I was working at Raylene's. Boys their age need role models, Gabe. Even ignoring the way he treated Adelia, I doubt Ernesto Hernandez was much of one."

Gabe had the same impression. Tomas was a little too hungry for someone to teach him guy stuff.

"I'm not sure I'm cut out for the role," Gabe said.

"Sure, you are. If you weren't, Tomas wouldn't have been telling Jeremy all about you. Obviously you handled the situation just right."

"Sure, I answered his questions. I taught him a couple of basic things, but that's not the same as being a role model for an impressionable kid," Gabe argued. "Heck, even some of the jerks my mom dated were nice to me when they thought they had something to gain from it. That doesn't mean I should have aspired to be like a single one of them."

"Definitely not," Mitch agreed readily. "But you learned from that, Gabe. You'll try real hard to be a good influence on Tomas."

"Why do I have the feeling that you think the kid's going to be as much of an influence on me as I am on him? Do you think I'll stay on the straight and narrow because of him?"

Mitch frowned at that. "To my way of thinking, you've never been that far off the straight and narrow in anyone's mind but your own, but, yes, I think you'll be good for each other. I think you need to start to see yourself as more than a rolling stone. You seem to have this crazy idea that you don't deserve to find real happiness, the kind that can last."

Gabe couldn't deny that Mitch had nailed it. He'd never seen himself as a good bet for happily-ever-after. The only examples he'd had — Mitch's side of the family — had certainly never given him much reason to believe in himself.

"And Adelia? How do you see her fitting in?" he asked his cousin.

Mitch gave him a considering look before saying, "Any way you want her to, I imagine."

Unfortunately, the way Gabe envisioned her fitting into his life had a little too much to do with toppling into his bed than it did with the straight and narrow.

CHAPTER SIX

For some reason it seemed as if every woman in Serenity had chosen today to shop at the boutique. Many of the women were contacts Adelia had made through her school committees. They'd come to rely on her fashion sense, more than doubling the boutique's business since she'd started working there.

Adelia closed the register after the last sale just past lunchtime and drew in a satisfied breath. She was exhausted, but it had been an excellent morning. Raylene was going to be over the moon when she saw the receipts.

Of course, today all those sales had come with a surprising number of questions about Gabe Franklin. Apparently word had already spread that Adelia had the inside scoop on the sexy construction guy who'd just returned to town. Since most of the women asking questions were married, she was a little surprised by the level of curiosity.

She'd managed to skirt the most intrusive questions by diverting attention to a new line of accessories and liberally tossing around compliments about the way the outfits being tried on fit perfectly or suited the customer's coloring. Because she'd developed a knack for sincere flattery and a reputation for her own personal style, which she'd always achieved on a budget, her tactics mostly worked.

"Nice job," Raylene said, startling her by emerging from the office in back.

"How long have you been here?" Adelia asked.

Raylene grinned. "Long enough to realize you could qualify for work at the State Department with those diplomatic skills you possess."

Adelia laughed. "I was dancing as fast as I knew how. Who knew that even the married women in this town were so interested in the latest gossip?"

Raylene gave her an incredulous look. "Oh, please, it's the town hobby," she said. "Fed by Grace Wharton and, though I'd never say it to her face, by Sarah over at the radio station. She and Travis do their part to stir the pot by announcing some of the juiciest tidbits on the air. Heck, they even invite Grace to drop by just to make sure their listeners always know the latest."

"Doesn't anybody ever consider going to the source?" Adelia asked in frustration. Of course, she'd been relieved at one time that no one had come directly to her when her marriage was crumbling.

Raylene looked amused. "Are you suggesting that people just ask Gabe whatever they want to know about him?"

"Well, he is the one with all the answers," Adelia replied. "I'm an innocent, uninformed bystander."

"But it's so much more fascinating to see how many of those answers you're already privy to," Raylene explained. "Were you really bothered by it? You know most of these women adore you. They're not just being nosy. They'd really like you to be happy after all you've been through."

"And they think Gabe is the answer?" Adelia asked. "Even though they profess to know nothing about him? One or two even seem to recall something about him being a troublemaker back in the day."

Raylene chuckled. "Who doesn't love a bad boy?" she asked. "Who cares what happened back then, anyway? The man is a serious hunk. He has a smile that makes women weak in the knees. I'd say that makes him a good candidate."

"For what? A fling?"

Her boss winked at her. "No woman I know deserves to have fun more than you do. Why not?"

Adelia gave her a horrified look. "I have children. I have responsibilities. Flings were Ernesto's thing, not mine."

"Do not tell me the thought of letting a sexy man show you just how desirable you are has never crossed your mind," Raylene said. "You'll disappoint me."

"Never," Adelia said staunchly, then thought of the way that smile of Gabe's made her toes curl. "Well, hardly ever."

Raylene laughed. "Thank goodness. I was getting a little worried there."

"But it's a fantasy," Adelia insisted. "I'd never act on it. My children need one parent with a sense of decorum. And if I did happen to lose my head and my self-control, I'd certainly never spread the news all over Serenity."

"Not even to rub it in Ernesto's sorry face?"

The thought of retribution did hold a certain appeal, Adelia thought, then immediately dismissed the idea. The momentary satisfaction wouldn't be worth the potential humiliation of having her children hear about it.

"Not even then," she said, though she couldn't keep a tiny hint of regret out of her voice. Determined to change the subject, she studied Raylene. "You're actually glowing. Pregnancy obviously agrees with you. How are you feeling?"

"The morning sickness seems to be over with, knock on wood. I feel pretty darn amazing." Her expression brightened. "We're going to find out the sex of the baby next week. At least I am. Carter's on the fence. He claims he wants to be surprised."

"You don't believe him?"

"Maybe I would if he hadn't bought four gallons of paint in various colors for the nursery this past weekend. If ever a man needed to have an idea whether he's having a son or daughter, it's my husband," she said, then confided, "I think he's secretly hoping for a boy."

"What makes you think so?"

"Three of those four gallons of paint were in different shades of blue," Raylene said with a smile. "It makes sense, too. He's been guardian to his two younger sisters for several years now. It would be natural for him to want to raise a son."

"How about you? Do you care?"

Raylene shook her head. "I'm just so thrilled to have a man like Carter in my life after the disaster of my first marriage and to be having a child I'd never expected to have, I honestly don't care. The girls were already in their early teens when Carter and I met, so it's not as if I've had baby girls in my life. But Carter's so amazing with all the kids in town. He spends a lot of his spare time helping Cal Maddox and Ronnie Sullivan coach all the sports teams. I'd love to watch him teaching his own son how to do all those little boy things."

Adelia smiled at Raylene's wistful expression. Then her friend sighed.

"The girls are rooting for a niece," Raylene admitted. "They came home the other day with a tiny pink outfit that they'd bought with their babysitting money. When I suggested perhaps they should have waited till we know for sure, they looked as if I were betraying them by even considering the possibility it could be a boy. They love that women are the dominant force in our household. They don't want to see the odds evened, not even a little bit by a kid who won't even be able to talk for a year or so."

Adelia could hardly relate to the excitement in Raylene's voice. She wished she'd shared that sort of excitement with Ernesto during her pregnancies. His daughters had been a disappointment to him. By the time Tomas had been born, he'd lost all interest.

"I am so happy for you," she told Raylene. "You deserve this."

Raylene laughed. "I really do, don't I? It took a long time to get past my ex's abuse and the agoraphobia that kept me a prisoner in my own home." She shook her head. "My gosh, I sound like I lived through my own personal soap opera."

"You did," Adelia said. And every time she thought of what she'd been through with her cheating husband, considering Raylene's past helped her to put it into perspective. No matter a person's own difficulties, there was always someone who'd been through something just a little worse and survived. It was good to remember that.

"You know what?" she said. "I think we deserve a little celebration. Why don't I run next door and get some decaf or tea, if you'd prefer, and a couple of cupcakes?"

"I'm all in favor of cupcakes, but what are we celebrating?" Raylene asked.

"Survival," Adelia replied at once.

Sometimes, she thought, she didn't give herself half enough credit for that.

At Sweet Things, Adelia was studying the

cupcake display case, trying to make a decision, when Sarah McDonald came in.

"I need caffeine," she announced with an edge of desperation in her voice. "I just finished a double on-air shift at the radio station." She sighed heavily, then retracted her order. "Make it decaf."

"You need more than coffee, with or without caffeine," Lynn told her. "I'll bet you haven't eaten all day. Pick out a couple of cupcakes on the house." She glanced at Adelia. "You, too."

"You can't be giving away your inventory," Adelia protested, her business instincts kicking in.

"Of course I can," Lynn replied. "Especially if it means I can put a sign on the door that says I'm sold out for the day and can go home."

Adelia and Sarah exchanged a worried look.

"Are you okay?" Sarah asked. "Now that I look closely, I can see the circles under your eyes. You're a woman in serious need of sleep."

"Thanks so much for noticing," Lynn replied wearily.

"Just an observation," Sarah said. "I know for a fact you're in here before dawn every day because I see the lights on when I go into the station for my morning show. And the lights are usually still on right up till dinnertime when Travis and I go for our walk before he goes in to do his stint on the air."

Lynn sighed. "For so long I dreamed about how wonderful it would be to have my own bakery, but I never believed it would happen. Then Mitch and Raylene and the Sweet Magnolias started pushing and convinced me I could pull it off. Baking's always been second nature to me. Running a business is not. If you say a word about this to my husband, I'll call you a liar, but I don't know how much longer I can keep up this schedule, especially now."

Adelia studied her intently, then gasped as she recognized the signs. "You're pregnant!"

Sarah's eyes widened. "You are, aren't you? Oh my gosh, it's like an epidemic. Raylene, you." She blushed furiously. "Me."

"You, too?" Lynn said, her expression brightening. "We're all going to have babies? That's amazing."

"Okay, that does it," Adelia said. "Bag up a half dozen or so of those cupcakes, put the closed sign on the door and come with me. We're having a party."

"A party?" Lynn echoed.

"Right this second," Adelia confirmed, a

127

little surprised by her own spontaneity. She couldn't recall a single time in her adult life when she hadn't had to consider a million things before moving forward on something fun. This was just one more indication that she was carving out a new path for her life.

"Next door," she told the two women. "Raylene's over there waiting for me to get back. We were just going to celebrate survival, but this will be so much more fun, like an impromptu baby shower."

"Without the presents," Sarah said, feigning disappointment.

Adelia laughed. "There will be plenty of time for the real thing, complete with lots and lots of presents," she promised. "This is just for us, and anyone else who wanders by."

Lynn nodded happily. "I'll just bring a whole tray of cupcakes. And I have a pot of decaf I just made."

"Then we have ourselves a party," Adelia declared.

"You know," Sarah said, her expression thoughtful. "The only other people I know who are so eager for parties at the drop of a hat are the Sweet Magnolias. Adelia, you'd fit right in. You get right into the spirit of a celebration."

Lynn's eyes immediately lit up. "You

would, you know." She turned to Sarah. "We'll have to work on making that happen."

"You don't have to do that," Adelia protested. "I wasn't angling for an invitation."

"Of course not," Lynn said. "But these are women you know, women who know what it means to be friends. Surely you're not telling us you have all the friends you need."

"Not possible," Sarah answered for her. "You may not know you need these women in your life, but you do. Alone, every one of us may be pretty amazing, but together . . ."

"We could run the world," Lynn chimed in, completing the thought.

"Or at least Serenity," Sarah amended.

Adelia couldn't deny that the prospect of having strong bonds with women who'd always have her back held a lot of appeal. She knew the original band of Sweet Magnolias — Maddie Maddox, Dana Sue Sullivan and Helen Decatur-Whitney — had been there for her sister-in-law even before Elliott had come into Karen's life. Raylene credited them with all but saving her life, too.

But Adelia didn't want to push herself into a clique where she might not be welcomed.

Sarah nudged her. "I can practically hear

those wheels in your head going round and round. This is not some exclusive secret society, I promise. You'll see. Of course with all these pregnant women these days, our wild margarita nights have gotten pretty tame. Everybody's drinking virgin cocktails."

"Frozen limeade," Lynn confirmed. "Amazingly, it seems to have the same effect as the alcohol-laced variety. We all get a little crazy. I think it's about knowing we can say absolutely anything and nobody's going to judge us."

"Exactly," Sarah said. "Adelia, we'll make sure you know the next time we're getting together." She gestured toward the display case. "Pack up those cupcakes, Lynn. I'm starving."

Adelia marveled at the way her trip to pick up coffee and a couple of cupcakes had suddenly turned into a special occasion. And when they trooped into the boutique, Raylene didn't seem to be the least bit flustered by the impromptu party.

"I'm calling Annie and telling her to get over here," she said at once. "Since we're going to be talking babies, she's going to want to be in on it." She glanced at Sarah. "Does she know about you yet?"

Sarah shook her head. "Not even Travis

knows, so I'm swearing you all to secrecy right this second."

"But it's okay if we let Annie in on the secret, right?" Raylene said. "How cool is it that we were best friends growing up and now the three of us are all having kids at the same time? Plus Lynn."

Adelia sat back and listened to their excited chatter. Not once when she'd been pregnant with any of her children had she been surrounded by girlfriends like this. She'd counted on her sisters, instead. While they'd all been great back then, it hadn't been the same as this. If that invitation to get together with the Sweet Magnolias truly did come her way, she wasn't going to hesitate. She felt a surprising longing deep in her soul for what these women had found together. Maybe real sisterhood wasn't about biology at all.

Gabe walked past Chic after six and was surprised to find the lights still on and laughter drifting from inside. He paused long enough to glance inside and see Adelia, Lynn and three other women he didn't recognize sitting on an assortment of chairs and stools with a large pastry box, napkins and Styrofoam coffee cups scattered across the counter. Judging from the tossed aside cupcake papers, the women had been having themselves a little party.

It was the laughter, though, that got to him, especially Adelia's. He'd been under the impression that she didn't have a lot of friends. Perhaps he'd based that on his own tendency to go through life alone.

Taking one final glance inside, he smiled to himself and walked on.

At the Serenity Inn, he showered, changed into clean jeans and a fresh shirt, then headed for his usual lonely dinner at Rosalina's. For once, though, the comfortable rut he'd carved out for himself bothered him.

As soon as he was settled in his regular booth, Debbie brought his soda. "Let me guess. A large pepperoni pizza," she said.

"Not tonight," Gabe said, startling them both. He gave a quick glance at the menu, then said, "How about the lasagna and a salad?"

A smile broke across her face. "Well, hallelujah! It's about time you started experimenting."

Gabe chuckled. "I take it you recommend the lasagna."

"I recommend anything other than pizza," she replied. "Not that there's a thing wrong with our pizza. It's excellent, but not as a steady diet. Who knows? Next time maybe you'll really cut loose and try the eggplant Parmesan."

"One step at a time," he said.

Debbie glanced across the restaurant just then and another smile lit her face. "Well, well, well, this is definitely a night full of surprises. There's Adelia and it looks as if she's all alone." She glanced at him. "You want some company?"

Gabe shook his head. "Skip the match-making and bring my dinner, please," he said, even though he couldn't quite take his gaze off Adelia. She was glancing around nervously. When her gaze fell on him, she actually looked relieved.

Gabe stood as she crossed the room. "You looking for somebody?"

"Not really. My mom has the kids, and when I left work, I didn't feel like going home, so I decided to stop by here for dinner. Then I walked in the door and realized I haven't eaten a meal by myself in a restaurant in years. I also realized I didn't much like the idea of it."

Gabe laughed. "Well, unless you were putting yourself to some sort of a test, you're welcome to join me. I wouldn't mind the company. I'm pretty sick of my own." He leaned closer and whispered, "It will make

Debbie very happy. She thinks I have no life."

"And you care what your waitress thinks?" Adelia said, clearly amused.

"No man likes being the object of pity," he told her.

"No woman, either," she confessed. "If you really don't mind, I'd love to join you." She hesitated. "It's not a date, just so we're clear. I'll buy my own meal."

"How about we negotiate that?" he suggested. "It might be even worse for my image if Debbie thinks I'm a cheapskate on top of everything."

No sooner had Adelia slid into place than the waitress reappeared. She gave Gabe a subtle thumbs-up, but Adelia caught it. He could tell she was about to launch into an explanation about this being a chance encounter, not a date, and decided that was a whole lot more than Debbie needed to know. He jumped in before she could speak.

"Debbie, can you hold back my order till Adelia's is ready?"

"Already done," she said, giving him a look that told him she was proud of her intuitiveness. "Hon, what can I get you?" she asked Adelia. "Gabe's breaking with his pizza tradition and having the lasagna and a salad. How about you?"

"Lasagna sounds excellent," Adelia said. "A small salad, too."

"Perfect. I'll be back in no time," Debbie promised.

Gabe met Adelia's nervous gaze. "Since you've made it abundantly clear that this isn't a date, why are you so nervous? Or are you just on a sugar high?"

She looked startled by the question. "A sugar high?"

"I passed the boutique on my way home and it looked as if you and some friends were gorging on Lynn's cupcakes."

She laughed. "Guilty as charged. I had three." Her expression sobered. "What on earth am I doing ordering lasagna after that? I should tell Debbie just to bring me the salad."

"Did you want the lasagna?"

She nodded. "It sounded wonderful when she mentioned it. I haven't had it in ages."

"Then you'll have a couple of bites if that's all you want and take the rest home," he said.

"Thank you for not making me feel guilty."

There was something in her voice that made him frown, a hint of an unspoken apology. "What would you have to feel guilty about?"

It was clear the question flustered her, but he couldn't imagine why. "Adelia, why would you feel guilty about ordering whatever you wanted?"

"You didn't know me a few years ago," she said softly, not meeting his gaze. "I was a mess. I'd gained some weight with each of the kids. Ernesto —"

"The man who cheated on you," Gabe said, not even trying to hide his disgust. "Was that his excuse, that you'd gained weight?"

She gave him a rueful look. "He didn't think he needed an excuse. But he did like to throw my weight in my face. If I'd just admitted to him I'd had three cupcakes and then ordered a big meal, I'd hear about it for days."

"Your ex-husband was a pig," Gabe declared forcefully, not even remotely inclined to censor himself.

A startled expression spread across her face. "Do you know him?"

"No, but I've heard enough to know the type. Don't waste a single minute worrying about his opinions. He doesn't deserve that much respect."

To his surprise, she frowned at his vehemence. "You won't say anything like that around the kids, will you? Ernesto is still

136

their father."

"Of course not," Gabe said. "It's not my place, though maybe they should know the truth about the kind of man he is."

She shook her head at once. "Selena knows and it's tearing her apart. I don't want the younger ones to be disillusioned. One day they may figure things out for themselves, but I'd like them to remain innocent as long as possible. They love their dad."

"That's more generous than he deserves," Gabe said.

She smiled. "I know that. I get to feel all noble. Maybe that's better than spending as much time as I'd like wanting to rip out his heart."

Her comment startled him, but as the heartfelt sentiment registered, he chuckled. "Now you're talking."

"You sound like my brother. He'd love it if I'd give him permission to beat the daylights out of my ex, but I won't do it."

"Nobility's not all it's cracked up to be," he said. "Sometimes plain old revenge is awfully sweet."

She studied him curiously. "You sound as if you know that firsthand."

Gabe sighed. "To be honest, I do, and those memories are not among my proudest moments."

"I'm sorry to have sent you back there, then."

He shrugged. "Protective instincts die hard."

"Who was it you were protecting?"

"My mother."

"What made you think she needed your protection? She was the grown-up, after all."

"She was older," he corrected. "That didn't make her mature. She got mixed up with too many guys like your ex-husband. She had a reputation around town as what you'd probably call a party girl." He shrugged. "Or maybe worse. By the time I was in my teens, I knew she deserved the label, but that didn't mean I liked hearing it."

"So you fought," Adelia concluded.

"And got kicked out of school eventually. I was a troublemaker back then, no question about it."

"Have you reformed?"

"I'd like to think so, which is probably the only thing that makes your ex-husband safe."

"You do know I don't need you to fight my battles for me," she said. "Any more than I want Elliott fighting them."

Gabe nodded. "But you'll let me know if

that ever changes, right?"

"Probably not," she said softly. "But I appreciate the thought, Gabe. It's been a long time since any man other than my brother wanted to look after me. It's a little disconcerting."

"Come to think of it, it's been a long time since I offered to be anyone's knight in shining armor," he told her. "That's a little disconcerting for me, too."

She smiled. "Then it's a good thing this isn't a date."

"Oh?"

"No obligations or expectations when it comes to shining up that armor."

But for reasons he didn't want to examine too closely, Gabe found that he was more disappointed than reassured.

Despite her nervousness, Adelia enjoyed dinner with Gabe more than she'd expected to. And somehow he'd managed to pay the check for both of them, probably when she'd made a visit to the ladies' room. Her protests had fallen on deaf ears, as had her perfectly reasonable arguments that he didn't need to walk her home.

"This is Serenity, for goodness' sake," she said as they stood on the sidewalk in front of Rosalina's. "The Serenity Inn is in the opposite direction from Swan Point."

"And I just ate a huge meal. A walk is just what I need," Gabe said, his jaw set stubbornly.

"I'm not going to win this debate, am I?" she asked in frustration.

"Not a chance," he agreed cheerfully. "Give in gracefully."

It was a pleasant night with a soft breeze and the scent of honeysuckle in the air. A tiny sliver of a moon lit the inky sky.

They'd stayed at Rosalina's much later than Adelia had intended. She was grateful that the kids were spending the night with her mother, so there wouldn't be the endless round of questions that would have ensued if she'd arrived so late to pick them up.

She and Gabe walked in companionable silence for a couple of blocks. She was very aware of the man next to her. Masculinity radiated from him in alluring waves. It was a little scary — no, a *lot* scary — that she was so aware of him. And when he tucked a steadying hand under her elbow when she stepped off a curb, the touch, rather than helping, almost caused her to stumble. It was like a jolt of electricity to her system.

Gabe glanced at her curiously. "You okay?"

"Of course," she said, though there was an unmistakably breathless note in her voice that belied that.

Another touch had her pausing in her tracks. She looked up in alarm to see his gaze on hers.

"Adelia," he said, his voice like a soft caress.

"Uh-huh," she murmured, lost in his eyes.

"I think I'm going to have to kiss you," he said, his lips curving slightly. "Tell me now if that's going to freak you out."

She swallowed hard. "It's going to freak me out," she whispered. Then, keeping her gaze locked with his, she added, "But I want you to."

He seemed startled by her candor. "You do?"

She blinked. "Unless you've changed your mind. I mean, if you have, it's okay. I really have no idea how to do this, Gabe."

"Do what? Kiss a man?"

"Uh-huh."

A smile spread across his face. "I'll bet you do," he said. "Let's see."

He lowered his head slowly until his lips were so tantalizingly close she could feel his breath whispering across her cheek. Her pulse jumped. Anticipation and heat built low in her belly. If he didn't do it soon, if

141

he didn't put his mouth on hers, she thought she very well might cry.

As if he sensed her nerves were at their limit, he closed that last bit of distance, touching his firm lips to hers. That tantalizing heat she'd been feeling exploded into a demanding fire. She put her hands on his shoulders, not just to steady herself, but because she needed to touch him, to feel his muscles bunch, telling her that he was as affected by this moment as she was. She needed to know she wasn't just some pitiful woman desperate and hungry for a man's touch and that he wasn't kissing her because he'd sensed that and felt sorry for her. She needed reassurance that the desire she was so sure was simmering between them went both ways.

The kiss, so gentle at first, deepened in a way she only vaguely remembered. That desperation and hunger curling inside her seemed to be matched by a similar intensity in Gabe. There was a moan low in his throat as their tongues tangled and he pulled her even closer.

Adelia couldn't think after that. Nothing mattered except that extraordinary demanding heat inside her and the wonder of discovering she was still desirable.

The sound of a car in the stillness of the

night seemed to shock them both. Gabe reluctantly drew back. Adelia even more reluctantly let him go.

"That was . . ." Words failed her.

"Unexpected," he said, looking as shaken as she felt. He smiled. "We might have to try it again sometime."

A profound relief spread through her. "We might," she agreed solemnly.

He ran a finger along her cheek as if he wasn't quite ready for the moment to end. "Soon."

Though a part of her wanted to demand that soon be, say, a half hour from now, she managed a teasing grin instead. "We'll see."

To her surprise, he laughed.

"What?" she demanded.

"Sweetheart, you haven't forgotten how to kiss or how to flirt."

Adelia couldn't think of a single thing he might have said that would have pleased her more. She was beginning to think her brother and Raylene might have been right, after all. Maybe Gabe was going to turn out to be the best thing to happen to her, the right man at the right moment in her life . . . even if nothing lasting ever came of it.

CHAPTER SEVEN

"How dare you!" Carolina Cruz Losado demanded of Adelia.

With her hands on her broad hips, her black hair windblown and the color in her cheeks high, she practically radiated indignation as she faced down her sister in the boutique.

Caught off guard by the unexpected attack in the middle of her workplace, Adelia gasped. Then her own temper flared. It was one thing for her family to feel compelled to question her choices and criticize her at home, but not here, not at Chic where anyone could wander in at any minute. It had taken her a long time to achieve professional respect and she wasn't about to let her judgmental sister destroy that.

"Whatever you have on your mind, Carolina, this is not the place to discuss it," she told her youngest sister. Though she kept her voice soft, but firm, she was more than ready to march her straight out the door if need be.

"Afraid you'll get fired if your boss hears what you've been up to?" Carolina taunted, her voice raised deliberately, obviously in the hope that Raylene would be in her office in the back.

Thank goodness Raylene had left for the bank just minutes earlier, Adelia thought. Not that Raylene would be shocked by anything Carolina might have on her mind, but Adelia didn't want her exposed to the kind of scene her sister was trying to cause.

"What about Mama?" Carolina pressed. "Does she know the kind of woman you're turning into?"

Adelia wasn't sure how to answer any of that since she had no idea what had brought Carolina into her workplace in such a mood. She was the more volatile of Adelia's sisters, but this was extreme even for her.

"I know that Mama taught us both better manners," she responded, still keeping her tone surprisingly calm. "We don't attack family with no provocation and we certainly don't do it in public."

"You're in no position to tell me how to behave," Carolina retorted. "It wasn't enough that you disgraced us all by tearing your family apart, but now you're making a

145

spectacle of yourself."

"I have no idea what you're talking about," Adelia said. "And, for the last time, whatever it is, we're not discussing it here. I want you to leave."

"Well, I want you to stop humiliating us," Carolina countered.

Adelia could see that she wasn't going to get her sister out of the shop without resorting to unseemly bodily force, at least not before she'd had her say. Sighing heavily, she said, "Okay, Carolina, out with it. What is it you think I've done?"

"It's not speculation. I saw you kissing that man, right in the middle of Main Street. Do you even know him? Or did you pick him up in some bar?"

Adelia flinched. So this was about that impulsive kiss she and Gabe had shared. She should have known it would come back to haunt her.

"Gabe is a friend," she said quietly. "I'm divorced. He's single. We weren't doing anything wrong. And just so you know, Mama and Elliott both know him. They approve. In fact, they've encouraged me to see him." That might be a bit of a stretch, but desperate times and all that.

The comment seemed to have the desired effect. It appeared to take the wind out of her sister's sails. "Mama knows you have a new man in your life when the ink's barely dry on your divorce papers?" she asked, her skepticism plain.

"The ink may barely be dry," Adelia said wryly, "but the marriage has been over for years. And I'm not the one who broke my wedding vows, Carolina. Ernesto did. Again and again. You know that. How can you continue to take his side?"

Her sister faltered at the hurt in Adelia's voice. "I wasn't taking his side," she murmured.

"It sure seems that way to me. You've done nothing but criticize me since I found the courage to walk out on a man who repeatedly betrayed me."

To her shock, tears filled her sister's eyes.

"I should go," Carolina said.

Adelia stepped around the counter and put a restraining hand on her sister's arm. "You started this. Let's finish it. Maybe it's past time we get all this anger and resentment out in the open."

"No," Carolina said in the same petulant tone she'd used as a little girl when she didn't want to do something.

Adelia smiled. "Now there's the sister I recognize. You sound like you did when you were ten and Mama asked you to do some chore that didn't appeal to you."

For the first time, a faint smile touched her sister's lips. "Spoiled and stubborn?"

Adelia nodded. "Pretty much." She brushed a strand of hair from her sister's cheek. "Talk to me, please. Why are you so angry with me because I walked away from an impossible situation? Staying would have destroyed every last trace of self-respect I possessed."

Carolina swallowed hard, her gaze avoiding Adelia's. "Maybe I was jealous," she admitted, her voice barely above a whisper.

The response all but confirmed Adelia's guess that her marriage, too, was on shaky ground.

"Is Ricky cheating on you?" she asked. Her opinion of Enrique Losado was almost as low as the one she held of her ex-husband, even without her sister's confirmation that he was cheating. He had the kind of macho, dismissive attitude that no self-respecting woman should tolerate.

"No," Carolina said a little too quickly. "At least I don't have any proof that he is."

"Because you don't want to know the truth?" Adelia suggested gently.

"Maybe," she said evasively. "Look, I've got to go. The kids will be home from school soon. They'll be expecting snacks." She finally dared to meet Adelia's gaze. "I'm sorry I came in here hell-bent on making a scene. I just saw you last night and lost it."

"Apology accepted," Adelia said. "And, sweetie, if you ever need to talk, I'm here. I'll always be here. And, believe me, I've learned not to make judgments. We all did it when Elliott brought Karen home, but now that I've had some serious problems of my own, I totally get why Karen made the choices she made. Lesson learned."

"I'll try to remember that," Carolina said. "You won't say anything to Mama or Elliott about this, will you? Not about me coming here or about my life being such a mess? Ricky and I will be fine." There was, unfortunately, more resignation in her voice than real conviction.

"Not a word," Adelia promised. "But just so you know, they'd be on your side, unconditionally."

"Probably, but I'm still hoping I'll never have to test that."

Carolina wrapped her arms around Adelia in an impulsive hug. "Thanks for not tossing me out the door. I know you wanted to."

"I kept imagining Mama's reaction," Adelia told her. Then she warned, "Next time, I might not let that stop me."

"There won't be a next time," her sister promised. "I'll think twice before throwing around accusations."

Adelia gave her a squeeze. "I plan to hold you to that."

She watched as her sister left and walked away, her shoulders slumped. She'd never seen Carolina looking so miserable. Adelia's heart ached for her. One thing she'd learned from her own experience, though, was that the only person who could make Carolina's life better was Carolina herself. And she clearly wasn't ready.

"You kissed Gabe!" Raylene emerged from the office and regarded Adelia with delight.

"You were eavesdropping?" Adelia said, humiliated. "I thought you went to the bank."

"I did, but I got back for the big show," Raylene said. "And I didn't intentionally eavesdrop, but you know how thin these walls are and your sister's voice wasn't exactly on mute. I knew you were aware I might get back at some point, so you could have insisted she leave or take her accusations outside or whatever."

Adelia regarded her with amusement. "Or once you realized she was determined to have her say, you could have slipped out the

150

back door to give us some privacy."

"After I heard her mention that kiss?" Raylene asked incredulously. "Come on. I'm only human. So, how was it?"

"I am not discussing that kiss with you."

"Hot, I'll bet," Raylene said, undeterred. "It must have been if you didn't even notice there were witnesses."

"It was late. The street was empty," Adelia corrected. "Except for one car that came along." She groaned. "What kind of bad luck was it that my sister happened to be in that car? It had to have been her, since she claimed to see us."

"Oh, so what if she did?" Raylene said. "You're entitled. Too bad she wasn't half as indignant when Ernesto was flaunting his affairs all over town."

"Yes, that is too bad," Adelia agreed. "But I think she had her reasons."

"You mean that it was hitting too close to home?" Raylene guessed. "It sounded like that to me, too, not that I know your sister all that well. And that said, I will now butt out of your business, especially if you're not going to spill all the juicy details about that kiss."

"I'm not even confirming there was a kiss," Adelia said. "You didn't witness it. You can't prove it. And anything else you might have heard in here just now is hear-say."

Raylene laughed. "Helen should hear you right now. She'd insist you go to law school." She held up a hand. "Not that I'm saying a word to her. You're indispensable around here."

"Thank you for that." She gave her boss a speculative look. "Maybe this would be a good time to ask for a raise."

"I just gave you a raise. If those commissions of yours keep mounting up, pretty soon I'll have to make you a part owner just to keep my costs down." As soon as the words were out of her mouth, Raylene's eyes lit up. Her expression turned thoughtful. "You know, that might not be a bad idea."

Adelia simply stared at her. "You'd consider letting me buy part of the business?"

Raylene nodded. "It might be a smart move for both of us."

"I don't have the cash to pay you," Adelia said, though she couldn't help being intrigued by the idea. Wasn't that exactly why she'd studied business, with the hope of owning her own retail store someday? But was she anywhere near ready to claim such a dream?

Raylene waved off her concern about money as if it were of no consequence.

"Let's keep mulling this over," she suggested. "We'll talk about it again after I have the baby. If I need to cut back my hours dramatically, this could be the perfect solution. For now, though, I'd better get back to that mountain of paperwork on my desk."

Adelia hesitated, then said, "I could start learning how you handle some of that. If it would help you out, that is. I'm familiar with the accounting program you use."

"I hired you to sell pretty clothes," Raylene reminded her, though her expression was hopeful. "Are you sure you want to deal with something that boring?"

Adelia laughed. "What can I say? I like making sure numbers add up."

Raylene threw her arms around her. "Bless you, bless you, bless you. This partnership idea is sounding better and better."

Adelia held up her hand. "You need to give it a lot more thought."

"Oh, believe me — I will," Raylene said.

The bell over the front door tinkled merrily.

"Go," Raylene said. "I'll deal with the paperwork for now. We'll have another talk about all the rest later."

Adelia stared after her. A part owner of her own business? How astonishing would that be? Even if it never happened, that the idea had even crossed Raylene's mind meant the world to her. Sure, she knew she was a good saleswoman. And the committees she'd organized for the schools had always run smoothly. But this was something else, proof that she was truly capable of making a real life for herself and her kids, that she'd been right all those years ago when she'd studied so hard and envisioned a shop just like this one for herself.

A morning that had started out leaving her shaken and questioning her actions by sharing that impulsive kiss with Gabe had turned around dramatically to boost her self-esteem.

"Yay for me!" she murmured, then went out to wait on the customer who'd wandered in.

After she'd sold the stranger an expensive handbag, she went back to straightening a display of colorful cashmere sweaters she'd encouraged Raylene to order. More than half had already sold in less than a week, yet more proof of her business instincts.

She sighed. If only she were half as confident about the personal choices she was making.

"Well, as I live and breathe, if it isn't Gabe Franklin," Grace Wharton exclaimed, putting her hands on her hips and regarding Gabe with a surprising amount of affection.

"You aren't planning to kick me right back out the door the way you used to, are you?" he asked, only half in jest.

"That depends. You here to start trouble?"

He laughed. "My days of stirring up trouble are behind me," he assured her.

She didn't look as if she entirely believed him, but she nodded. "Then you can stay."

"I'm glad because I've had a hankering for one of your burgers ever since I got back to town."

She regarded him skeptically. "There's that charm I remember. Too bad you didn't use that to talk your way out of trouble back then, instead of using your fists."

"I have to agree with you," he said. "I'm glad to see you still don't hesitate to speak your mind, Grace."

"Never saw any point to it," she replied. "What would you like to go with that burger? Are you ready now or will Mitch be joining you?"

"He's on his way," Gabe told her. "You can put my order in when he gets here, but I'll take a large soda now."

"Will do." She started away, hesitated, then turned back, her expression filled with sympathy. "I'm real sorry about your mama,

155

Gabe. I wanted to tell you that when she died, but you took off before anyone could let you know how much we cared. A lot of folks in town did."

Funny, he didn't remember much evidence of anyone caring, not about either one of them. Grace's expression suggested she knew exactly what he was thinking.

"It probably didn't seem that way to you," she told him. "People talk, sometimes without thinking. I'm one of them. It's a curse as much as it's a blessing. You'll always know what's on my mind, even when I should be wise enough to keep my mouth shut. It was one thing to say cruel things about your mama. She chose her own path. It was quite another to say them openly where a young boy would hear them. I regret that. I really do."

The sincerity of her words resonated in a way they might not have years ago. "I appreciate your saying that," he told her.

"None of the gossip was meant to be malicious," she told him. "But it must have seemed that way to you."

"Grace, I know you mean well now, and maybe you did back then, but not everyone was the same as you. Even as a boy, I recognized the joy some people took in spreading rumors about my mom. She did plenty to cause talk, but I always wondered if things would have been different if anyone had reached out to help her. The only ones who did were after what she had to offer them, a willing body."

Grace might pride herself on being candid, but she looked uncomfortable at his straight talk. "I'm sorry," she said again.

Gabe merely nodded. "I'd like that soda now, if you don't mind."

"Right away," she said, clearly eager to have an excuse to leave.

Mitch showed up in time to note her relieved expression. He frowned at Gabe. "What was that about?"

"Just catching up," Gabe claimed.

Mitch didn't look as if he bought that, but he let it go. When Grace returned, he ordered his own burger, then sat back in the booth with a sigh.

"Problems on the job?" Gabe asked him. "I mean other than those I already know about."

"Not on Main Street," Mitch said. "I may have mentioned, though, that I have a customer in town who's changed his mind at least once a week about what he wants done. Then he goes crazy when I tell him the change is going to cost him." He shook his head. "My bad. I should never have taken the job. I've regretted it practically from day one."

"Anyone I know?"

"Ernesto Hernandez," Mitch admitted, his expression rueful. "And you don't need to say a word. I've already gotten an earful from my wife and every one of her friends."

Gabe bit back his own indignation since Mitch looked as if he'd already paid a heavy price for his decision. "Why'd you take the job?" Gabe asked curiously. "You don't need the work."

"The call originally came from Mary Vaughn Lewis. She said she had a client who wanted some renovations done and she'd told him I was the best. You know how persuasive Mary Vaughn can be when she wants something."

"You let a little flattery get you to take a job working for a piece of slime like Ernesto Hernandez?" Gabe made no attempt to hide his incredulous reaction. He'd never thought his honorable, upstanding cousin could be flattered or bought.

"I told you, it was Mary Vaughn who got me to take the job. She took me to look at the house, told me what the client wanted and that money was no object. It wasn't until I saw Ernesto's name on the contract that I realized who I'd be dealing with. By then, it was too late to back out. I'd given Mary Vaughn my word."

"Didn't it occur to you that it was odd that the Realtor was setting up the deal instead of the client? Hernandez must have known you'd never agree to work for him."

Mitch flushed. "Of course it occurred to me," he said. "Unfortunately, though, not till after I'd agreed to do the job."

Gabe frowned, still confused about how a smart man like Mitch could have been taken in. "You didn't realize it was Ernesto's house when you went there to check out what he wanted done?"

"It's not his house," Mitch revealed. "To top off a lousy situation, it belongs to his mistress. He apparently wants to get top dollar when she sells it and moves in with him."

Gabe could only think about how that scenario must feel to Adelia, knowing that her husband's mistress was about to move into her old home. His opinion of Ernesto sank a little lower, which he'd thought was pretty much impossible.

"I suppose you could take some comfort by charging him an arm and a leg for everything you do," Gabe suggested.

Mitch laughed. "Believe me, that would give me a great deal of pleasure, but it's not in the cards. The man's a cheapskate. He wants a top-dollar renovation on a shoestring. Apparently Mary Vaughn was overly optimistic about cost being no object."

"I see the dilemma," Gabe told him. "Better you than me." He gave his cousin a long look. "No one would blame you if you tore up the contract and walked away from the job. Sounds as if he's given you plenty of cause. I imagine Helen Decatur — isn't she the best lawyer in town? — could find a loophole for you."

"I'm sure she could and she'd be eager to do it, too," Mitch conceded. "But I don't do business that way. Once I give my word, I like to keep it."

Gabe nodded. It had been a long time before anyone took his word. He understood, perhaps even more than Mitch, how important that kind of respect could be and why a man would do anything he had to in order not to violate that trust. Sure, people might understand or even cheer if Mitch halted his dealings with Ernesto, but Mitch would find it hard to live with himself.

"Let's talk about something else," Mitch pleaded. "Have you gotten together with Adelia to go over those cost estimates?"

Gabe shook his head.

His cousin's expression turned puzzled.

"Didn't I hear you had dinner with her at Rosalina's just last night? The subject of the renovations never came up?"

Gabe could tell his cousin was fishing for details that had absolutely nothing to do with any home renovations. "Nope. Forgot all about it."

Mitch didn't even try to hide his amusement. "Then what was the topic that was so fascinating it kept the two of you there till closing?"

A frown spread across Gabe's face. "Do you have some sort of pipeline to what's going on at Rosalina's?"

He was half joking, but Mitch apparently took him seriously.

"Well, let's see," Mitch said. "You got there about seven-thirty, the way I heard it. Adelia came in right on your heels and joined you. You were huddled over lasagna and salad for at least a couple of hours. Then you ordered pie. She turned down dessert."

"You mean to tell me you missed out on the kind of pie I ordered?" Gabe inquired sourly.

"Apple with ice cream on top," Mitch said. At Gabe's incredulous expression, he added, "That was just a guess. I happen to know it's your favorite."

"Well, thank goodness the gossips left out a few of the details," Gabe muttered.

"Did I forget to mention the kiss?" Mitch asked innocently. "Word on the street is that it looked pretty memorable."

Gabe groaned. "I have to leave town," he muttered. "Who can live like this?"

"Most of us survive," Mitch said. "The reports about Lynn and me flew around town pretty quickly, too. I learned to ignore it. Lynn had more trouble with it than I did, because her ex-husband got worked into a frenzy every time he heard we were together, never mind how he reacted when he spotted me with his kids."

"I now have an inkling of what my mom must have gone through," Gabe said wearily. "No wonder she drank herself to death."

Mitch looked alarmed by the bitterness in his voice. "Different situation entirely," he said firmly.

"Really? You think so? You think she deserved to have people in her business?"

"No, of course not. People, especially family, should have been more understanding. We should have stood up for her."

Gabe closed his eyes against the pain that washed over him just thinking about how all that talk had eaten away at his mom. Sure, it was the alcohol that had killed her, that and a long string of bad choices, but being picked at by everyone in town certainly hadn't helped. She'd had no one but him on her side, and he'd been a kid who hadn't really known how to help. Bailing him out of scrapes at school had just added to her downward spiral.

"Words hurt," he said softly. "I wonder if some of the gossips in this town understand that. They may think that it's all harmless fun, but it's not. Sometimes careless words can destroy lives." He met Mitch's gaze. "I won't subject Adelia to that."

Once more his cousin looked startled by the ferocity of his words. "Gabe, if you like this woman, don't back off, not unless she asks you to. Both of you are tough enough to weather a little gossip. She's certainly been through worse, thanks to Ernesto."

"Then she deserves a break," Gabe said. "Find someone else to oversee that job at her place, Mitch."

Just then Grace arrived with their meals. Gabe held up a hand. "Could you make that to go, Grace? I have someplace I need to be."

She looked from him to Mitch and back, then nodded. "Give me a minute. Mitch, are you staying?"

Mitch nodded. She set his plate in front of him.

When she'd gone, Mitch regarded Gabe with real concern. "I'm not putting anyone else in charge at Adelia's," he said, his tone unyielding. "Not until you've had time to think this through or unless she asks me herself to make a change."

"Don't do this," Gabe pleaded, determined to do the honorable thing. "It's for the best."

"I don't see it that way," Mitch said. "And last time I checked, you were working for me."

Gabe frowned at his cousin pulling rank. "That could change in a heartbeat," he said angrily.

Fortunately Grace returned just then with his meal. He took it, turned and walked out before he could lash out further at Mitch. He had a hunch if he said what was on his mind, he'd live to regret it. He already had enough regrets on his plate for one day. That amazing kiss he'd shared with Adelia was suddenly right at the top of the list.

CHAPTER EIGHT

Adelia had no sooner walked in the front door than Selena stormed out of the kitchen, her expression sullen.

"What's wrong?" Adelia asked. "Has something happened? Are your sisters and brother okay?"

"*They're* just fine," she replied sourly. "Maybe I'm just tired of babysitting."

Selena had suggested that she be responsible for watching her younger siblings after school since she was confined to home, anyway, so Adelia wasn't sure what to make of her sudden change of heart. One thing she was sure of, she didn't like the attitude.

"I don't know where this mood of yours is coming from, but I don't appreciate it," she told her daughter.

"Well, I don't like a lot of things," Selena retorted.

"Okay, that's it," Adelia said, pointing to the living room. "In there right now."

Though she didn't look happy about it, Selena went into the living room and sat down. Only when they were both seated on the sofa, albeit with a good bit of distance between them, did Adelia ask, "What is going on with you? You were perfectly fine when you left for school this morning."

"I want you to lift my grounding," Selena said.

Something in her tone suggested she thought she had the upper hand. "And why would I do that?" Adelia asked. "We agreed that a month was appropriate for leaving school without permission."

"Well, I don't agree anymore," her daughter replied, her expression belligerent. "Not after what you did."

"Watch your tone with me, young lady." Adelia looked into Selena's increasingly stormy eyes and went still. "What is it you think I've done?"

"You made a spectacle of yourself, that's what," Selena said angrily. "Just like Dad. Why should I respect anything you say after that?"

Given her choice of words, Adelia had a pretty good idea where Selena had gotten her information. "Since you were in bed at your grandmother's last night when I made this so-called spectacle of myself, I suppose your cousin is the one who filled you in." Jose, Carolina's oldest son, would happily spread bad news. Only a year younger than Selena and possessing a surprisingly mean streak, even at twelve he had a knack for trying to make her life miserable. "What did he tell you?"

"Joey saw you kissing that Gabe person right on Main Street. He was with Aunt Carolina coming home from shopping at the mall in Columbia. He said it just proved you were no better than Dad." Suddenly there was more hurt than anger in Selena's expression. "Is it true? Did you kiss Gabe?"

"Sweetie, you're my daughter and I love you, but I don't have to keep you posted on my actions, much less justify them to you. And this is nothing like what your dad did. Men and women sometimes kiss. It's very different when that kiss is between two single people who haven't made vows to other people. What your dad did was a betrayal." She watched Selena's face closely to see if her words were registering. "You do understand the difference, right?"

Tears welled in Selena's eyes and she sighed heavily. "I guess," she admitted.

"Then what is it you're really upset about?"

"Do you like him?" Selena asked, her tone

plaintive. "Gabe, I mean. It looked like you might when he was here for dinner."

"We hardly know each other," Adelia said honestly.

"But you were on a date. You must have been if you kissed him."

Though she chafed at having to explain herself to her thirteen-year-old daughter, Adelia wanted Selena to understand. She'd already seen too much for a girl her age. It was little wonder she was angry and confused so much of the time.

"It wasn't a date," she said. "Gabe and I ran into each other at Rosalina's. He invited me to join him. Then he walked me home. I told him he didn't have to, but he insisted. That's the way a true gentleman treats a lady." It was behavior both of them had far too little experience with, and she wanted Selena to learn to watch for and appreciate such gestures.

"But what about the kiss?" Selena persisted. "Was that some kind of weird coincidence? Your lips just accidently locked?"

Adelia smiled. "It was . . ." She thought of the word Gabe had used the night before. "It was unexpected."

Selena frowned. "Did you like it? Are you going to do it again?"

"It was a nice kiss," she said, her voice

softening as she remembered. "I don't know if it will happen again. Would you mind so very much if it did?"

"Yes," Selena said forcefully. "You said it yourself. We don't even know him. Things are already changing too fast."

"Does it feel to you as if I'm betraying your dad?"

The troubled expression on Selena's face answered the question, but her words came more slowly.

"I know you're divorced," Selena replied carefully. "And I totally get why. I'm even glad about it."

"But you miss your dad."

"I don't!" Selena all but shouted, clearly agitated by the suggestion that she missed a man she'd sworn to hate forever.

"Of course you do," Adelia soothed. "And, sweetie, it's okay to miss him. No matter what happened between your father and me, it's okay for you to love him. And he will always love you."

"Like I believe that," Selena said, her voice radiating skepticism and pain.

"Well, I believe it," Adelia told her. "He might not always show his love in ways you might like him to, but I remember the look on his face when you were born. You were this tiny little bundle with the most amazing lungs on any baby ever. Your face was scrunched up and red. You were screaming your head off, but he looked as if he'd just seen the most perfect angel."

That story — and the snapshot commemorating that exact moment — had always calmed Selena. At one time, when she was struggling to accept her father's actions, she'd clutched that photo and asked to hear the story over and over as if she needed reminding that at one time they'd been a happy family and she'd been the center of it.

"Not anymore," Selena said wearily. "He hates me now."

"Never," Adelia said.

"Mom, I know you're trying to make me feel better, but you can just stop. I'm not a little kid. I know the kind of man Dad is. Why would I still want anyone like that in my life?"

"Just because someone we love has flaws, we don't always stop loving them. There's even a part of me that can remember the good times I had with your dad. We've talked about that."

"Well, I don't love him, not anymore," Selena said fiercely. "Not after what he did to you. And I don't want anyone else to hurt you like that again."

170

"No one will," Adelia told her. "I'd like to think I'm smarter now. I certainly have more self-respect." At least she was working on that, she amended to herself.

Selena studied her intently. "So you're not going to let Gabe hurt you the way Dad did?"

"Not the way your father did, no. But, sweetie, falling in love comes with risks."

Alarm immediately crossed Selena's face. "You're falling in love already?"

"Of course not. It's much too soon. But I hope I'll be open to the possibility someday, whether it's with Gabe or someone else," she said, aware of the irony that she was echoing Elliott's words to her, advice she hadn't been interested in hearing. Her brother would be thrilled by her apparent change of heart. She knew, though, she was saying them for her daughter's benefit. She didn't want Selena to grow up bitter and jaded, always keeping herself safely protected against any pain love might bring.

"But no matter when it happens," Adelia continued when she was sure Selena was listening, "it won't come with any guarantees that I won't get hurt. That's just life."

"Then why would you take a chance? You have me, Juanita, Natalia and Tomas. Aren't we enough for you?"

171

Adelia smiled at her naïveté. "You all are the very best part of my life," she said. "But when relationships work, they can be wonderful. You'll find that out for yourself someday." She gave her a meaningful look. "A long, long time from now. Maybe when you're thirty."

Selena giggled, but her expression sobered quickly. "Do you think this thing with Gabe can be wonderful?"

"I have no idea. We're just starting to get to know each other. I don't even know how long he's going to be in town."

"So it might not get serious?" Selena asked, sounding a little too hopeful.

"It might not," Adelia confirmed.

"Isn't kissing supposed to be serious?"

Adelia hid a smile. It was a refrain she'd repeated to her teenage daughter a million times, hoping to keep her from making a mistake when she was still so young. "Yes, it is," she said. "But this was just one kiss and, like I said, it was unexpected."

"Well, I'm going to be keeping an eye on him," Selena declared.

"You do that," she said. It would be just one more person keeping him under close scrutiny.

"Do I have to like him if you do?"

"No, but just remember that we should

always give people a chance to prove themselves. And we're nice to everyone, no matter what reservations we might have about
them. Understood?"

Selena nodded, though she didn't seem
entirely happy about it. Adelia realized that
the reminder was one she needed to heed,
as well.

Her conversation with Selena was still very
much on Adelia's mind when she opened
the boutique in the morning. She told
herself that was the only reason her pulse
scrambled when she looked up as Gabe
opened the door and walked inside. She was
feeling guilty that she was glad to see him,
she told herself. That's all it was.

"You shopping for a gift?" she asked,
aware that her voice betrayed her nerves.

He shook his head. "I came to see you."

"Oh."

She studied him closely and realized he
looked just about as nervous as she felt.
"Everything okay?"

"I'm not sure," he said candidly. "Did you
catch as much flak yesterday over that kiss
as I did?"

She laughed, oddly relieved that his feet
had apparently been held to the fire, as well.
"Probably more," she told him. "My sister

accused me of making a spectacle of myself. Her son filled my daughter in on my unseemly behavior, and then I had to answer a whole lot of questions about relationships, kissing and betrayal. Oh, and did I mention that my boss wanted to hear all the juicy details?"

His jaw dropped as he listened. "I thought it was bad enough that Mitch put me on the hot seat."

Adelia shrugged. "It's just Serenity."

"You seem to be taking the gossip in stride," he said, seeming surprised.

"Have you forgotten that I was married to a man who was having serial affairs for years? I had to tune out the gossip to survive."

He shoved his hands in his pockets. "Well, I don't want to be the one to put you through anything like that again. I told Mitch I thought he ought to assign someone else to handle your renovations."

The sensation that washed over Adelia caught her by surprise. She realized it was disappointment. "If that's what you think is best," she said stiffly.

He frowned. "Don't you?"

"I suppose it depends on why you're suggesting it. If you think you're protecting me, I don't need it. If you don't want to do the job, that's something else entirely. I liked the ideas we discussed the other night when you were at the house. I suppose another man could handle the work, but I'm comfortable that you and I are on the same page." She smiled at him. "And I'm not sure anyone else will want my eight-year-old son on his crew."

"What about the gossip, though?"

"Like I said, I'm used to it."

"And it doesn't bother you? Honestly?"

She suddenly realized she wasn't the only one whose name was going to be spread all over town amid speculation, disapproval and who knew what else. "Gabe, does this bring back too many bad memories for you? If that's it, I totally understand. I don't remember the talk about your mom all those years ago, but you've told me how painful it was."

"It was a long time ago. I should be over it by now."

"But are you?"

He paused a moment. "I guess I'm not. I still remember how helpless I felt and how angry I was at the whole world. I don't want to be the guy who brings that kind of unwanted attention to you. I'd hate to have to start punching people out again."

"And you think you'd be tempted to do that?"

"If I thought what they were saying might be hurtful to you? I'd like to think I'd find a more mature way to handle it, but I can't swear to that. Old habits die hard."

"How about this? We can keep things strictly professional, if that's what you want," she suggested. "No more impulsive kisses."

He gave her a disbelieving look. "You and me under the same roof for days on end," he said. "There are going to be more kisses, Adelia. Right this second it's taking every ounce of willpower I possess to keep from dragging you into my arms and we're smack in the middle of a conversation about what a bad idea that would be. Just imagine what might happen if we stop telling ourselves it's a bad idea."

She felt a little frisson of relief just knowing that he was struggling with the same impulse that she was. The fact that he was trying so darned hard to do the right thing for her made him even more appealing. Frustrating but appealing.

She met his gaze. "What did Mitch say when you told him you wanted someone else to take over the renovations?"

"That he disapproved of the idea and

expected me to do the work. He reminded me that he was my boss."

She laughed, though it was evident he found no humor in the situation. "Maybe we should trust his judgment. He's lived here his whole life, too. He knows a thing or two about the Serenity grapevine and how to live with it."

"You honestly think I'm making a big deal out of nothing?"

"Not out of nothing," she corrected. "I'm just saying I think we can handle it. Most of the time the talk isn't meant maliciously. It's just curiosity and some crazy need to be the first to know what's going on around town."

He didn't look as if he was entirely pleased by her conviction. "Okay, then," he said, relenting. "I'll be by tonight with the cost estimates and a timetable."

"Come for dinner," she said on impulse. "It won't be anything like my mom's cooking, just burgers on the grill."

For a minute it looked as if he might refuse. Instead, though, he shook his head as if unsure what to make of her. "I'm told I can grill a pretty mean burger myself," he said at last. "If you'll let me cook and bring dessert, it's a date."

"A date? Really?"

He frowned at her teasing. "Not that kind of a date. Not the boy–girl kind. Just a professional appointment at a specified time that happens to include food."

She bit back a grin. "Duly noted."

But no matter what he insisted on calling it, she found that her pulse was skipping merrily in anticipation.

Tomas was like a little shadow from the instant that Gabe arrived at Adelia's. Natalia and Juanita were a bit more reserved, and Selena was downright hostile. Gabe realized he was going to have his work cut out for him trying to win her over, not because he needed her approval, but because it was going to be awkward doing the work for Adelia if Selena set out to make the situation intolerable.

"Is it just me she doesn't like?" he asked Adelia when he'd slipped into the kitchen and caught her alone.

"She wouldn't approve of any man hanging around right now," Adelia reassured him. "As I mentioned this morning, she got word of the kiss, though, and that definitely didn't help. She may not want me back with her dad, but she doesn't want me with anyone else, either."

"I guess the divorce was hard on her," he said.

"Not the divorce so much as the reason for it. She knew all about her dad's infidelity. Not only didn't he work very hard to hide it, he actually flaunted it toward the end."

Gabe frowned. "What kind of a man does that to his kid?" he said, then winced. His mom had been no better. He'd been well aware of all her affairs. She hadn't cared enough to keep them secret. And she'd made him her shoulder to cry on when things had gone south, as they had each and every time. He doubted she'd had any idea of the damage she'd done to him.

"Never mind," he said. "I think I know just how she must have felt. Discovering that your parents have feet of clay is never easy."

Adelia studied him intently. "Did you swear off of love because of what your mom did?"

"Pretty much. I've dated over the years, but not once have I allowed things to get too serious. Anytime I sensed they might, I broke things off and moved on. I didn't want to be responsible for hurting anyone the way my mom's lovers hurt her."

"So no string of brokenhearted girlfriends

for you," Adelia said lightly.

"Nope."

"But what about you? Were there any of them you were sorry to leave?"

Gabe frowned at the question. "What are you asking?"

She looked directly into his eyes. "I'm asking if it was always so easy to keep things light and casual or if you ever fell in love along the way, but then broke things off because that was the pattern you were determined to follow?"

"I never let myself get that serious," he insisted.

"I find that a little sad," Adelia told him.

Gabe shrugged. "It was for the best. I'm not the kind of man who puts down roots."

She held his gaze. "So, fair warning? Now that you've made yourself clear, you're off the hook if I get any crazy ideas?"

"I didn't mean it like that," he said, not liking the implication that he was looking for a cop-out. "You asked a question. I tried to answer it honestly."

She gave him a bright smile that seemed a little forced. "No need to get defensive. Message received." She turned to stir the mayonnaise into the big bowl of potato salad on the counter.

"I wasn't sending a message," he said

impatiently. "Adelia, look at me."

She turned slowly, the spoon still in her hand.

"I was *not* sending a message."

She smiled slightly, though her eyes looked a little sad. "Sure you were. Now, maybe you'd better get those burgers going. Everything else is just about ready."

Gabe wanted to stay right there and argue, tell her she'd misunderstood, but the truth was, she probably hadn't. He just didn't happen to like the conclusion she'd reached. It didn't say anything good about him, and, for reasons he didn't care to examine too closely, he wanted her to think well of him.

Dinner had been a little tense, at least between her and Gabe, but the chatter of Tomas and the younger girls had overshadowed their awkward silence. Adelia was furious with herself for pressing him earlier, for getting a little too deeply into his personal business. He was here to do a job. One kiss didn't give her the right to start questioning his behavior and his motives with women.

After she'd sent the younger children off to their rooms to settle down for the night and managed to discourage Selena from standing guard over her and Gabe, Adelia sat across from him at the dining room

181

table. Her lists were spread between them, along with his notations and cost estimates.

"Gabe, I owe you an apology," she said.

His head snapped up. "For what?"

"I had no right cross-examining you earlier. If I made you uncomfortable, I'm sorry. I know how much I hate it when people start asking me about stuff I don't want to discuss."

He met her gaze. "I only hated it because you might have hit a little too close to the truth. I do keep women at a careful distance to protect myself, as much as I do to be fair to them. It's an ingrained habit." He paused. "But I don't regret it. I figure it's saved me a lot of pain."

"It's also kept you from loving deeply," she suggested.

He looked startled by her words. "Are you such a big proponent of love after everything Ernesto put you through?"

"Right this second, not so much," she told him candidly. "Elliott's been on my case about that. So has Mama. I even told Selena she shouldn't let what happened between her dad and me discourage her from giving her heart to someone someday."

"But you're not ready to take that chance?"

"Not today," she said. "Maybe not even

tomorrow or the next day. But I hope someday I'll change my mind and open my heart again. I don't want to give Ernesto the power to rob me of a full and rich life. That's what I'd be doing if I never took another chance on love."

"And you think I let my mother's bad experiences cost me this full and rich life you're talking about," he said, looking skeptical.

"Did you?"

"Maybe I just think my life is full and rich as it is," he replied.

She smiled. "You only say that because you've never experienced what it could be. It's like saying you love mashed potatoes and could live on a steady diet of them your whole life, but never having discovered a great enchilada or a pizza with everything, the claim wouldn't mean all that much."

Gabe laughed. "You're comparing love to food?"

"In a way. Think about it. Bland food may sustain you, but life is better with lots of spices. You can survive without love, but you'll miss all that heat and excitement."

Even as she spoke, she realized that she herself had come up with the most convincing reason of all to let love back into her life. She'd had heat and excitement once.

Sure, it had died a long time ago, but deep down she knew that she'd only be living a half life if she didn't reach for that again. Someday. That kiss she'd shared with Gabe had reminded her of that.

She looked into Gabe's eyes and saw the spark of amusement there. "Heat and excitement, huh?"

"Definitely," she said, daring to hold his gaze.

"I could get behind that," he said softly.

Adelia felt her cheeks burn. "I wasn't . . . I'm not . . ."

"What?" he asked, his grin spreading. "You're not talking about sex?"

"No. Well, yes. I mean that's a part of it, of course," she said, rattled.

"I happen to like sex," he said.

"What's not to like?" she said impatiently, then blushed even more furiously. "We need to change the subject. Show me those cost estimates."

He held her gaze for another beat, then dutifully pushed the papers across the table. His hand deliberately grazed hers, sending heat rushing through her veins. Blast the man. He was heat and excitement all wrapped up in one sexy, contradictory, infuriating bundle. But she knew without a doubt that he possessed the power to drag

184

her back into the world of the living. She just wasn't sure she was entirely ready for it.

CHAPTER NINE

Adelia came home from work two days after her touchy conversation with Gabe and found a half-dozen men swarming all over her roof. A Dumpster was overflowing with the old roofing materials and it looked as if more than half the roof had already been replaced with new shingles. Tomas was standing wide-eyed at the bottom of a ladder, practically dancing with excitement.

"Mom! Mom!" he shouted when he saw her. "Gabe's fixing the roof and I'm helping."

"Are you really?" she said, tousling his black hair, loving the way it curled around her fingers. If he had his way, he'd have a crew cut, but Adelia couldn't bring herself to have those beautiful curls shorn. Someday soon, though, she wouldn't be able to fight him.

"What's your assignment?" she asked. Thankfully it didn't appear to include scampering around two stories above-ground.

"First, I was supposed to pick up stuff if it didn't go into the trash when it got tossed off the roof. Now I have to wait right by the ladder to make sure it's there when they need it to get down. Gabe says that's really important because otherwise the guys could get stuck up on the roof and have to jump and maybe even break a leg."

"Then it's definitely an important job," she acknowledged, appreciating Gabe's cleverness in making the menial task sound so critical while keeping Tomas on solid ground.

"Gabe says if I do it really well, he'll take me up on the roof later so I can see what they've done up close," Tomas told her excitedly. "He promised to explain how they put on the new shingles and maybe even to let me do one myself."

She frowned at that, glanced up and caught the eye of the man who'd told her son he could climb onto the roof. "Did he now?"

Tomas must have heard the dismay in her voice and seen the direction of her gaze, because he patted her arm. "It's okay, Mom. Really. Gabe will be with me."

Just then the man in question climbed

187

down the ladder and put a hand on Tomas's shoulder. "Good job today, buddy. How about you scout around the yard and make sure everything's picked up while I speak to your mom? Take the big magnet and use it like I showed you in case there are any nails around."

The second they were alone, Adelia looked Gabe in the eye. "You promised him he could go on the roof? Are you nuts?"

He laughed. "It's not as if I'm giving him a hammer and nails and putting him to work up there unsupervised. I gave him an incentive to stay safely on the ground while we worked. And now, with me hanging on to him for dear life, he can go up for a couple of minutes and check things out. It's a fitting reward for a job well done."

"He said you were going to let him put on a shingle, so he could learn how to do it himself. Doesn't that involve a hammer and nails?"

"And very, very close supervision," Gabe reminded her.

She sighed. "You think I'm overreacting."

"Maybe just a little."

"But, Gabe, what if he decides he likes it up there and goes up on his own later?" she said, knowing how her son's mind worked.

"There won't be a ladder in sight that he

can get to," Gabe promised. "I bought a big combination lock for the shed and the ladders and tools will all be stored in there when we're not here working."

Even as he spoke, the crew was scrambling down the ladder and taking their tools to the shed. Adelia finally released the breath she felt as if she'd been holding ever since her child had made his big announcement. "I guess that's okay then."

"Adelia," Gabe said softly, tucking a finger under her chin and forcing her to meet his gaze. "I'm not going to endanger your son. Not ever. That's a promise."

"I know that," she said, relenting. "And I keep forgetting that he's growing up and has an inquisitive mind that should be encouraged, not stomped on by an overly protective mother. In some ways, I felt better that he had a dad like Ernesto. Ernesto wasn't the sort of man who'd put himself into dangerous situations, much less Tomas."

"Roofing isn't dangerous if you know what you're doing," Gabe reminded her.

She smiled. "And you do."

"And I do," he confirmed. "Okay? You can stand right here at the bottom of the ladder and hold on tight every second we're up there if it'll make you feel better." A grin lit his eyes. "Or you could come up there with us."

The dare in his voice actually had her glancing up and considering the idea, but only for a second. "I think I'll wait right here and be prepared to catch him if he slips."

"And me?" he asked, amusement sparkling in his eyes. "Will you catch me if I fall?"

"I've seen you on the roof. You're as agile as a mountain goat, but, yes, if you slipped, I'd try to catch you, too."

"The view's pretty amazing from up there," Gabe said, deliberately continuing to tease her. "I can see all the way to the park. I'll bet it's beautiful when there's a full moon. Maybe you'll sneak up there with me then."

Adelia got lost in his eyes for just a heartbeat and temptation licked through her. "Maybe I will," she said softly.

Gabe winked at her. "I'll hold you to that." He raised his voice then. "Tomas, you ready to hit the roof?"

Tomas came around the house at a run, his eyes bright with excitement. "You bet. Mom, are you gonna watch?"

"I am," she said, smiling at him. She'd be watching both of them like a hawk until they were safely on the ground again.

■ ■ ■ ■

"I'm not sure I'm going to survive this renovation," Adelia told Lynn when she stopped by the bakery for coffee a couple of days later. For once neither Gabe nor Mitch were there. Lynn said they'd been called to a job site where there were ongoing problems with a difficult client.

Lynn sat across from her, flour on her cheeks and circles under her eyes. "I heard about Gabe taking Tomas up on the roof. You didn't approve."

"Once Gabe explained his theory, I actually got it, but that doesn't mean I wasn't scared out of my wits the whole time they were up there."

"I can imagine," Lynn said. "When I found out Mitch was letting Jeremy use power tools, I flipped out. He finally got me to see that it was better he try things with strict supervision than sneak in there on his own and try them with nobody looking."

"That's pretty much what Gabe said, too. What is it with little boys and danger?"

Lynn laughed. "They want to be like the big boys, especially the ones they admire. It's a guy thing. Since neither of our sons had especially good role models as dads, at least when it comes to that sort of thing, I think it's natural that they gravitate to guys like Mitch and Gabe."

"You're probably right," Adelia said, trying to resign herself to accept reality. "And I certainly don't want to turn my son into some sort of sissy who's scared of his own shadow, but I'm not sure if I can live with my heart in my throat every time I walk into my own yard."

"The roof is done now, right? The worst is over."

Adelia laughed at her friend's naive comment. "And now the demolition starts inside. Oh, boy! Sledgehammers and saws. Fun stuff." She shuddered at the thought. "Okay, enough about me. Are you okay? Are you getting enough sleep?"

"No, and Mitch has noticed. He's caught me napping when he comes home at night, but so far he's pretending not to see it. I know he's just waiting for me to say something, and that almost makes it worse. He's so blasted determined to let me make my own decisions."

"How is that a bad thing?"

"Because I'm stubborn," Lynn said, her expression rueful. "I almost wish he'd take this one decision out of my hands and tell me I need to cut back or hire help or something."

"But he wants you to reach that conclusion on your own," Adelia said.

Lynn nodded. "When we were first dating, I really appreciated his letting me get back on my feet on my own. I needed to know I was strong enough to handle things."

"But now you wouldn't mind leaning on him just a little?" Adelia guessed.

"Something like that," Lynn said. "I know he'd step up in a heartbeat if I told him I needed help, but to me that feels like conceding defeat."

Adelia understood the dilemma. "It's not, you know. It's being smart. You're having a baby. If you want a healthy baby, you can't wear yourself out."

"But I wasn't this tired when I was pregnant with Lexie and Jeremy," Lynn complained. "Do you think there's something wrong with me?"

Since there was real worry in her voice, Adelia held back a chuckle. "Nothing more than that you're a few years older now," she said gently. "And trying to run a demanding business."

Lynn gave her a chagrined look. "Oh, that."

"You're not Superwoman. You're just human."

"But I want Mitch to think I'm Superwoman," she said plaintively.

Adelia did laugh at that. "Honey, I think he knows better, and you know what's best about that?"

"What?"

"He's crazy in love with you, anyway."

Lynn's expression brightened at last. "He really is, isn't he?"

"Seems that way to all of us watching the two of you enviously."

"You envy me?" Lynn asked, looking surprised.

"Of course. You're my role model. You went through a crappy marriage just like me, and look at you now. You have your own very successful business. Your kids are happy again. You have a baby on the way. And then there's Mitch, who adores you. It can't get much better than that."

"I predict you'll have all that, too," Lynn said. "Your kids are already doing better. They come by after school every now and then on their way to see you next door. They're chattering away with their friends and laughing. It's really good to see."

"All of them except Selena," Adelia corrected. "I think it's going to take a while for her to get over what her father did."

"But she will," Lynn said. "And I have it

on good authority that Raylene is considering making you a half owner in the boutique. Your life is definitely turning around."

Adelia regarded Lynn with surprise. "Raylene told you about that?"

"She mentioned it. She said it made a lot
of sense, that she'd be making a decision
once the baby's here and she sees how
demanding he or she is." Her eyes narrowed. "She also said you seemed hesitant.
Why?"

"Only because I don't have the money to
invest right now," Adelia admitted. "Well,
mostly that, anyway."

"Trust me, that's the least of your worries," Lynn said as if it were of no significance at all. "The Sweet Magnolias have a
way of making things happen. They did that
for me. They did it way back with The
Corner Spa, when Helen and Dana Sue put
up the cash and Maddie put in the sweat
equity. Your own brother got his interest in
Fit for Anything the same way."

"I know about that, but I don't want to
feel beholden to anyone," Adelia told her.
"After being under Ernesto's thumb all
those years, I want to make my own way."

"Accepting a helping hand does not make
you beholden," Lynn corrected. "I had to
learn that lesson myself. You'll find ways to

pay it forward. We all have. If Raylene brings this up again once the baby's here, don't even hesitate, Adelia. You've earned the right to be more than just an incredibly good salesclerk."

When Adelia remained silent, Lynn studied her intently. "You said it was mostly about the money. What's the rest?"

"I know that so far my instincts about the business have been pretty decent —" Adelia began.

"More than pretty decent to hear Raylene tell it," Lynn said.

"But I'm not really experienced," Adelia said. "Not with running a company, that's for sure."

Lynn laughed. "Honey, do you think any of us had a ton of experience when we got started? Dana Sue knew she could cook, but she'd never run a restaurant. Look at Sullivan's now. It's listed in guidebooks all over as one of the best in the state. As for The Corner Spa, when Helen, Maddie and Dana Sue opened it, they didn't even like to exercise. They just believed this town needed a gym that catered to pampering women. This bakery's the same for me. I'm flying by the seat of my pants most of the time. You'll be just fine, the same as the rest of us."

Apparently satisfied with her pep talk, Lynn stood up then. "Break's over. At least for me," she said, pouring more coffee into Adelia's to-go cup. "I've got cookies in the oven that should be ready."

"And I need to get to work," Adelia said. "Thanks for the company and for the advice."

"Back at you," Lynn said. "Maybe one of these days you and Gabe will come over for dinner."

Adelia immediately frowned at the suggestion. "I'm not sure . . . I mean we're not . . ."

Lynn grinned. "I'm no fortune-teller, but I predict one of these days you will be all those things you can't bring yourself to say," she said confidently.

"What things?"

"Dating. A couple." She laughed at Adelia's expression. "I know," she soothed. "Now I get why everybody had so much fun listening to me protest that there was nothing between Mitch and me."

Adelia couldn't think of anything to say to that, so she took her coffee refill and left. While it was great to have someone she could bounce her worries off of, in some ways she was leaving with more on her mind than she'd had before.

■ ■ ■ ■

Gabe studied Ernesto Hernandez and wondered how a woman like Adelia could have given him the time of day, much less years of her life. Successful people in Serenity dressed well enough, but none of them put on the show that Ernesto did with his fancy watch, Italian shoes and a suit that had evidently been custom-tailored. His silk-blend shirt even had monogrammed cuffs, for goodness' sake. Most men in town figured they were dressed well enough if there was a little starch in their collars when they got their oxford cloth shirts back from the laundry.

"I gave you a budget for sprucing up this kitchen," Ernesto complained to Mitch. "Now you want to charge me double what we agreed on."

Gabe watched as his cousin struggled to hold on to his temper. Gabe wondered if Mitch would be able to pull it off. The pulsing vein in his forehead seemed to be working overtime. Gabe was tempted to step in and help him out, but this was Mitch's company and his call.

"It's not a matter of *wanting* to charge you double," Mitch corrected, his voice surprisingly quiet. "I *have* to charge you double because you've upgraded everything we talked about. You're the one who decided only granite countertops would do and that the appliances ought to be stainless steel."

Ernesto sighed. "Not me. That's all Kendra."

"If you're going to let her start calling the shots, then you have to pay for the changes," Mitch said. "Or we can go back to the original plan and stay on budget."

"We're selling the blasted house. I don't know why she even cares," Ernesto grumbled.

Without ever having laid eyes on Kendra, Gabe had his own theory. He had a hunch the woman wanted the house upgraded her way just in case things didn't work out with Ernesto. If he'd cheated on his wife, he was likely to cheat on her. She wanted a nice place to go home to, that is, if the relationship even lasted long enough for her to move out. The woman might have the morals of an alley cat, but she was clearly smart enough to see Ernesto for the lousy bet he was.

Mitch sat at the kitchen table, his gaze on Ernesto. "What's it going to be?" he asked eventually.

"Do the upgrades," Ernesto said after a pause.

Mitch nodded and pushed a piece of paper in his direction. "Then I'm going to need you to sign this change order."

Ernesto frowned. "My word's not good enough."

Now there was a minefield, Gabe thought as he awaited Mitch's reply.

"It's standard procedure to have a change order when the original contract is amended in any way."

Ernesto glanced toward Gabe. "Are witnesses necessary, too?" he inquired sourly.

"Gabe's my second-in-command," Mitch said easily. "He oversees a lot of the work. It's just smart business to have him aware of any changes we're making."

Ernesto's frown deepened. "You're the man I hired. I thought you were overseeing this yourself. That's the impression Mary Vaughn gave me."

"I oversee all my company's work," Mitch explained patiently. "And I stand behind it. But I learned to delegate a long time ago. Gabe's taking over a lot of the details and he's very good at what he does."

"No way," Ernesto said heatedly. "I won't have a man who's been hanging around with my wife in charge of a job I'm paying for."

Gabe stilled at his words. Instinctively his hands balled into fists. Just like the old days, he was ready for a fight. Only out of respect for Adelia and Mitch did he manage to control the urge to use them.

"Excuse me," he said softly. "Are you referring to Adelia? Isn't she your ex-wife?"

"Technically," Ernesto said, not looking one bit happy about the concession to reality. "But she's bound to influence how you feel about me. I know she doesn't hesitate to tell everyone how mistreated she was, even after I gave her everything she could possibly need."

"Except fidelity and respect," Gabe snapped before he could stop himself. He glanced at Mitch. "Sorry."

Mitch sat back, barely restraining a smile. "Not a problem," he said, clearly happy to let Gabe say all the things he'd managed to keep himself from saying.

Ernesto stood up and squared his shoulders, radiating indignation. He scowled down at Mitch. "Are you going to let him speak to a client in such a disrespectful way?"

Mitch stood up, as well. He might not be wearing outrageously expensive business attire, but he towered over Ernesto. There was little question who was the more intimidating presence in the room.

"I believe you started it," he said calmly. "I don't think this is going to work out, Mr. Hernandez. I'll return your deposit. Get another company to do the job."

"I'll sue you for breach of contract," Ernesto warned.

"Try it," Mitch said, waving the unsigned change order under his nose. "You wanted to make changes to that contract but didn't want to pay for them. That nullifies the contract. I'm pretty sure Helen Decatur-Whitney can counter any claim you want to make. She did a pretty good job for your wife in the divorce. Do you really want to tangle with her again?"

"Get out!" Ernesto said. "I want you off my property."

"I don't believe the property is yours," Gabe said as they were on their way out. "And if your girlfriend is even half as smart as I think she must be since she convinced you to do all these fancy renovations for her, eventually you'll be the one who's escorted from it by the police."

Ernesto blinked at Gabe's words. "You don't know what you're talking about."

Gabe grinned, surprisingly satisfied to let

words win this particular battle. "Sure I do. I always recognize a good con when I see one. Now you have yourself a nice day."

Mitch didn't say a word until they were in his truck and on their way back to town. Gabe studied him, worried that he'd gone too far and cost his cousin this job.

"I'll go back and apologize if you want me to," he offered. Then he added, "Though I'd probably choke on the words."

Mitch chuckled then. "No, absolutely not. You said everything I'd been dying to say. I told you days ago I didn't want to do this job. Thanks to you, Ernesto finally gave me the perfect way out."

"Then you're not furious with me for what I said back there?"

"Nope. I just wish I'd guessed what his girlfriend was up to the way you did. I never look for devious motives."

"Because you're a nice guy," Gabe told him. "You never see the bad in anyone. Me, I've seen more than my share of good cons over the years."

"Do you really think his girlfriend is just after a sugar daddy to fix up her house before she calls it quits?"

Gabe shrugged. "I've never laid eyes on her, so who knows, but I can't imagine she thinks the man who cheated so openly on

Adelia would be a good bet for a long and happy life. I imagine she'll take him for whatever she can, then shed very few tears when she sends him on his way."

"Well, apparently Ernesto just realized that's a real possibility, too, because he looked pretty shaken when you said it." Mitch glanced over at him. "Seemed to me as if he knew there might be more to your relationship with Adelia than renovating her house for her. Any thoughts about how he knew that?"

Gabe barely contained a groan. That kiss was going to haunt them forever. "There might have been a little talk around town recently," he said eventually.

"About the kiss," Mitch suggested, his amusement plain.

"Yes, about the kiss," Gabe responded ruefully. "Apparently that's been a hot topic."

"It certainly has been at my house," Mitch said. "Lynn's convinced she should start polishing the silver."

Gabe stared at him. "Why would she do that?"

"Wedding shower," Mitch said, then chuckled when Gabe's jaw dropped. "You might want to hold off on any more kissing in public if you want to limit that kind of speculation."

"It was a stupid kiss," Gabe grumbled. "Nobody caught us naked."

Mitch's expression sobered at once. "Well, let's hope when the two of you do get naked, it won't be in the middle of Main Street."

"Nobody's getting naked," Gabe retorted.

Mitch laughed then. "Yet," he corrected. "Never say never, Gabe. Sooner or later you'll wind up eating those words."

Gabe was very much afraid he was probably right about that. Getting naked with Adelia was on his mind way too much lately. It had been ever since he'd discovered the power of a single kiss.

Gabe was atop a ladder painting Natalia and Juanita's room with pale pink on the walls and lavender on the ceiling when Adelia got home from work.

She stood in the bedroom doorway, a smile on her face. "Don't you look cute all splattered with pink and purple. Very princessy."

Gabe gave her a disgruntled look. "You should have seen me with the tiara on my head."

Her eyes widened. "Excuse me?"

"They thought we ought to have a tea

205

party before I started painting. Juanita persuaded me to wear this shiny tiara thing. She said something about princesses always being in charge and I had to do what they said. Since I wanted to get this room finished sometime before midnight, I cooperated."

Adelia tried to swallow a laugh, but she couldn't pull it off. A giggle slipped out. "I am so, so sorry I missed that."

"I believe there are pictures," he said, his expression disgruntled but his eyes twinkling. "Selena actually smiled while she was snapping them. I consider that worth it."

He climbed down from the ladder and crossed the room in three long strides. "And because of all that, I think I earned this."

He leaned in and stole a kiss. It didn't last more than a heartbeat, but it tripped her heart into overdrive.

He winked at her. "Thanks."

He climbed back on the ladder and went back to work while Adelia still struggled to catch her breath. When she remained silent, he turned back around.

"You okay?" he asked eventually.

"You just caught me by surprise," she said. "Again."

"Well, I've been told that kisses in the middle of Main Street stir up too much talk, so this is my last resort." He grinned. "Since I doubt you came up here just in case I decided to lose my head and kiss you, was there something on your mind? Or were you just checking on today's progress?"

"I came looking for you because I heard you told off my ex-husband this morning. And that he fired Mitch because of it. I didn't even know Mitch was working for him."

Gabe suddenly looked uncomfortable. "Mitch only took the job because Mary Vaughn somehow tricked him into it. If you know Mary Vaughn at all, you can understand how that sort of thing can happen. She's sneaky. Mitch didn't realize Ernesto was the client until it was too late to back out. And technically Ernesto didn't fire Mitch. Mitch fired him. Pretty happily, I might add."

Adelia felt a lot better about that. "Seriously?"

"He definitely had a good time doing it."

"And you? Did you have a good time telling him off?"

"I have to admit, I enjoyed it," Gabe said. "I figured I owed it to you to get in a couple of good shots." He gave her a lingering look. "I'm not sure what came over me, but I cut him down with words instead of punching him out. I consider that progress in my evolution. You must be a good influence on me."

She didn't entirely buy his claim. Knowing his history, she felt compelled to warn him. "While I can't say I don't appreciate the protectiveness, please stay away from him, Gabe. Ernesto has ways of getting even with people he perceives as enemies. It's better just to stay out of his path."

"How about this? I'll promise not to do or say another thing to the man as long as he doesn't give me cause to."

"I'm not sure I like the loophole you left for yourself."

Gabe shrugged. "Take it or leave it. That's the offer."

"He's not worth it, Gabe."

"No question about that, but if I think he's doing anything to hurt you or your kids, I'm not going to ignore it. Not my nature."

"We're not talking about a school-yard bully throwing insults about your mom," she told him.

For an instant she thought she'd gone too far. Gabe's expression went hard.

"A bully is a bully, Adelia," he said flatly. "It doesn't matter where he is or how old he is. And nobody hurts the people I care about. Not ever, if there's a single thing I can do to stop it."

"I don't want or need you to fight my battles for me," she argued, worried that things that had been dismissed as the actions of a troubled teen could turn into something else entirely when two grown men were involved.

Gabe studied her for a minute. "You're not worried about me embarrassing you or causing more trouble for you, are you? You're actually afraid for me."

"Somebody has to worry about you," she said, not denying it.

His expression immediately softened. "Nobody ever has before," he said very, very quietly.

She heard something in his voice that reached in and touched her soul. She heard the pain of a kid who'd spent too many years trying to protect someone only to pay a heavy price for it without ever getting so much as a word of thanks. She couldn't help wondering if all those years ago when he'd been fighting his mom's battles if anyone at all had ever fought his. It didn't sound like it.

She straightened her shoulders and met his gaze. "Well, now you have me. I'll have your back." She smiled to lighten the moment. "But you probably ought to know, I'm not much good in a brawl."

He laughed at that. "I'll keep that in mind and try to stay out of trouble."

She nodded. "All I'm asking."

CHAPTER TEN

Adelia hurried downstairs to keep herself from crossing the bedroom and dragging Gabe into her arms for a hug he seemed to desperately need. Or maybe that was her need, to show him that he was no longer alone. She couldn't help thinking about how long it had been since any man had needed her. Ernesto certainly hadn't, at least not for anything other than being able to claim he was respectably married to a woman who was a terrific mother to his kids.

Downstairs, Adelia found Selena at the kitchen table, along with Natalia, Juanita and even Tomas. To her shock, their homework was spread out on the table.

"I'm impressed," Adelia told them. "And the casserole I left for dinner is in the oven?"

Selena nodded. "I put it in when I heard you come in. I waited till then, because I didn't think you'd want to eat the second you walked in. I figured you'd be a while

211

with Gabe."

Since Selena didn't sound especially distraught by that, it was evident something had changed. Adelia wondered how much it had to do with that impromptu tea party and the tiara.

She leaned down to give her two younger girls a hug. "I hear you had a tea party. That must have been fun."

Selena actually giggled at that, filling Adelia's heart with hope. If her teen's sense of humor was back, perhaps she was finally emerging from the dark place she'd been in ever since she'd discovered what Ernesto was up to.

"It was dumb," Tomas said, his voice radiating masculine disgust. "They made Gabe wear this shiny crown thing. He did it, too. I don't get it. Guys shouldn't do stuff like that."

"And why is that?" Adelia asked.

Tomas looked confused by the question. "Just because," he said stubbornly.

Adelia kept her tone even as she told her son, "Someday you'll understand that men will do a lot of unpredictable things for women they like."

"Well, not me," Tomas said. "Daddy wouldn't have done something stupid like that."

"No, he probably wouldn't have," Adelia agreed quietly. "But personally I think it says a lot about Gabe that he would do something silly to make your sisters happy." She turned to Selena. "What do you think?"

"I think he looked pretty cute," she said. She frowned at her brother. "And it was cool that he went along with it." She held her cell phone out to Adelia. "Want to see?"

Sure enough, the younger girls were seated at the kitchen table with Gabe, doll-size teacups in front of all of them. Natalia and Juanita were wearing their favorite princess costumes. Gabe was adorned not only with that ridiculous tiara, but a pink feather boa. Neither could do a thing to take away from his potent masculinity, though. If anything, he looked sexier than ever, at least to her.

Adelia chuckled at the image. She really did owe him big-time for going along with her girls' request. It had clearly been an attempt to win her daughters' approval. And judging from the broad grins just now, it had worked, even with Selena, at least temporarily.

"Looks like a lot of fun. I wish I'd been here," she told the girls. She gave Selena a measured look. "So, how many people have you texted that picture to?"

"A few," she admitted, then added with a touch of defensiveness in her voice, "Come on, Mom. It's a great picture. Gabe knew I was taking it."

"I imagine he also knew you'd delight in making him a laughingstock all over town."

Selena flushed guiltily at the gently spoken accusation. "Do you think he's going to be mad?"

"No," Adelia told her. "I think he knew exactly what your intentions were and went along with it to try to win a couple of points with you. He wants to get along with you, you know."

"Maybe he's not such a bad guy," Selena conceded.

Adelia patted her shoulder. "Remember that the next time you see him. Cut him a little slack."

"Is he staying for dinner?" Selena asked.

"I didn't mention it to him."

"Can I ask him?" Selena requested.

Relieved by Selena's willingness to make more of an effort with Gabe, Adelia nodded at once. "I think he'd really appreciate that."

"We'll come, too," Natalia said, jumping up.

"No," Adelia said, stopping her. "Let Selena do this."

She could see from her oldest's expression that Selena understood not only just how much this gesture meant to Adelia, but how much it might matter to Gabe.

Selena wrapped her arms around Adelia's waist and gave her a fierce hug. "I'll try harder, Mom. I promise."

Adelia tucked a finger under her chin. "It makes me very happy to hear you say that. All I'll ever ask of you is that you be open-minded."

"Because everybody deserves a chance," Selena said, echoing what Adelia had said only a few days earlier. She glanced at the photo still on the screen on her cell phone. "Gabe might really, really deserve one."

She gave Adelia another grin and headed upstairs. Watching her go, Adelia breathed a sigh of relief. She didn't need her daughter's approval for whatever might happen between her and Gabe, but it was nice to know it might not be withheld. Things between her and Gabe were complicated enough without having to fight that particular battle. Of course, she was wise enough to recognize that winning one battle did not win this particular war. Selena's mercurial moods could change on a dime.

Gabe had finished painting the ceiling and was working on the trim when he noticed

Selena standing hesitantly in the bedroom doorway.

"Hey," he said. "Everything okay?"

"I thought you might want to see the picture I took earlier," she said, then grinned. "Or maybe not."

Gabe chuckled. "I have a hunch I'll be begging you to delete it."

She shook her head at once. "Not a chance."

"Good blackmail material?" he asked.

A smile tugged at her lips. "Really good."

He beckoned for her to come closer. "Let me see."

He took in the tiara, the pink boa and the miniature teacups and barely contained a groan. Sadly the picture was clear as a bell. Too bad it wasn't so blurry no one would be able to identify him.

"Nice shot," he commented.

"That's what everyone thinks," she said, then winced, her expression filled with guilt.

"Everyone?"

"I might have texted it to some people. Sorry." She tried to look contrite, but failed at it.

"If I had a picture this good, I'd want to share it, too," he said.

She looked surprised by that. "Really?"

"Sure."

"You aren't humiliated that it's probably all over town by now?"

"Was that your intention, to humiliate me?"

"Maybe," she confessed. "At least until I thought about it."

"And then?"

"I realized it was really nice what you did, going along with Natalia and Juanita. My dad would never have done something like that. He'd be too freaked out about his image." She made a face. "As if his is all that great in the first place," she added.

There was real anger in her voice. Or perhaps it was disappointment Gabe heard. Either way he wasn't about to go down that road with Selena. "Well, if you promise not to tell anyone," he said, "I'll tell you a secret."

She looked intrigued. "I won't tell. Cross my heart."

He leaned closer. "I had fun. I'd never been to a tea party before. Or worn a tiara and whatever that feathery thing was."

"A boa," she said, giggling. "You liked it?"

"I liked that it made you laugh and it made your sisters happy," he corrected.

To his surprise, his words seemed to cause tears to well up. Unsure of what he'd said to bring them on, he regarded her worriedly.

"Selena, what did I say? I didn't mean to upset you."

"I'll bet you wouldn't have made a big deal about going to a father–daughter dance with your daughter, would you?" she blurted, the question seemingly coming out of nowhere.

Gabe regarded her with confusion. "I don't understand. What's a father–daughter dance got to do with this?"

Her expression turned sad. "I asked my dad to take me to one at school a while back. He said he'd go, but at the last minute he tried to bail, just like always when something was important to me. He said he was too busy. My mom made him go, but he didn't want to be there. It was awful. My uncle Elliott took Daisy and he loved being there. That made it worse."

Gabe heard the misery in her voice and added yet one more reason to dislike Ernesto to his rapidly growing list. "I'm sorry," he said.

She swiped angrily at the tears on her cheeks, then asked, "Would you have gone?"

There had never been an opportunity for such a thing in Gabe's life, but he was pretty sure he'd never disappoint a child the way Ernesto had disappointed Selena. "If I had a daughter, there's nothing I'd be more honored to do than to take her to a father–daughter dance if she wanted me to be there."

"That's how Uncle Elliott felt, too." She sighed. "I guess some people can't change who they are and how they feel about stuff, huh?"

No, but they ought to try, especially if their actions were going to hurt their kids, Gabe thought. "People can always change," he said carefully.

"You're nice," she said, as if that was a huge surprise to her.

"Not always," he confided just to see another smile on her face. She rewarded him with a bright one.

"Yes, you are." She stuffed her phone into her pocket, then regarded him hesitantly. "I came up here to see if you want to stay for dinner. We're having Mom's enchilada casserole. Actually it's *Abuela*'s recipe, but Mom's getting pretty good at making it. It'll be ready in about ten minutes."

"I would love to stay," Gabe said, not just because the promise of good food was tempting, but because she'd made the unexpected overture. "Thanks, Selena."

"Okay, I'll tell Mom." She got to the door and turned back. "Mr. Franklin?"

"You can call me Gabe, if that's okay with

your mother."

"Okay, Gabe. Do you like my mom?"

"I do," he said.

"I mean a lot. Do you want to date her and stuff?"

Gabe wasn't sure what sort of "stuff" Selena had in mind, but he knew admitting to it was probably a very bad idea. "We're getting to know each other," he said, choosing his words carefully.

"That's what she says, too."

"Are you okay with that?"

"I'm not really sure."

Gabe nodded at her honest reaction. "You don't have to be sure right this minute. Nobody's on a timetable here."

Her expression brightened again at that. "That's good then. Thanks."

"No thanks necessary," he said, watching as she left.

While the whole conversation seemed like a giant step forward, it was also a very big reminder that the situation was a whole lot more complicated than he'd ever imagined. If he did decide to see where things might go with Adelia, he needed to remember that there were a lot of other people who'd be affected by their actions. Was that a risk he was willing to take? Especially when he'd already made it clear, to Adelia at least, that he didn't do the whole happily-ever-after thing?

"You were awfully quiet during dinner," Adelia said as she and Gabe cleared the table and put dishes into the dishwasher. He'd insisted on helping, so she'd let the younger kids go outside to play and allowed Selena a half hour of phone time with her friends.

"Seriously?" she'd asked, looking shocked at the special dispensation from the rules of being grounded.

"Seriously," Adelia had told her. "I think you showed some signs of real maturity today. I think you deserve a break, just this once." She'd given her a stern look. "Though from now on, would you please remember that no phone includes no texting. You seem to be having a little trouble with that."

"I know. I'm sorry," Selena said, sounding suitably contrite. A genuine smile had broken across her face then. She'd thrown her arms around Adelia. "Thanks, Mom." Then she'd grinned at Gabe. "Thank you, too."

Gabe had regarded her with bewilderment. "Me? What did I do?"

"You've made Mom all mellow," Selena

responded, then darted off.

Now Adelia focused her attention on Gabe, who seemed to be avoiding not only her comment, but her gaze. "What's going on, Gabe?"

"I have a lot on my mind, that's all," he said, an oddly defensive note in his voice.

"About work? Is it getting to be too much, doing my renovations after hours?"

"No."

"Am I going to have to play twenty questions to get the truth out of you?"

His lips quirked up at that. "No. It was something Selena said earlier. It got me to thinking."

"What did she say?" Adelia frowned. "She wasn't rude, was she? I told her she could call her friends because I thought she'd made amends with you."

"She never needed to make amends with me, but, no, she wasn't rude. Nothing like that. It's just that some of the things she said made me realize that what's going on with us . . ." He glanced at her quickly. "Not that anything is."

"Right. Not that anything is."

"It's just that the decisions we might make down the road don't just affect us."

Adelia began to understand. "You're absolutely right. I will always have to think about my kids and put them first."

"Which means I have to think about them, too," he said. "I've never had to look beyond my own wants and needs before."

"Of course you have," she said impatiently. "For years you put your mom's needs first."

"Since then," he said, conceding the point. "And let's just say it — that situation was all upside down. I was a kid. She was the parent. I'm not sure what I took away from that, maybe just an understanding that I didn't ever want to be responsible for anyone's happiness or well-being again."

"Which is why you don't do relation-ships," she said. "Yes, you've mentioned that."

"I just want to be up front with you."

"And you have been. You're doing it again right now, making it clear that I shouldn't have any expectations where you're con-cerned."

Gabe frowned. "You make that sound like a bad thing. Would you prefer me to start something with you and then take off with no warning when the situation gets to be more than I can handle?"

Adelia sighed. She knew that wouldn't be better. But what made the most sense of all was to never start anything in the first place, not with a man who'd declared very clearly that there would be no commitment, not ever. It didn't matter that she thought he was selling himself short. It only mattered what he thought.

And while she might not be anywhere near ready for a commitment herself, she wasn't so sure she was cut out for a flirtation that had absolutely no potential for going anywhere.

"Gabe, are we crazy for spending even a single second with each other?" she asked.

"What do you mean?"

"We both know there's some kind of attraction thing going on. Heaven knows, I liked kissing you."

"Right back at you," he said.

"Then it seems to me we're playing with fire. I don't think I'm capable of having some sort of passionate fling without expecting it to go somewhere. And you're very clear about where you stand on anything more than a fling. One of us is bound to get hurt, and, frankly, I've had about all of the misery I can handle."

"It would kill me to know I'd made you miserable," he said, gently cupping her cheek with his hand. "It really would. I don't ever want to give you a reason to lump me in any category in which a man like Ernesto is the star offender."

She smiled at that. "I doubt I'd ever compare you to him. You've already shown me more thoughtfulness and consideration than he had in years."

"Still, it's not a risk I'm willing to take."

"So, where does that leave us?" she asked, already knowing the sensible answer. "Do we agree just to be friends? Do we avoid each other entirely?"

Gabe looked genuinely taken aback by the limited options she'd presented. "Friends isn't going to work, Adelia. Not for me. That attraction thing isn't going to go away. Sooner or later one of us will cave in to it. I'm betting it will be me." He gave her a self-deprecating grin. "And given my excellent powers of persuasion . . ."

She couldn't help smiling at that, too. "Really?"

"Oh, yes. I'll be very persuasive. You'll give in and then you'll wind up hating me for it."

She understood his logic and bought the argument. Even now, if he reached for her, she knew she'd be unable to resist.

"Then I suppose we have to avoid each other," she said with real regret. She drew herself up, though, and said with resolve, "We can do that. I know when you're likely to be at the bakery. I'll go in at a different time or not at all. As for the work here, I can call the kids and let them know when I'm heading home. They can alert you and you can be gone by the time I get here. That should be easy enough."

"Or I could insist that Mitch replace me on this job," he said.

"That's not fair," she protested. "I don't want you to lose the income and I like the work you're doing. I'll just make sure to limit the times we cross paths."

Gabe sighed, clearly reluctant to agree to her plan. "I have to tell you, Adelia, I hate this."

"I'm not wild about it, either, but it's the only sensible way to handle things so they don't get out of hand," she said.

"Preventative medicine, so to speak."

She nodded. "Exactly."

Even as she managed to sound determined, her heart was aching. The thought of not seeing Gabe anymore like this, of not witnessing the growing bond between him and Tomas or the laughter he stirred with her girls, made her incredibly sad. Sure, this was the smart decision, perhaps the *only* decision, but that didn't mean she had to like it.

Just when she was trying to mentally congratulate herself for making the tough choice, Gabe stepped closer. His heat drew her the way that giant magnet he had Tomas using in the yard drew metal. She swayed toward him, just as she'd predicted she would.

He put his hands on her shoulders and held her in place, his touch gentle but firm.

"One last kiss?" he said.

It was posed as a question, but there was a quiet urgency, a command to the words, too.

Adelia nodded, her heart in her throat.

His hands — his big, strong hands — left her shoulders to frame her face. His gaze held hers, his eyes darkening with desire.

And then his lips were on hers. This wasn't a tender, exploratory kiss like the one they'd shared on Main Street, or the teasing kiss he'd bestowed on her earlier. This was passion and heat and longing all wrapped up in a moment that seemed to last forever. It stole her breath and left her pulse racing.

And it filled her with a longing she'd never expected to feel again.

I just ended this, she thought to herself incredulously. *I just declared this man off-limits? Am I nuts?*

The kiss stopped too soon and yet not nearly soon enough. It had lasted long enough to give her second thoughts, maybe even third thoughts. From the dazed and hungry look in Gabe's eyes, it had done the same to him.

"No second thoughts," he said, as if he'd read her mind. "We've agreed that this is for the best."

"It is," she managed to say, even though she found it hard to believe that anything this good could possibly come to a bad end.

He caressed her cheek one last time, then regarded her with unmistakable regret. "Good night, Adelia."

The regret in his eyes was almost her undoing. Then she steadied her resolve. "Bye, Gabe," she whispered as he walked away, closing the back door oh so quietly but emphatically behind him.

If this was so right, she thought, why did it feel as if she'd just given up the best thing to come into her life in years?

CHAPTER ELEVEN

It had been a slow morning at the boutique. None of the new merchandise Adelia had helped Raylene select had turned up. Customers had been few and far between. Adelia had straightened up all the displays, dusted every surface and looked through half a dozen catalogues for potential new stock. Raylene always took her recommendations seriously, which had given her self-confidence a much-needed boost.

Typically on a day like today, she'd lock up for a ten-minute break and head next door for a pick-me-up cup of coffee, maybe even one of Lynn's tart lemon-blueberry bars. Ever since her most recent encounter with Gabe, though, she'd grown more skittish than ever about dropping into her friend's bakery. She and Gabe had an agreement, and while he was rarely at the bakery in the middle of the day, she couldn't take a chance on running into him, not while this agreed-upon separation of theirs was so new. It would be far too easy to backslide.

At the sound of the bell over the door, she bounced up eagerly and walked into the front of the store.

"It's just me," Raylene called out. "I thought you might be ready for a break, so I brought coffee."

"Thank goodness," Adelia said, accepting the cup.

Raylene grinned. "Quiet day?"

"You have no idea. It's as if everyone in town is all shopped out. I suppose that's to be expected after the crazy busy days we had last week."

"You should know by now that it's feast or famine in retail," Raylene said, not sounding particularly upset by the decline in business.

Adelia couldn't make herself be so blasé. She'd spent the morning thinking of ways to generate more customers. "Maybe we need to have a sale," she suggested. "Or send out an announcement about the new lingerie line. We have email addresses for all our customers. I could do that this afternoon."

"And that is why you're going to make an excellent business partner," Raylene said. "Ever since you came to work here, you've been coming up with ways to build the business. I hope you know how much I value your input. If you want to do an email blast to our customer base, go for it."

"I'm going to blunder sooner or later," Adelia warned.

Raylene laughed. "No doubt about it. You weren't working here at the time of my great Christmas sweater catastrophe."

"What was that?" Adelia asked, intrigued.

"I ordered a ton of what I thought were really fun Christmas sweaters before I realized that my customers were looking for style, not things that would be passed around at parties as the year's worst gifts. I'll bet you would have steered me away from that disaster."

"Absolutely," Adelia said. "This shop has become the fashion trendsetter in town. Those sweaters sound as if they might have been just a bit off the mark."

"And there's that diplomatic skill of yours again," Raylene said, laughing. Her expression sobered as she held Adelia's gaze.

She studied Adelia over the rim of her own take-out cup of decaf. "Is there some particular reason you're so jittery today?"

"I'm not jittery," Adelia said. "I'm bored. It's ironic really. Before I started working full-time for you, I was on so many committees for the schools that I never had a spare minute. Now it feels as if I'm at loose ends, even when I'm here on days like today."

"That's not boredom, my friend," Raylene said, her eyes twinkling with mirth. "I'm guessing this has something to do with Gabe Franklin."

Startled by the assessment, Adelia stared at her. "Why on earth would you jump to that conclusion?"

"Because Lynn told me you've stopped coming by in the morning to pick up coffee. She has the feeling you're avoiding him." Raylene gave her a penetrating look. "Are you? Did the two of you have a fight?"

Adelia sighed. It was useless to try to pretend with Raylene. She'd keep poking and prodding till she got the answers she wanted. In recent months, Adelia had discovered it was something friends did. She still wasn't sure how she felt about the habit.

"There was no fight," she told Raylene, then tried to minimize the situation that had left her more shaken than she'd expected to be. "He's still doing the work at the house. It's all good."

"Then why do you sound so unhappy and why is Gabe storming around as if someone stole his favorite power saw?"

Adelia actually took some comfort from hearing that Gabe was no happier than she was. Of course, neither of them had genuinely wanted this separation. They'd just agreed it was for the best.

"I can't explain Gabe's moods," Adelia claimed. "As far as I know, everything's just fine."

"I'm not buying it," Raylene said. "You're saying all the right words, but the look in your eyes says something else entirely. What really happened between you two? He didn't cross a line, did he? I certainly know the two of you kissed."

"Everybody in town knew the two of us kissed," Adelia said wryly.

"Well, I thought it was something you were into," Raylene said. "Was I wrong? Gabe wasn't making unwanted advances, was he? Was he pressuring you?" Indignation immediately laced through her voice.

"Absolutely not," Adelia said quickly. She certainly didn't want the full weight of a bunch of riled up women coming down on him, not when he'd done nothing to deserve it. "He'd never do anything like that."

"And the kids like him okay?" Raylene prodded, clearly determined to find the missing piece to the puzzle she was trying to unravel. "I know Tomas is like his little shadow, but the girls? How do they feel about him?"

Adelia regarded her with exasperation. "You need a hobby, something other than my life."

"Probably so," Raylene said unrepentantly. "But for right this second, you're all I've got. Were things okay with Gabe and the kids? You didn't dump him because of them, did you?"

In a way that's exactly what had happened, Adelia thought, but she wasn't prepared to admit it. Instead, she said, "You're absolutely right that Tomas thinks he hung the moon, or at least he did before Gabe went along with Natalia and Juanita and attended one of their tea parties. He's struggling a bit with why a real guy would do that."

Raylene chuckled. "Yeah, that picture made the rounds. I thought it showed a lot about the kind of man Gabe is. Not many men could pull off a tiara and a feather boa and still look sexy as sin."

"Not many men would be willing to try it just to make a couple of little girls happy," Adelia commented.

"So, we have a man who puts a blush in your cheeks, is a good role model for your son and makes your girls happy," Raylene assessed. "I'm not seeing the downside. What am I missing?"

Adelia finally gave up on keeping the situation under wraps. "It was never going to work," she confided.

Raylene stared at her incredulously. "And you knew that after a couple of weeks and not even one real date? How?"

"It just wasn't. We have very different ideas about what we want in life. Better to end it before it got started and anyone got hurt, especially my kids."

Understanding dawned in Raylene's expression. "Now I get it. You did call it off to protect your kids, just not the way I was talking about."

Adelia shrugged. "Pretty much."

"But he's still at the house. He's still in their lives on a daily basis. How is this helping to protect them?"

"They won't get any ideas about the two of us," Adelia said. They'd miss any displays of affection, any stolen kisses.

"Ah," Raylene said, nodding. "And what about you? Do you feel all safe and secure now, too?"

"I did what I had to do," Adelia said defensively. "Gabe agreed with me."

"Well, that is just plain wrong," Raylene said.

"How is it wrong to want what's best for my family, especially after all they've gone through with the divorce?"

"Putting your family first is always good," Raylene agreed. "It's what mothers do. But smart *women* know that sometimes what's best for a happy family is taking care of their own needs, too. Remember that expression, 'If Mama ain't happy, ain't nobody happy'?"

Adelia smiled. "A simplified slogan isn't necessarily the best motto for living your life."

"I think this one has merit," Raylene said. "Happiness is contagious. Even in the very limited time you and Gabe have been acquainted, I've seen a change in you. You were happier, Adelia. Don't even try to deny it. This job may be giving your self-esteem a boost when it comes to your professional skills, but with Gabe you were rediscovering your worth as a woman."

Adelia didn't bother trying to deny it, because she knew it would be a lie. "It wouldn't have lasted," she said instead. That wasn't a lie. It was the inevitable truth.

"Gabe doesn't do forever," she revealed to Raylene. "How could I get involved with someone who openly made that clear from the outset? I've already been with one man who was incapable of sticking to his wedding vows. Gabe was pretty clear he'd never even take the vows."

Raylene scowled at the comment. "Don't you dare compare him to Ernesto. It's not fair."

"That's not what I'm doing. Gabe said —"

Raylene cut her off. "Men say stuff. They even believe it to be true. It gives them an easy out if they decide down the line that they need one. It's very rare for anyone to fall head over heels in love in a minute. It takes time. People have to get to know each other, to trust each other. Look at Carter and me. We had enough issues and past history to scare off any sane person. But we hung in there. Actually I should say that he did. He was persistent even in the face of all my doubts. In the end, love won out."

"If it were just me," Adelia began, unable to keep a wistful note from her voice.

"You'd take the chance," Raylene said triumphantly. "That right there tells you that you're giving up too easily."

"My kids," she protested.

"Your kids deserve to have a happy mom who has a wonderful man in her life. He's already won over Tomas, Juanita and Natalia, right?"

"Even Selena has fewer reservations,"

237

Adelia admitted. "That whole tea party thing, even though it was for the benefit of the younger girls, made an impression on her, too, probably because it was such a contrast to anything Ernesto would have done to please her or her sisters."

"Well, there you go."

"But if Gabe and I can't make it, I'll be dragging them through a whole big drama all over again," Adelia said. "I can't do that. I won't."

"You're scared," Raylene assessed. "And who can blame you? This is a man who flirts, who makes you feel like a woman, who makes you feel alive. That's scary stuff after too many years of being dismissed as unworthy and competing with a string of mistresses."

"Okay, yes. I'm finding it hard to trust that Gabe's even attracted to me, but I swear that is not why I called it quits. It was the sensible thing to do." She gave her friend a defiant look. "And I'm not changing my mind."

"Okay, this calls for an intervention by a higher authority," Raylene said.

Adelia stared at her, surprised. "You think I should pray about it?"

Raylene grinned. "Well, that probably wouldn't hurt, either, but I was thinking that what you really need is a margarita night with a bunch of women who've been there, done just about everything."

"The Sweet Magnolias," Adelia guessed, then shook her head. "I don't know."

"Come with me," Raylene ordered, pointing to the back room. "Let's think about this." She led the way into the tiny office. "Sit."

"I don't want to," Adelia said, then chuckled. "What is wrong with me? I sounded like Selena then, just like a sullen teenager."

"Want to know what I think?" Raylene asked, then continued without waiting for Adelia's reply. "I think of all the women I know, nobody deserves the chance to flirt and feel like an attractive woman again more than you do. Ernesto took that skill set away from you. He played havoc with your self-confidence by going after all those other women. You're entitled to have a little fun. Flirt with Gabe if you want to. Let him make you laugh. Let him make you blush. It doesn't have to lead to anything more, not if you don't want it to."

"I have to concentrate on being a good mom right now," Adelia argued yet again, even though it seemed her words were falling on deaf ears. Raylene was nothing if not stubborn. "The kids need me more than ever to make sure they feel safe and loved."

"And who's supposed to make you feel that way?" Raylene asked.

"Not Gabe Franklin," Adelia said.

"Maybe not," Raylene agreed. "But there is a man out there who is right for you. Think of Gabe as practice, if you want to."

Adelia frowned at the suggestion. "That hardly seems fair."

"Sweetie, I don't know Gabe that well yet, but something tells me he can take care of himself. Worry about what you need for a change."

"And you think what I need is to flirt outrageously?" Adelia asked skeptically.

Raylene gave her wicked grin. "Couldn't hurt. And if you don't trust my opinion, then come over to my place tonight. The Sweet Magnolias are getting together for a margarita night. You can run the idea past everyone. And before you get all crazy and say something about the Sweet Magnolias being some secret society, let me assure you that everyone is on board with you joining us. Karen will be there. So will Lynn and Sarah. You'll know all the others, too. You should at least give us a chance."

Adelia had to admit that the prospect of forming a bond with other women, many of whom had been through what she'd been through and, in some cases, even worse, held a lot of appeal. She'd already promised herself that if she ever had the chance to get to know them, she'd grab it.

And she needed a night like this, not so much to kick up her heels, but to do something for herself. It had been all about the kids lately, especially the decision to walk away from Gabe before they got too attached or misinterpreted why he was around. It was one thing for Tomas to idolize Gabe as a role model. It would be quite another for him to start thinking of Gabe as potential dad material.

"Okay, I'll come," she said at last. "What can I bring?"

"Nothing this time," Raylene told her. "But next time we're going to want you to bring one of your mother's famous Mexican dishes and maybe that secret mole sauce I've been hearing so much about."

Adelia laughed. "Not even I have that recipe, but I'll talk Mama into making it for us. Maybe Dana Sue can dissect it and figure out the ingredients since she's such a great chef. My sister-in-law is pretty good at that, but Karen hasn't been able to figure it out. It's driving her a little nuts."

"So, you'll be there," Raylene pressed.

"I'll be there," Adelia agreed.

"Perfect. I'll see you tonight around seven," Raylene said. "If you need someone to stay with the kids, I can send Carrie or Mandy over. Babysitting gigs on margarita nights keep them in pizza money. Or is Selena babysitting them these days?"

"I don't mind leaving her in charge after school, but nights are another story. I'll check with my mother. The kids could use a night with their *abuela*. If she's not available, I'll let you know."

She watched as her boss left the store without asking a single question about anything work related. She'd even left it to Adelia to decide about sending out those email alerts. Surprisingly, that felt wonderful. She realized it demonstrated just how much Raylene trusted her to be on top of things. Being invited to a margarita night was just the icing on the cake.

"I brought coffee," Mitch said, settling onto a folding chair across from Gabe. He handed over a supersized to-go cup from the bakery.

"Thanks. To what do I owe this?"

"I thought maybe the caffeine would improve your mood," Mitch said. "I've had half a dozen complaints today that you're behaving like a bear with a thorn in its paw."

Gabe studied his cousin with narrowed eyes. "Is that so? Who's running to you to tattle?"

"Not the point. Is it true? And before you try to deny it, you should probably know that I have to believe it must be true because of all those reliable sources."

"Then why even ask?"

"Because I wanted to give you a chance to explain."

Gabe regarded Mitch curiously. "And if I have nothing to say?"

"Then I will be forced to remind you that I am the boss and that I don't like dissension on my work sites, especially when the man responsible for it is my cousin and my second-in-command."

"There you go, pulling rank again."

"Frankly, I don't like doing it," Mitch said, looking surprisingly uncomfortable. "I shouldn't have to."

Gabe sighed. "No, you shouldn't. And I'll apologize to, well, everybody, I guess, since you refuse to be specific about whom I've offended."

"Just correct the attitude," Mitch suggested. "And talk to me."

"About what?"

"Whatever put you in this mood."

Gabe regarded him incredulously. "Do

you honestly want to have some long talk about my feelings and that sort of stuff?"

Mitch looked horrified, just as Gabe expected.

"Absolutely not," Mitch said at once. "Lynn just thought I ought to try to get to the bottom of it." His eyes narrowed. "She doesn't think it's a coincidence that Adelia seems to be making herself scarce at the bakery."

Gabe avoided his cousin's penetrating gaze. "I wouldn't know about that."

"Because the two of you had some sort of falling out?"

"Mitch, please do not go there. My personal life is just that, personal."

"So this is about Adelia," Mitch concluded, looking pleased with himself. Or maybe he was just happy at the proof that his wife had nailed the problem. "Want to talk about that?"

"No!" Gabe said emphatically.

Mitch tried to hide a grin but couldn't pull it off. "Interesting."

"Go to blazes!"

His cousin's laugh echoed through the work site. "And there's the attitude I've been hearing about."

At Gabe's sour look, Mitch's expression sobered. "Okay, here's the deal. The women are all getting together for one of those Sweet Magnolia things tonight. I imagine they're going to roast you for whatever you did."

"I didn't do anything," Gabe protested.

"Doesn't matter. Perception is everything. My point is that when they get together like that, the men play hoops. Frankly, my knees are giving out, but it's nice to hang out, work up a little sweat and tell tall tales with a bunch of the guys. You're coming along tonight."

"Was that an invitation or a command?" Gabe grumbled.

"Call it whatever you want, as long as you're on the court in the park by seven. Want me to pick you up?"

"I can find it," Gabe said.

Actually the idea of a little physical exertion sounded good. Maybe if he was sweating hard, gasping for breath and making a few baskets, he could push all the thoughts of Adelia out of his head. Of course, that might be asking an awful lot of a casual basketball game with the guys. He was pretty sure his steamy thoughts about Adelia weren't going to go away so easily.

When Gabe turned up at the basketball court that night at seven, he was surprised to find several men he remembered there, including Ronnie Sullivan, who now owned the hardware store on Main Street, high school baseball coach Cal Maddox and Adelia's brother, Elliott Cruz. A lot of the others were new to town, proving that Serenity had provided a draw to men from very diverse backgrounds. It made him look at the town with a new perspective.

Perhaps most surprising were Travis McDonald, a former pro baseball player who now owned the country music station, his cousin Tom, who was the town manager, and Carter Rollins, the police chief who Mitch said had moved to town from Columbia in search of a quieter place to raise his two sisters after their parents had been killed in an accident. These were men who could have settled anywhere, but they'd chosen Serenity, seen its potential.

Before the game started, Elliott pulled Gabe aside. Expecting a lecture or worse, he tensed. Instead, Elliott merely asked how the work was coming along at Adelia's.

"The roof's solid now and the demolition is mostly completed. I'm trying to get all the kids' rooms painted so they'll feel settled," Gabe reported.

A smile tugged at Elliott's lips. "I'm surprised you've had the time to accomplish all that, what with the tea parties you've had to attend."

Gabe groaned. "You saw the picture?"

"Oh yeah," Elliott confirmed. "Selena sent it to my daughter. Naturally she shared it with her mom and me and heaven knows how many other people."

Ignoring yet more evidence of how far that blasted picture had spread, Gabe focused on the rest of what Elliott had said. "I didn't think you and Karen had been married long enough to have a daughter Selena's age."

"Daisy's actually a little younger. She was my stepdaughter, but we started adoption proceedings a while back. She and her brother, Mack, will be my kids officially before long."

Something in his voice suggested there was a story behind that, but Gabe didn't pry.

"Are you guys ready to get on the court?" Carter called out. "I, for one, could work off a little steam. I had to deal with the mayor today, and that usually tests my patience."

"Amen to that," Tom McDonald said in heartfelt agreement.

The men chose sides and hit the court. It didn't take long for Gabe to realize that most of them played for blood. He was panting in no time, but he felt as if he was holding his own as he blocked a shot by Travis McDonald, then took the ball down the court and dunked it to score the winning points.

Mitch was bent over, but there was pride in his voice, when he said, "And, gentlemen, that is how it's done. Now, if you don't mind, I need water and maybe some oxygen."

Tom followed Mitch to the bench and sank down beside him, then handed out water bottles all around.

"I hate to admit it," Ronnie Sullivan said, "but I might be getting too old for this."

"Join the club," Mitch said, clearly commiserating with him.

"If you guys suggest we quit this and take up golf, I swear I'm going to have to leave town," Travis said. "I can't be surrounded by a bunch of wimps."

"Say that when you're my age," Ronnie countered.

"Or mine," Mitch said.

Travis shook his head. "Pitiful. Just plain pitiful."

"Oh, cut them some slack," Cal suggested. "Old geezers deserve our respect."

Gabe laughed at the indignant expressions that spread over Ronnie's face and his cousin's. Since Mitch was only a couple of years older than Gabe was, he probably shouldn't be laughing at all.

"Maybe we should change the subject," Carter said, "before I have to call in deputies to break up a brawl." He turned to Gabe. "So what's this I hear about you dating Adelia Hernandez?"

Gabe flushed at suddenly having all the attention focused on him. If they'd been asking about the Main Street renovations or even his work at Adelia's, it would have been one thing, but this was clearly a trap he'd fallen into.

"I have no idea where you got your information," he said carefully, only to see Elliott's expression darken.

"I had the impression you were seeing my sister," Elliott said.

"Were, past tense," Gabe said, aware that silence had fallen and all the men were listening attentively to his response. "She and I agreed we should stick to being friends."

That was a bit of a stretch, but it was better than revealing the truth, that they'd called it off before it really got started, mostly because he'd made it clear they had no long-term future.

"I warned you," Elliott said, his voice low,

his scowl firmly in place.

Gabe leveled an even look on him. "Her decision," he said quietly. "Ask her if you don't believe me."

"Oh, I will," Elliott assured him. "And if I don't like the answer —"

"Guys, guys!" Carter said, intervening again. "I think we could all use a time-out and something cold to drink."

"Beers at my place," Ronnie said. "Or more water, if that's your preference. And the pizza will be delivered by the time we get there. I've just called the order in to Rosalina's."

Gabe turned to Mitch. "Maybe I should take off."

Mitch shook his head. "No need. These are good men. They're a little protective of their women, but they're not unfair. You need to stand your ground." He held Gabe's gaze. "That is, if you've done nothing wrong."

Gabe wanted to believe Mitch was right. He'd never had buddies like these men appeared to be. It had been nice to feel like a real part of something, even if it had been a casual basketball game.

He nodded eventually. "I'll hang out and see what happens."

After all, he really hadn't done anything

wrong. All he'd done was let himself be tempted for just a minute by a strong, beautiful woman. Not a one of these men, all of whom were happily married from what he knew, could possibly believe that was a crime.

CHAPTER TWELVE

The Sweet Magnolia women gathered in the new family room at Raylene's, with its high ceiling and soaring windows, were all people Adelia had known most of her life in one capacity or another. Two or three were even friends.

She was really looking forward, though, to getting to know the original trio of women who'd formed the group. Dana Sue Sullivan, the owner of Sullivan's restaurant, and Maddie Maddox, who ran The Corner Spa, were practically legends in town.

In a way she already knew Maddie as Elliott's boss and an indirect partner in the men's gym he'd created with some of the husbands of the women in this room. Their brief exchanges when Adelia had gone to the spa to try to get fit in a last-ditch effort to save her marriage had been mostly casual, though. She also knew that Maddie had coached Lynn through making her business plan for the bakery. She was obviously generous and kind. Like all the Sweet Magnolias, she was someone worth knowing.

Adelia already knew the third member of that original group, Helen Decatur-Whitney, professionally. Helen had been her divorce attorney, and she'd fought to ensure that Ernesto provided well for her and for the children. Adelia was determinedly setting most of that support money aside for college for the kids. Some of her lump-sum alimony would go toward the house renovations. Beyond that, she wanted to prove they could live on what she was able to provide on her own these days. Amazingly, thanks to her budgeting skills, which she'd practiced even when living under Ernesto's roof, they were making it. She headed in Helen's direction to thank her yet again for her support. She wondered if a lifetime would be long enough for her to convey the depth of her gratitude for Helen's fierce loyalty.

"You look incredible," Helen said, studying her outfit. "I wish I had your sense of style."

Adelia laughed. "You must be kidding. I recognize that blouse you're wearing. It's from the new designer collection I saw in a boutique when I was over in Charleston a couple of weeks ago. And your shoes are Jimmy Choo." She leaned down for a closer look. "Stunning."

Maddie joined them just then. "We *all* know those are Jimmy Choos, even if we don't have a lick of style. Helen's expensive taste in shoes is her trademark. Before she had a daughter and college expenses to worry about, she indulged in shoes. Lots and lots of shoes."

Helen held out a foot and regarded it with a sorrowful expression. "These are beautiful, aren't they? Sadly, these days I seem to spend a lot of time in sneakers, trying to keep up with my daughter."

Maddie turned to Adelia. "I'm so glad you were able to come tonight. I'm looking forward to getting to know you better. I've watched your progress at the spa and listened to your brother bragging on you."

"Elliott brags about me?" Adelia asked, surprised.

"He takes personal credit for turning you into an exercise junkie," Maddie reported.

"No way," Adelia said adamantly. "I show up. I work out, but I hate every second. I'm there in spite of my brother, not because of him. That's why he's not my personal trainer."

Maddie chuckled. "Working out with your

brother might be counterproductive. If I know anything about sibling relationships, I can guess you'd probably do the opposite of anything he suggests."

"Exactly," Adelia confirmed.

"Well, I know Raylene thinks the world of you," Maddie said. "She says she can take time off to be with the baby when it comes, because she knows the boutique will be in excellent hands. She says she really lucked out the day you walked in the door looking for a job."

Though she'd heard the same thing from Raylene herself, it was praise Adelia never tired of hearing. Raylene's confidence in her had been the first step on her path toward rebuilding her confidence in herself. "I certainly intend to try hard not to let her down," she told Maddie.

Raylene came over just then. "No way could you let me down. My business doubled after you came to work for me." She turned to Maddie. "Adelia has this amazing eye for what women should wear and she has this soft-sell approach that always works. Nobody walks out without buying something and they usually buy a lot more than they intended to. Earlier today she sent out an email to our top customers about a new line of lingerie. By the end of the day most of it was sold."

"And this coming from a woman who traveled in very chic social circles in Charleston once upon a time," Maddie said, then winced. She gave Raylene's hand a squeeze. "Sorry, sweetie. I know that time of your life doesn't bring back such good memories, but I wanted Adelia to understand that coming from you, what you said was high praise."

"It's okay," Raylene said. "There are some days when I can actually remember the positive things about that time of my life." She focused on Adelia. "Maddie's right, though. You need to take me seriously when I tell you how good you are."

Adelia flushed at all the compliments. "Thank you."

Helen gave her a sympathetic look. "Okay, fair warning. All this sweetness and light ends now. This group is notorious for asking inappropriate, intrusive questions. You are always free to tell us to butt out."

"But we'll hate you for it," Dana Sue said, joining them. "We pride ourselves on knowing the inside scoop about everything."

"Only Grace Wharton knows more gossip than we do," Helen said with a resigned sigh. "I don't know how she does it, but it's annoying."

"I'm afraid I'm way out of the gossip loop," Adelia apologized. "If that's the card that grants me entry, you're all going to be disappointed."

"Maybe you're not current with *everything,* but the way I hear it, you have the inside track on at least one thing," Dana Sue said, her expression mischievous. "I hear you're getting tight with the sexiest man to hit Serenity this year, Gabe Franklin. What's the scoop with him? He was a couple of years younger than Maddie, Helen and me, but I remember him from years ago. He had quite a reputation as a trouble-maker back then. He was nothing at all like Mitch."

Adelia blinked and tried to scramble for an answer that wouldn't reveal much of anything about how Gabe rattled her. She knew instinctively that she shouldn't jump in to defend his past behavior, no matter how great the need. A quick, fierce defense would be far too telling.

"I don't really know much about him," she said evasively, glancing frantically around the room until her gaze landed on Lynn. "Ask her. Gabe is her husband's cousin."

"Which means Gabe doesn't flirt outrageously with her," Maddie said. She glanced at Lynn and grinned. "At least I hope he doesn't."

"Of course he doesn't," Raylene chimed in. "Mitch would kick him out of town if he so much as looked at Lynn." She cast a sympathetic look toward Adelia. "Nope. You're the one he has in his sights. We've all heard the stories."

"Which stories and from whom?" Adelia said, another fiery blush heating her cheeks. Did she have to steer completely clear of the bakery — or maybe even all of Serenity — to put an end to the already rampaging gossip?

"I believe Grace was at Rosalina's on a recent Saturday night when you were there with Elliott and your kids. She says she caught a glimpse of something," Sarah McDonald explained as she joined the group. "She couldn't wait to tell me the next morning. And if she told me, you can bet she told every single customer who walked into Wharton's."

"But nothing happened that night at Rosalina's," Adelia protested, dismayed. "We never even spoke to each other. I didn't meet Gabe till a couple of mornings after that at the bakery."

"Grace thinks of herself as being intuitive about these things," Sarah said. "She says she can spot a budding romance a mile away. Surely having grown up in Serenity, you know that."

"I was probably one of the few kids in town who didn't hang out at Wharton's as a teenager," Adelia explained. "My mother was pretty strict back then. She was worried to death about my sisters and me getting into trouble. She considered a teen hangout to be trouble just waiting to happen."

She grinned as she recalled the lectures about spending time at the local soda fountain. Of course, those lectures had made it sound even more alluring. "Forbidding us to go there was probably a big mistake," she told them. "As it was, I was pretty inexperienced when I met Ernesto in college. Believe me, if I'd dated or hung out at Wharton's the way most other girls in town did, I might not have fallen for him. I might have recognized the sort of macho cheater he turned out to be."

"Ernesto is in the past," Helen declared forcefully, dismissing her ex with a wave of her hand. Then she grinned. "Let's get back to Gabe instead. We've all heard about the kiss." She glanced around as the other women nodded. She used her best interrogator's voice on Adelia. "Care to tell us about that, Ms. Hernandez?"

So this was what friendship was like, Adelia thought, suddenly feeling completely out of her depth. Being surrounded by women who thought they had the right to ask about her innermost private thoughts was beyond disconcerting. Maybe she'd misjudged the value of the whole friendship thing.

"Careful," Raylene warned Helen. "She's starting to look a little pale. Remember, Adelia's not used to being cross-examined by people she barely knows."

Before Adelia could thank Raylene for trying to intervene, Helen merely smiled and came at her from a different, more subtle direction. At least Adelia assumed Helen considered it more subtle.

"Gabe's definitely a good-looking man," she said casually, then gave Adelia a sly look. "Don't you think so?"

"I wouldn't kick him out of my bed," Dana Sue commented, drawing a shocked look from Helen and Maddie. "Oh, get over it. I'm alive, aren't I? Ronnie's the man for me. Always has been. Always will be. But I can have the occasional fantasy. That's perfectly healthy. And don't either of you dare tell me that you haven't had your share of daydreams about someone other than your husbands."

Helen and Maddie exchanged guilty looks. "Okay, maybe, from time to time, I fantasize about Brad Pitt," Maddie conceded. "Even if he is way, way out of reach. And even if Cal is the perfect husband."

That drew a few dreamy sighs from around the room. Adelia laughed, finally relaxing. "You all are a little bit crazy," she said, then added apologetically, "If you don't mind me saying so."

Raylene put an arm around her shoulders and gave her a comforting hug. "And now you know our dirty little secret. We are all a little nuts and a little delusional. Have another margarita."

Adelia held out her glass. "I believe I will."

She just hoped the drinks weren't like truth serum. She didn't want to find herself an hour from now spilling her guts about her own unwanted fantasies about Gabe Franklin. Of course, given the speculative looks she'd been receiving, she doubted a single woman in this room would be surprised to hear anything she had to say. They'd probably respond with a fervent "Amen!"

The morning after his night with the guys, Gabe found himself taking a break from the work site at nine-thirty. He swore to himself that he was heading to the bakery at that hour because he hadn't had time to stop there earlier for his usual cup of coffee. He needed a solid caffeine fix.

The fact that he'd chosen the precise time that Adelia tended to get to Chic to open up was purely coincidental. He'd stick to that claim with his dying breath, if need be.

Sure enough as he stepped outside, he saw her at the door to the boutique. She seemed to be fumbling with the key. He frowned as she dropped it, then struggled again to get it in the lock with fingers that were clearly shaking.

Making up his mind, he walked quickly down the block, stepped up behind her and placed his hand over hers. She jumped a good foot in the air, panic on her face.

"Sorry," he said. "It's just me. You looked as if you were having a little trouble with the lock."

Color flooded her cheeks. "I'm a little shaky this morning," she confessed. "I have no idea why. Well, I do know why. It's probably the three margaritas I had last night. Everybody warned me to quit after two, told me they don't call them lethal for nothing." She gave him a shy, almost bewildered look. "They were really good, though."

Gabe bit back a smile. "But you don't

drink much."

She frowned. "Are you implying I'm a lightweight who can't hold my liquor?"

He laughed. "Are you?"

She held his gaze with a defiant look, then sighed. "I must be if I can't even unlock a stupid door this morning."

"How's your head?"

"I believe a jackhammer has taken up residence," she admitted.

Gabe pushed open the door to the boutique and handed her the key. "Go on inside and do your thing. I'll be back."

When she seemed about to protest, he held up a hand to cut her off. "I'll be back, Adelia. Leave the door unlocked, okay?"

"Okay," she said, sounding surprisingly meek.

That meek response alone told him just how off-kilter she was feeling.

He headed straight for the bakery and told Lynn, "I need two coffees, both large, one with lots of sugar."

"You drink your coffee black," she said, looking startled.

"It's not for me."

"Then who?" she said, then went perfectly still. "Adelia?"

He nodded. "She's feeling a little under the weather. What the heck did you women do last night? She mentioned three margaritas."

Lynn winced. "I think it was actually four. She might have lost count. That happens."

"Sweet heaven," he said. "I don't imagine they're watered down as the evening goes along."

Lynn looked horrified. "I think Helen would rather give up her entire wardrobe of designer shoes than water down a margarita. Most of us have learned to pace ourselves. And, of course, those of us who are pregnant stick to frozen limeade so we at least look as if we're fitting in. Then we jealously keep count of the drinks the others are consuming."

Gabe thought of what Mitch had told him about these Sweet Magnolia get-togethers. "Not to sound egotistical, but did my name come up last night?"

She chuckled. "Oh yeah."

Gabe groaned. "And you all were on Adelia's case about me and our relationship, that sort of thing?"

"We might have asked a few intrusive questions," Lynn confessed. "All in the spirit of sisterhood, of course. We wanted her to know she has backup." She hesitated, then added, "We might have been a little too inquisitive about any juicy details she might want to share."

No wonder the woman had been downing margaritas like water, Gabe thought. "Maybe you should tell these so-called friends to butt out," he suggested. "Not everyone wants to have their private business hung out like laundry for everyone to see." He gave her a stern look. "And don't you think Adelia might have had more than enough of that with the whole Ernesto fiasco?"

Lynn flushed guiltily. "We didn't think of it like that," she said. "And if you must know, we were all encouraging her to give you another chance. You should be thanking us."

Gabe understood that Lynn at least meant well, but he suspected their efforts had been counterproductive. "Adelia and I are perfectly capable of figuring things out for ourselves."

Lynn leveled a disbelieving look at him. "Are you still seeing each other?"

"No, because —"

She cut him off. "Because you are not capable of figuring things out. She's vulnerable and scared. You're . . ." She hesitated, then blurted, "Okay, I'll just say it, if you let her go, you're an idiot."

"You don't know what you're talking

265

about," Gabe said.

"Of course I do. I was just as stubborn and stupid about Mitch, that's how I recognize all the signs. And every one of those women there last night has been through something similar. We're experienced with putting up defenses and pretending that we don't need or want some man in our lives. And we don't *need* a man, not a one of us." She held his gaze. "But we'll all tell you now that we're better off for deciding to take a chance."

Gabe sighed at the heartfelt conviction in her voice. "Lynn, I appreciate what you're saying, but could I just have those coffees and maybe a couple of pastries? Whichever ones Adelia likes."

She gave him a long look, but she poured the coffees and put several pastries in a box. "Tell her to call me if she needs anything."

Gabe nodded. "Will do."

"And I don't care what you say, I think it's sweet that you're looking after her."

Gabe frowned. Sweet was the last thing on his mind. He'd taken just one look at the state Adelia was in this morning and felt his heart plummet. No matter how he looked at it, he couldn't help thinking he was responsible for it. If Elliott got wind of this, he was going to punch Gabe's lights out and Gabe wouldn't do a darn thing to try to stop him. A good thrashing was probably just what he deserved.

The simple act of opening the cash register was almost more than Adelia could manage. And the familiar sound the drawer made to signal it was being opened seemed to echo in her head.

This is so wrong, she thought. Women her age should not be suffering from a hangover. They were supposed to have better sense.

The bell over the door rang and she clamped her hands over her ears at the sound and groaned. If this was going to happen every time a customer came in today, she might die. Or at least wish she could.

This, though, was Gabe returning and the look on his face was filled with pity or sympathy. She looked closer and thought she saw just a tiny touch of amusement that he was trying valiantly to hide.

"Head hurt?" he asked lightly.

"You have no idea."

"Here," he said, holding out his hand. "It's just aspirin. That and the caffeine and sugar in the coffee might help."

"I don't like sugar in my coffee. Lynn knows that."

"She made an exception today at my insistence." He shoved the container a little closer. "Drink up."

Adelia thought about arguing, taking a stance, in fact, but the thought of caffeine held a little too much appeal. As did those aspirin he'd set in front of her. She took those, then a sip of coffee.

"Why are you being so nice to me? We're not even supposed to be speaking."

"I feel a little responsible," he admitted.

She stared at him incredulously. "Why? You weren't there shoving margaritas down my throat."

"Might as well have been," he said. "At least the way I hear it."

She frowned at that. "What did you hear?"

"Lynn says we were a hot topic last night." He held her gaze. "Adelia, I never meant for you to be in that position."

He looked so apologetic and dismayed, Adelia found herself taking pity on him. "Gabe, you don't know these women. Heck, I don't even know them that well, but even I could tell that they make a hobby out of butting in. They're all happily married. We've just provided them with some new fodder. Sooner or later some other couple will come along and they'll meddle in their lives."

"But in the meantime, you shouldn't have to deal with this. That's what I told Lynn, too."

"You told Lynn that everybody needed to back off?"

"Yep. In no uncertain terms."

Adelia started to laugh, but it hurt, so she settled for saying, "You're delusional if you think she's going to pay a bit of attention to you. If anything, she's probably more convinced than ever that there's something between us."

He looked thoroughly, charmingly confused. "How? Why?"

"Because you immediately leapt to my defense. And because you went over there to get me coffee and pastries and aspirin."

"Why is that a bad thing?" he asked. "And, for the record, I didn't get the aspirin from Lynn. I had them in my car."

She gave him a pitying look. "That is so not the point."

Gabe sighed. "You're going to have to explain this to me. Clearly I, a mere man, am not privy to the way women's minds work."

"What you did for me just now is not a bad thing at all," Adelia explained patiently. "It is, however, exactly the kind of thing that Lynn will report to all the others and they'll sigh happily and conclude that they were exactly right to try to push us straight into each other's arms."

"Are all women this crazy or do these Sweet Magnolias have some kind of a lock on that?" Gabe asked.

Since Adelia had wondered almost the same thing the night before, she shared the conclusion she'd reached. "I think it's these women. They care about their friends. They're intrusive and a little crazy, but they're well-meaning. That makes them more dangerous, I think."

Gabe frowned. "Dangerous? How so?"

"They're all so sweet and normally trust-worthy that they make you want to believe them, to make them happy."

"What are you saying? That we ought to take another look at this thing between us?"

She hesitated, because that was exactly what she'd been thinking by the time she'd left Raylene's the night before. Now in broad daylight with her head pounding, she was having second thoughts. "No, of course not. We decided . . ."

He held her gaze. "Adelia, do *you* think we made a mistake? Do you want to go back to the way things were? You know, hanging out, just seeing how things develop?"

"What do you think?" she asked, not

wanting to crawl out on that shaky limb all by herself.

"I think we made the decision for all the right, sensible reasons," he said.

She fought to hide her disappointment, not just because it was humiliating, but because she didn't want to admit even to herself that she felt so much as a tiny bit of regret. "Yes, of course we did."

He leaned across the counter and tucked a finger under her chin, his eyes locked with hers. "But if we want to change our minds, to maybe reassess, that's up to us, too."

Hope spread through her. "Is that what you want, to reassess?"

He drew in a deep breath, then nodded. "To be honest, this separation hasn't been working as well as I'd hoped it would. If anything, it's just made me think about you more. I can't seem to get you out of my head."

"Me, too," Adelia said softly.

Gabe studied her, then nodded. "Okay then. Dinner tonight?"

She took a deep breath. "Sure, why not. I left another casserole with Selena," she said. "There's plenty for one more."

Gabe shook his head. "Not this time. I think maybe you and I need to go on an actual date, just the two of us."

"Not Rosalina's," she said at once. "There seems to be a direct pipeline from that place to gossip central. And, of course, Wharton's *is* gossip central."

"I've been hearing a lot about Sullivan's since I got back to town," Gabe said. "Everybody says it's the place to go for a nice meal."

"The food's amazing," Adelia confirmed, then thought of the implications of the two of them being seen in the town's best restaurant together on what couldn't possibly be mistaken for anything other than a date. "It'll be like tossing a teaser morsel to a lion, though. Everyone's going to pounce. It might be even worse than Rosalina's."

"But at least we'll have had an excellent meal." He grinned. "Or we can always hope they'll be too busy congratulating each other to bother messing with us."

She thought about it and laughed. Since Dana Sue, who owned the place, would probably have the news of their arrival all over town within seconds, that's probably exactly what they'd be doing.

"Either way," she told him, grinning herself, "I don't think I care."

"That's the spirit."

Of course by the time tomorrow morning rolled around, she might be facing all sorts of regrets. Come to think of it, though, they couldn't be any more uncomfortable than the regrets she'd had this morning after drinking all those margaritas. She glanced at Gabe and allowed herself a brief moment of pure feminine satisfaction. And just look at how well today was turning out.

CHAPTER THIRTEEN

"Mommy, Gabe left again!" Tomas complained when Adelia arrived home from work. "I liked it when he was staying for dinner. I asked him to stay, but he said no."

"Gabe has plans for tonight," Adelia told him.

"What about tomorrow night?" Tomas persisted. "Can he stay then?"

"You'll have to ask him," Adelia said. "Selena, could I speak to you upstairs?"

Her daughter regarded her with suspicion but followed Adelia up to her room. It was still filled with boxes from the move. She'd seen no point in unpacking until her room had been painted. She'd told Gabe to leave it for last, so the kids would start to feel better about their new home by having their rooms decorated just the way they wanted them to be.

"What's going on?" Selena asked her, sitting on the edge of the bed as Adelia opened her closet door and looked at the few outfits she'd pressed and hung up, mostly for work.

"I'm going out for dinner tonight," she announced, keeping her tone casual. "I won't be late, but do you mind being here alone with your sisters and brother, or would you prefer me to call someone to come over?"

Selena regarded her suspiciously. "Where are you going? You were just out last night."

"I'm having dinner at Sullivan's."

Selena's eyes narrowed even more. "But that's for special occasions," she said slowly, clearly trying to make sense of her mother's unusual behavior. "Is this a special occasion?"

"It's just dinner with a friend," Adelia said evasively.

Selena looked even more skeptical. Then her eyes widened. "You're having dinner with Gabe tonight, that's why he's busy, too. It's a date, isn't it?"

"It's just dinner," Adelia repeated.

"It's a date with Gabe," Selena said again. She didn't seem that unhappy about her conclusion, just puzzled. "I thought you weren't gonna see him anymore, not like that, anyway. I thought that's why he'd made such a big deal about leaving before you got home."

"Well, tonight's an exception," Adelia said, then sat down beside her daughter, clinging to a simple black dress. She met Selena's gaze and sighed. "It's a date. How do you feel about that?"

Selena was silent for a long time. "Do you really need to date somebody?"

Adelia held back a smile at the plaintive question. "I don't have to," she said. "But I do enjoy Gabe's company. It's nice to have another grown-up to talk to."

"You have *Abuela,*" Selena said, then sighed. "That's not the same, though, is it?"

"No. Someday you'll understand the difference. You'll much prefer being out with a boy instead of home with your sisters, brother and me."

"First, I'd have to not be grounded," Selena replied ruefully.

Adelia laughed. "Yes, that would be a requirement." She brushed a strand of hair from her daughter's face. "So, can you accept it if I go on this one date with Gabe?"

"I suppose," Selena said grudgingly, then glanced at the dress Adelia was holding. "But you can't wear that! No way. Mom, you'll look like a nun."

Adelia studied the simple dress and saw her daughter's point. "Maybe that's not such a bad idea."

"No, no, no," Selena protested, jumping up and diving into the closet. "Here," she said, tossing a filmy flowered skirt at Adelia. "And this," she said, adding a low-cut sleeveless top. "You look fantastic in this."

Adelia studied her with increasing surprise. "You sound like you're okay with this, after all."

Selena shrugged. "I told you a while back that I'd decided Gabe wasn't so bad. I guess if you have to go out with a guy, he's okay. I liked it better, though, when you were avoiding each other." She gave Adelia a very grown-up look. "But you weren't happy. Neither was he. It was nice when he made you laugh. You and Dad hadn't laughed in a long time."

"I liked that, too," Adelia confided. "But this is just one date, sweetie. Don't say anything to your sisters or brother. I don't want them to make too much of it. You shouldn't, either."

"I won't ask him if I can call him Daddy, if that's what you're worried about," Selena said.

Adelia regarded her with stunned silence. When she could find her voice, she said, "I certainly hope not."

Selena laughed. "I was just kidding."

Adelia caught the sparkle in her daughter's

eyes and realized that maybe she wasn't the only one in the house who was better off with Gabe being in their lives. It seemed he was having much the same effect on Selena, at least when it came to brightening her mood. And that had to be a good thing, worth every one of the butterflies that were currently fluttering crazily in Adelia's stomach.

"What did the kids say when you told them we were having dinner?" Gabe asked when they were settled in a quiet booth at Sullivan's, albeit under Dana Sue's speculative, delighted gaze. She'd been darting out of the kitchen, peering in their direction every few minutes, a cell phone pressed to her ear. There was little doubt every Sweet Magnolia in town knew about this date by now.

"I just said I was having dinner with a friend," Adelia replied. "Selena knows it's you, though."

"And?"

"She approves."

Gabe looked as surprised as she'd been. "Really?" he said.

"Don't count it as a ringing endorsement," Adelia warned. "She doesn't actually want me to date at all, but if I have to go out with someone, she seems okay with it being you. It was a nice change of heart on her part. It was especially nice to have her teasing me rather than berating me."

"But you're still worried about how the others will react," he guessed. "That's why you insisted on meeting me here instead of letting me pick you up. You didn't want Tomas, Natalia and Juanita getting any ideas."

Adelia nodded. "I still believe we need to be very cautious, at least until we know how this is going to go. You should know, though, that Tomas intends to ask you to stay for dinner again tomorrow."

Gabe studied her. "What should I tell him?"

"That's up to you."

He held her gaze. "Not entirely. What do you want me to tell him?"

Flustered under his penetrating look, she could barely manage a whisper. "That you'll stay."

A smile spread across his face. "Okay, then. And, Adelia, we need to be clear about one thing."

"What's that?" she asked, worried about his suddenly serious tone.

"When it comes to how much time I spend with your kids or what we tell them, you're in charge. I don't want to mess with their heads any more than you want me to."

"You're good for them," she admitted. "You treat them like real people. I can see them blossoming under all that attention, Tomas especially. I don't want to take that away from them. I just don't want them to get too far ahead of themselves when it comes to us. I don't want them to be hurt."

Gabe nodded. "It's a fine line," he agreed. "But we'll figure it out." He reached under the table, laced his fingers with hers and gave her hand a squeeze. "Could we focus on us now?"

She shivered under the intensity of his gaze. "I guess so," she said, not sounding very certain.

He smiled. "You're not used to having the attention focused on you, are you?"

She shook her head. "Not like this."

"Did you and Ernesto ever have date nights?" he asked.

Adelia knew that was something a lot of married couples did. It was a way to solidify their relationship and keep the romance alive without all the demands of being parents, at least for an evening. She knew it was something Elliott and Karen credited with getting their marriage back on track after a rough patch. She'd suggested it once to Ernesto and he'd looked at her as if she were nuts.

She shook her head. "Never."

"Why not?"

"He didn't see the point," she said, then shrugged. "I suppose he figured he'd already paid for the rings and the fancy house. Why bother courting me?" She winced at the bitterness in her voice. "Sorry."

Gabe frowned. "Why are you apologizing? The man should have been down on his knees every night thanking you for making a nice home and taking such great care of his kids."

"He was too busy chasing other women to bother with that."

Her reply seemed to anger Gabe.

"You do know that reflects badly on him, not you, right?" Gabe said. "I may not think I'm a good candidate for marriage, but I do know that a husband should treat his wife with more respect than that. He shouldn't be taking her for granted."

"Maybe it was me," she ventured, voicing the fear that she still hadn't totally overcome.

Now there was no mistaking the heat in Gabe's eyes. "Absolutely not," he told her.

"You don't know. You didn't know me then. I've gotten myself together in the past year or so."

"Meaning what?"

"I did what I thought Ernesto wanted. I went to the spa and lost weight. I tried to compete with those other women."

"You shouldn't have had to compete with anyone," Gabe told her. "And in a matchup with any woman who'd get involved with a married father of four, you'd come out way, way ahead in all the areas that matter."

He said it with such conviction that Adelia sat a little taller. "You really mean that, don't you?"

"I really mean it," he said quietly. "And if you doubt me, let me tell you that everyone I've met since I got back to town feels the same way. If your name comes up, it's always said with respect. Don't let one idiot make you question yourself."

"Even if that one idiot was my husband, who knew me better than anyone?" she said wryly.

"Not even then. It just shows what poor judgment he has."

He'd just carved another big chunk out of her wall of defenses. "You know something, Gabe Franklin?" she said lightly.

"What?"

"The kids aren't the only ones you're good for."

Now it was his turn to blush. "Just calling it like I see it," he said. Then, clearly flustered, he opened the menu. "Maybe we should order. Any suggestions?"

His sudden nervousness actually served to calm her own nerves. "Everything I've ever had here is great," Adelia said, more than willing to go along with the change in topic. "The meat loaf is a specialty. So is the fried catfish."

Gabe's expression turned nostalgic. "My mom used to make meat loaf. It was terrible, but it was the one thing she thought she could cook, so she made it for special occasions."

"Well, Dana Sue's version takes it to a whole new level," Adelia told him.

"Then I think I'll have that, for old times' sake."

Adelia studied him closely. "There were good times with your mom, weren't there? Mostly you make it sound as if it was all bad."

For a moment, she thought he might not answer. He looked as if he'd gone someplace far away, or more likely just back in time.

"There were good times," he said eventually. "Christmas, my birthday. Those were the occasions when she tried to do something special. Of course, at Christmas she went crazy with decorations and a big meal, not because the holiday meant much to her, but to take her mind off the fact that whatever man was in her life was home with his own family that day."

Adelia winced at the stark pain in his voice. "I'm sorry things weren't better for you."

"Hey, I survived it, didn't I? I just wish her life had been better, but I was way too young to know how to help."

"That didn't stop you from trying, though. Remember that."

"I went about it in all the wrong ways," he said. "At least that's what a lot of people in town would have said back then, including my aunts and uncles and grandparents. They just lumped me in with her and considered us both a lost cause."

"Mitch, too?" she asked, shocked.

"Mitch was just a kid himself. I don't blame him or any of the other cousins. He's more than made up for it now by giving me a fresh start."

Dana Sue arrived at the table just then, clearly in search of hot new information to impart. "Have you all ordered yet?" she asked, studying them with amusement. "Or have you been too engrossed with each other?"

Ronnie Sullivan appeared at her side almost immediately and tucked his wife's arm through his. "Leave them alone," he told her firmly.

"I'm just checking on my customers," Dana Sue protested, though she flushed guiltily.

"No, you're being nosy," Ronnie said, giving them an apologetic look. "Sorry. She can't help herself."

Gabe chuckled. "Maybe you can send over our waitress," he suggested.

"Now there's a thought," Ronnie said. "Darlin', as the owner of this fine establishment, why didn't you think of that? Go get their waitress, then get back in the kitchen and make something delicious."

Dana Sue gave Ronnie a mock scowl, then kissed his cheek. "You stay and ask questions," she suggested.

Ronnie looked after her with tolerant amusement, then called out, "Nobody's asking questions." He winked at Gabe and Adelia. "You should be safe for an hour or so, but I'd suggest you get dessert to go. I'm not sure how long I can keep her in the kitchen. I'm sure she's back there texting half the town right now, even though she has very little to report."

Adelia chuckled. "Thanks for the tip."

"Maybe we should get the whole meal to go," Gabe said.

Ronnie shook his head at once. "And have the whole town speculating about where you went to eat it?"

"They would, too," Adelia confirmed with a resigned sigh.

"Then let's just wolf down our meal and take off," Gabe said.

"Wolf down one of Dana Sue's meals?" Adelia asked. "That's practically sacrilegious."

"She's right," Ronnie said. "The only thing worse than keeping my wife in the dark about your relationship would be insulting her food."

Gabe shook his head. "Who knew that eating out in Serenity could get this complicated?" He turned to Adelia. "Next time we're going to Charleston."

Ronnie chuckled, but one look into Gabe's eyes told Adelia he was 100 percent serious. Since the thought of a night on the town in Charleston sent a shiver of anticipation straight down Adelia's spine, she didn't find anything even moderately amusing about the prospect.

"You went awfully quiet when I mentioned going to Charleston," Gabe said to Adelia after they'd savored every bite of their dinner and even shared a dessert.

"It's a long way to go just to have dinner," Adelia said carefully.

"Might be worth it, though, to avoid all these prying eyes in Serenity."

She gave him a long look. "And it would just be about dinner?"

He regarded her with confusion. "That's what I said, isn't it?" Understanding dawned. "Oh, I see. You thought I meant, well, something more than dinner."

"Like I said, it's a long drive for a meal."

"Adelia, I honestly wasn't suggesting we go off for some intimate overnight rendezvous." He studied her. "Or am I getting this all wrong? Were you hoping that was exactly what I was suggesting?"

She blushed furiously. "Don't mind me. I don't know what I was thinking. You made the suggestion and I guess I let my imagination run wild."

He smiled at that. "Well, I'm certainly open to negotiation. I didn't think you were ready for anything more than dinner."

"I'm not," she said firmly. "At least I don't think I am."

"But you're tempted."

She didn't meet his gaze but gave an almost imperceptible nod. "I might be tempted," she conceded, then buried her face in her hands. "What is wrong with me? Just a few days ago I was telling you we should stop seeing each other and now here I am practically throwing myself at you."

"I don't mind," he said. "You're not saying a thing I haven't fantasized about myself."

She glanced up. "You have?"

"Of course. I'm not sure we wouldn't be jumping into something we're not ready for, but I've thought about making love to you about a million times since the first night I saw you at Rosalina's."

A tiny self-satisfied smile tugged at her lips. "About a million times, huh?"

"At least."

Her smile spread. "Good to know. Maybe that'll hold me for now."

"So no secret overnights to Charleston?" he asked, not even trying to hide his disappointment.

"Not just yet," she said, though she sounded even more intrigued by the possibility.

Even though he doubted he'd be able to get the idea out of his head so he could sleep tonight, Gabe was glad she'd gone there. She'd taken a tiny step out of her shell by admitting that the thought of sleeping with him had crossed her mind. Actually doing it might take a little longer, but anticipation was going to be half the fun.

Adelia was surprised to find her mother waiting for her in front of the boutique when she arrived the morning after her dinner with Gabe.

"Mama, what are you doing here so early?" she asked as she led the way inside. "Do you have a wardrobe emergency?"

Her mother gave her an as-if look. "I came to see you, since I can't seem to catch up with you in the evening. You dropped the kids off the other night and took off before I could ask you a single question."

Adelia smiled. "Did you ever think that maybe that was on purpose?"

"Of course it was. I know how skilled you are at evading my questions. I tried again last night, but when I called the house, Selena said you were out. Then I heard from my friend that you were with a handsome man at Sullivan's. Were you on a date?"

Adelia sighed. It had been too much to hope that her mother would be far removed from the gossip loop. "I was."

"With that Gabe Franklin person?"

"You say that as if you'd never laid eyes on him or as if you disapproved of him,"

Adelia said. "Have you suddenly changed your mind? You seemed to like him well enough when he stayed for dinner and you got to cross-examine him to your heart's content."

"That was before," her mother said.

"Before what?"

"Before I thought you were going to jump into something with both feet and parade your indiscretions around town the way Ernesto did."

Adelia froze at her words. "Excuse me? You did not just compare what I'm doing with what Ernesto did."

At the scathing, furious note in her voice, her mother backtracked at once. "Of course it's not like that. I just mean that it's awfully soon after your divorce to be seen all over town with someone. People might make too much of it."

"People? Or is this Carolina again? She's already told me that she thinks I'm making a public spectacle of myself. And Joey said the same thing to Selena."

That last had the desired effect. Shock registered in her mother's eyes. "Joey said something like that to your daughter?"

Adelia nodded. "Clearly he's under his mother's influence."

"I'll speak to Carolina and to Joey," her

mother said with grim determination. "It won't happen again."

"Mama, you can't control them. Let it go. I've dealt with them. I just don't like hearing the same sort of judgmental comments from you. I thought we'd established a different relationship the past few months."

Her mother sighed. "I'm just worried."

"About me? I can take care of myself."

"I'm not so sure that you can after years of letting Ernesto erode your self-confidence, but actually I'm more worried about your children. They can't stop talking about Gabe."

Now it was Adelia's turn to sigh. "I know. I worry about that, too. That's why Gabe and I decided to take a break."

"And dinner last night was part of this so-called break?"

Adelia smiled at her mother's incredulous expression. "Not exactly. We had second thoughts and decided to keep seeing each other. We're taking it slowly, though, because of the kids. Neither of us wants them to get the wrong idea."

"The wrong idea being that you might have a future with this man?"

Adelia nodded.

"That's a big risk," her mother warned. "And this time I'm not talking about my grandchildren. Are you ready to take such a risk?"

Adelia thought of the way Gabe made her feel. "Apparently I am," she said softly. "I enjoy being with him, Mama. He makes me feel special."

Her mother's expression softened at that. "You deserve that. You *are* special, and I am so sorry that Ernesto caused you to think otherwise for even a single minute."

"Me, too," Adelia responded. "I'm not deluding myself that this is going to lead to some big thing, but it's right for me now."

"Then I'll focus my prayers on that," her mother said. "That Gabe will be exactly what you need in your life right now."

Adelia understood what a concession that was for her rigidly moral mother. "Thank you, Mama."

"Of course, I might also say a prayer or two that he'll be wise enough to make an honest woman of you."

Adelia laughed and gave her mother a fierce hug. "Of course you will. Thank you for that, too."

"Perhaps he'll join us for Sunday dinner one of these days," she suggested slyly.

Adelia choked at that. "No way," she said. "We are definitely not ready for that."

Her mother shrugged. "In time then. I

only want what's best for you, for all my children. Sometimes I credit myself with knowing what that is, but the truth is each of you must decide for yourself. I'm adjusting to that concept."

"Keep trying, Mama. I think you're pretty darn close to getting it exactly right."

Her mother looked pleased by that. "Now I'll leave you to your work."

"Not without looking at these new sweaters that just came in," Adelia told her, leading her to the display. "Feel how soft they are. Pure cashmere."

Her mother put a tentative hand on the sweater, then stroked it gently. "It is soft."

"And look at this red one," Adelia encouraged her. "It's your favorite color."

Her mother looked at her, amusement dancing in her eyes. "Now I see why everyone says you have a magic touch as a saleswoman. I'll take it, even though it's far too indulgent."

"I'll give you my discount," Adelia told her, already heading for the register.

"It's still an indulgence, but given the joy I'll get wearing it, it will be worth it." She touched Adelia's cheek. "And seeing the color here, that makes me even happier."

Adelia watched her mother leave, then realized a tear was rolling down her cheek.

No matter how grown-up and independent she thought she was, receiving her mother's unequivocal approval was an unexpected blessing.

CHAPTER FOURTEEN

Gabe was grabbing a burger at Wharton's when he overheard one of the men in the booth behind him mention Mitch's name. He wasn't in the habit of eavesdropping on conversations, but he couldn't help it since the tone of the remark had been derogatory. He put his burger down. Though he didn't turn around, he did tune in.

"Well, I'm not buying it," another man responded. "Mitch Franklin is one of the most honorable men in this town. He'd never cheat a customer. And look at what he's doing for downtown. Main Street's going to be revitalized once he's through with the renovations. It's already showing more signs of life than it's shown in years."

"You can thank Ronnie Sullivan for that," the other man said. "He bought that old hardware store and got things started."

"And Raylene Rollins opened her boutique not long after that," a third voice added.

"But she and Mitch bought up all those other neglected properties and are fixing them up," Mitch's defender argued. "We're already hearing from a few businesses that are interested in locating downtown."

By now Gabe had recognized that the man who was standing up for his cousin was Howard Lewis, the mayor, one of the town's biggest boosters and a proponent of improving the economy of Serenity. After a glance over his shoulder Gabe still couldn't put a name to the other two.

"If you ask me, whoever's been spreading those lies has an ax to grind with Mitch," Howard said. "I'd say it was Ed Morrow, but I thought he'd learned his lesson when he tried it before and most of the town sided with Lynn and Mitch."

"I can't name my source, but it wasn't Ed," the first man revealed.

"That leaves Ernesto Hernandez then," Howard said, his voice filled with disgust.

"Makes sense," the more neutral of the other men said. "I did hear that Mitch tore up the contract he had to do some renovations for Ernesto. I imagine Hernandez didn't like that one bit. This sure sounds like payback. Walter, you should know better than to listen to anyone like that."

"I'm not confirming that my source was Hernandez, but it sounded like he had the facts to back up what he was saying," Walter said defiantly. "I believe him. I think somebody ought to take a long, hard look at what Franklin's up to on Main Street. And we all remember that cousin of his, Gabe. The kid was nothing but trouble, and now he's back here and in the thick of that whole scam."

"Walter!" Howard said, casting a warning glance at him. Clearly he'd caught sight of Gabe in the next booth.

Walter, however, didn't take the hint. "Who knows how many shortcuts they're taking with building materials and such?" he continued. "The whole dang thing could fall down a year from now."

That brought Gabe out of his seat. Temper barely leashed, he moved swiftly to stand beside their table. He put his hands down and leaned in. First he directed a look at Howard. "Mr. Mayor. Nice to see you," he said pleasantly.

Howard looked even more uncomfortable. "Son, no need to get worked up," he told Gabe, clearly hoping to avoid a scene, no matter how justified he might think Gabe was in causing one. "Walter here didn't mean anything by what he was saying. And you must have heard me tell him he was way off base."

"I did hear what you said, and I appreciate that," Gabe replied, then turned his attention to the man who'd just been identified as Walter. "But this gentlemen just suggested my cousin and I might be doing something illegal by skirting around regulations or using questionable materials." He looked the man in the eye. "That is what you were saying, isn't it?"

"It's what I heard," he said, his face bright red now.

Gabe gave him an incredulous look. "And you heard this from a man who cheated on his wife and then tried to hire my cousin to renovate his mistress's house, correct? Did he mention he kept asking for changes and upgrades, then wanted Mitch to shave his costs down to nothing? That's the kind of man you find believable? What do you suppose that says about you?"

Walter clearly wasn't ready to give up yet. "He said he had proof," he countered, a triumphant note in his voice.

"Did you see any? Because if you did, it was phony. Mitch doesn't cut corners. Neither do I. And if I find out you're spreading those lies, I'll encourage Mitch to sue you for slander." He gave him a hard look. "But first I might forget that I'm no longer the town troublemaker and deal with you myself."

"Your gripe's with Hernandez, not me," Walter responded, though he looked shaken by the threat of a lawsuit or worse, just as Gabe had intended.

"Oh, believe me, I'll deal with him," Gabe said readily. "But you're the one doing his dirty work by spreading it all over town, so right now I'm concentrating on you. Are we clear?"

"He won't be saying another word about this," Howard promised. "I'll see to it."

"I can speak for myself," Walter said belligerently.

"Then do it," Howard said. "Or I'll encourage Mitch to sue you myself. I'm not sure I'll even bother with discouraging Gabe from getting even, either."

The two men locked gazes, but it was Walter who blinked first. "Not another word," he said grudgingly.

Though Gabe didn't entirely buy that this would be the end of it, he gave a nod of satisfaction, then turned to Howard. "Thanks for backing me up and for defending Mitch."

"No problem," Howard said, clearly relieved to have the matter settled without a single punch being thrown. "And just so you know, this project of Mitch's has my full support. The town manager's, too. Main Street's already looking better than I ever imagined it could."

"It'll look even better when we're done," Gabe said, appreciative of the vote of confidence.

His appetite gone, he tossed some bills on his own table and left without touching the rest of his burger. Mitch needed to hear about this, but maybe not till after Gabe could have a few words with Ernesto Hernandez.

The carpet in Ernesto's fancy suite of offices was a light beige. Coming into the suite from a sudden downpour that had left him soaked, Gabe took a certain amount of delight in tracking mud across that pristine carpet as he headed for Ernesto's office. He waved off the secretary who jumped up and tried to block his path.

"This won't take long," Gabe told her, pushing open the office door without bothering to knock.

Ernesto had removed his jacket, but that was his only concession to being all alone in his office. He was in another one of those stiff fancy shirts, a silk tie knotted at his throat. Gabe harbored a strong desire to tighten that knot until it made the man squirm. Instead, he took a seat across from Ernesto, settling in as if he had all the time in the world. He couldn't help hoping that his rain-soaked clothes would ruin the fancy upholstery.

"How're you doing, Ernesto?" he inquired casually.

Ernesto's eyes narrowed. His secretary hovered uncertainly in the doorway. Apparently aware that anything Gabe was likely to say wouldn't be anything he'd want the woman to hear, Ernesto waved her off.

"It's okay. I'll handle this," he said tightly. "Close the door."

"Are you sure?" she asked worriedly.

Ernesto nodded, his gaze never leaving Gabe. "Okay, what do you want?" he demanded when they were alone.

"I want you to stop spreading lies about Mitch," Gabe said, his voice quiet but unyielding.

"No idea what you're talking about."

"Yet another lie," Gabe said. "But I can refresh your memory if you like. You've been telling people that he's cutting corners, using faulty materials."

Ernesto shrugged. "I might have mentioned to a couple of friends that I had my

301

suspicions about the quality of his work. If that happened to get around town, that's on them."

Gabe stood up, then leaned down until he was just inches from Ernesto's face. Adding this latest offense to everything Ernesto had done to Adelia made him want desperately to plant his fist squarely in Ernesto's smug face. Only the thought of Adelia's reaction and the reminder that this man was the father of her children kept him from acting on the impulse.

"First of all, I think I can safely say that you have no friends in this town, not after what you did to Adelia and your kids. Second, the instant those deliberate lies came out of your mouth, you were guilty of slander. The law has reasonably stiff penalties for that. I think my next stop will be Helen Decatur-Whitney's office to check into just how long you might rot in jail if we pursue charges."

For the first time a tiny hint of panic flickered in Ernesto's eyes. "Who's going to believe a man who was in trouble with the law as much as you were in this town?" he said with pure bravado.

Gabe allowed himself a faint smile. "There's not a thing on my record but a string of warnings about fighting back against some bullies who were talking about my mom. I may have mishandled things back then, but I was standing up for someone I care about, the same way I'm doing right now. And if you know anything at all about those incidents, you probably also know that I know how to use my fists when I'm worked up. Right this second, I'm getting pretty worked up."

"Are you threatening me?"

"I suppose you could test me and find out for sure," Gabe said.

Suddenly a smirk settled on Ernesto's face. "I wonder how much time you'll be spending around my ex-wife and my kids once a judge hears about this. Two can play at this game."

Having Adelia and the kids dragged into this fight nearly got the best of Gabe. He wanted desperately to wipe that smug look off Ernesto's face, but once again he restrained himself. He knew nothing good would come of it.

"I thought that might shut you up," Ernesto said, obviously pleased with himself.

"It is only out of respect for Adelia that I'm not wiping the floor with you right this second," Gabe told him. "But don't push me too far, Ernesto. And stop with the

303

mudslinging about Mitch. If I hear one more word that's attributed to you, we'll both see you in court."

He walked out of the office without looking back, aware that the secretary went rushing in, probably to make sure her boss was still in one piece.

He was just exiting the building when a patrol car pulled up out front. Carter Rollins gestured for him to come over, then nodded in the direction of the building.

"Everything okay in there?"

"Ernesto's pretty face is untouched, if that's what you're asking."

"Too bad," Carter muttered, then regarded him sternly. "You did not just hear those words come out of my mouth."

Gabe bit back a grin. "Never heard a thing. I imagine I can thank his secretary for alerting you that trouble was on the horizon."

"She said you'd stormed in without an appointment and she'd heard raised voices. I decided given the complicated dynamics of the situation, I'd better check it out myself."

Gabe's expression sobered. "I threatened him," he told Carter.

"I do not need to hear that," the Serenity police chief said.

"Yes, you do. You also need to understand why." He explained about the campaign Ernesto had been waging to undermine Mitch's reputation. "My next stop is Helen's office. I want her to be aware of this, too. I don't know that Mitch will want to take action, but I need to know what the options are." He nodded toward the building. "And just so you know the whole ugly story, since he wasn't real happy with me, Ernesto threatened to find a way to keep me away from Adelia and his kids."

Carter groaned. "Gabe, I know you're in the right here, especially since you gave him a warning and didn't lay a hand on him, but watch yourself. I wouldn't put anything past him. Ernesto may not have many supporters around here, but the courts have to be above that. If a judge sees you as a threat, he'll have no choice but to order you to steer clear of the kids. He probably can't do the same when it comes to Adelia, but you know what it would do to her. If she's forced to make a choice, you'll lose."

Gabe sighed. "I know that. I'm just praying it won't get to that point."

"Warn her, okay? Ernesto's unpredictable and he's angry. You don't want Adelia to be blindsided by any of this."

"Got it," Gabe said. "Thanks, Carter."

"I'll have your back as long as you don't cross any lines. Understood?"

Gabe nodded. "Understood."

For the first time ever in this town, he felt as if he wasn't totally alone when it came to standing up to a bully. And when it came right down to it, that's what Ernesto was, nothing more than a grown-up version of the sort of thugs Gabe had seen far too much of as a kid.

Gabe's conversations with Helen and with Mitch to fill them in went reasonably well. Helen was ready to start legal proceedings right away, but Gabe told her to hold off, that it was Mitch's call whether he wanted to go that route.

To his surprise, Mitch laughed off Ernesto's underhanded campaign against him. "Gabe, people in this town know me. He's not going to be able to say a thing that will hurt my reputation. All I have to do is say, 'Consider the source.'"

Gabe thought he was being naive. "That kind of talk is insidious. Once he plants the idea that you do shoddy work, if a single shingle falls off a roof anywhere in town, people will start to wonder."

Mitch's expression sobered at that. "Okay, you may be right. It is dangerous to let his lies circulate without fighting back, but a lawsuit might be overkill. I'll just have Helen send some kind of cease and desist letter just to let him know that I'm taking the matter seriously. That ought to put him on notice to shut his mouth." He held Gabe's gaze. "Will that suit you?"

Gabe nodded. "I just saw red when I overheard Walter in Wharton's. Who knows how many other people heard him?"

"They also heard the mayor standing up for me. And you," Mitch reminded him. He smiled. "Thanks for that, by the way. As for Howard, he's respected in this town. He's been reelected time and again. He may be a figurehead for all intents and purposes, but his faith in my work will carry a lot of weight."

"I suppose."

"I'm not worried," Mitch insisted. "You need to let it go for now. Take off and go over to Adelia's. You need to fill her in sooner rather than later."

Because he knew both Mitch and Carter were right, Gabe agreed. "I'll make up for all the time I missed this afternoon," he promised.

"Not to worry," Mitch said. "You were on company business." To Gabe's shock, Mitch pulled him into a bear hug. "Thanks for standing up for me, Gabe."

"Hey, it's what family does."

"I didn't, not back when you needed someone on your side," Mitch said.

"We agreed that's in the past," Gabe told him.

At Adelia's a few minutes later, he found Tomas sitting glumly in the middle of his bedroom, awaiting Gabe's arrival. He glanced up when Gabe walked in.

"Hey, buddy," Gabe greeted him. "Something wrong?"

"You're late. I thought you weren't coming."

"I told you I'd be here, didn't I?" Gabe said, sitting on the floor beside him. "I'll always keep my word."

"Like I believe that," Tomas said. "Nobody does."

Gabe had a sick feeling he was being tarred for someone else's neglect. He had a pretty good idea who that might be.

"Somebody let you down?" he asked. "Besides me, that is?"

"My dad said he was going to get me today and play catch with me in the park."

"He didn't show up?"

Tomas shook his head, fighting tears. "I called him when he wasn't here when he said he would be. He said he didn't have time, that he had a lot of important work to do. It's what he always says," Tomas said in a resigned tone.

Gabe muttered a harsh curse in his head but refrained from saying a word against Ernesto aloud. "I'm sure he does have a pretty busy schedule at work," he suggested instead.

Tomas brushed impatiently at the tears on his cheeks. "He's not at work. I called there first. He's with that lady, the one he picked over Mom. I heard her telling him to hurry up and get off the phone."

"I'm sorry," Gabe said, unable to think of a single comforting thing he could possibly say, much less any defense he could offer for Ernesto's behavior.

"It's not like it's the first time," Tomas said. "I should be used to it, huh?"

His plaintive words took Gabe straight back to his own childhood when he'd struggled time and again to prepare himself to be let down by his mom.

"It's not the kind of thing you should have to get used to," he told Tomas honestly. "But the truth is that sometimes adults make choices kids don't understand. It is hard, but one of the important lessons of life we need to learn is that we have to find some way to accept that people we love have

309

flaws. It takes a real grown-up to understand that. Do you think you can try? Personally I think you're pretty mature for a kid your age."

Tomas sat a little taller. "I can try," he said.

"Good for you. Now, are you going to help me get this room painted?"

For the first time the boy's eyes lit up. "I get to help?"

Gabe wasn't sure how much help Tomas would be, but he nodded. "Put on some really old clothes, so you don't ruin what you're wearing, and you can help," he confirmed. "And later on, if it's okay with your mom, I'll take you to the park and we can play catch."

"Cool," Tomas said, racing over to dig through a box of things still packed from the move. "Mom says these are ready to be turned into dust cloths," he said, holding up a pair of shorts that looked practically threadbare and a faded T-shirt.

"Those look perfect to me," Gabe said.

When Tomas ran off to the bathroom to change, Gabe drew in a deep breath. As sleazy as Gabe thought Ernesto was, he still couldn't grasp how he could so easily dismiss the needs of a great kid like his son. Gabe might not be the best person to make up for a dad's attention, but he sure as heck intended to try.

Adelia waited until dinner was over, Gabe and Tomas had returned from their game of catch and all the kids had gone upstairs to bed before she walked across the kitchen to Gabe and kissed him firmly on the lips. Shock and a quick flash of desire lit his eyes.

"What was that about?" he asked, his expression incredulous.

"To thank you for the way you handled Tomas earlier this afternoon."

"You were here? I thought you were still at work."

"I would have been, but Selena called me and told me what Ernesto had pulled and that Tomas was really upset. By the time Raylene could get in to cover for me and I got home, you were with him."

"Why didn't you say something?"

"Because you were already saying all the right things," she told him. "And, to be honest, it made me cry."

Gabe looked dismayed. "I made you cry?"

"You were so sweet, exactly the kind of man my son should have as a father. Instead, he has this thoughtless, careless jerk in his life, a man who will always put his own needs ahead of his son's."

Gabe seemed uncomfortable with her praise. "You might not feel that way when you've heard about what I've been up to today," he suggested direly.

"Gabe, you put a smile back on my son's face and made him feel as if he matters. You took him to the park for a game of catch, when I know you must be beat. I can't think of a thing you could tell me that would negate that."

"Don't be so sure," he said and described what had apparently been quite the confrontation with Ernesto.

Adelia heard him out. "Of course you had to stand up for Mitch," she said.

"That's not all of it, though."

She stood silently as he described Ernesto's reaction.

"He threatened to go to court to keep me away from you and the kids," he concluded.

Adelia laughed. "It's all bluster," she said. "He wouldn't dare set foot in that courtroom again. The judge wasn't any happier than Helen that I let him off as easily as I did when we divorced. He's not going to listen to anything Ernesto has to say, especially when it comes to throwing mud on someone who's been as great with my kids as you've been. Don't you get it, Gabe? You're everything that Ernesto's not. That's why he's so upset."

"He could complicate things for us," Gabe countered.

"Not a chance," Adelia insisted. "You don't know him like I do. It took me a very long time, but I finally realized that despite the way he behaved when it came to honoring our wedding vows, Ernesto craves respect. He liked the image he presented of being this terrific family man with a big house and four kids who excelled in school and a wife who was involved in all sorts of community activities. He didn't give two hoots about us, but he did like what it said about him. We mattered to him just a tiny bit more than his designer suits and his Rolex watch."

"But the whole blasted town knows now that it was a lie, that your kids are great because of you, that you were the person to be admired."

Adelia didn't even try to deny it. In fact, the knowledge satisfied her need to feel a sense of pride in the way she'd lived her life despite Ernesto's philandering. "But he's not going to want to have any of that mud slung in his face again. He won't risk it by attacking you."

"He's already attacking Mitch," Gabe countered.

"Not the same thing, at least as he sees it. That's all about business. This would be personal, and he wouldn't come out smelling like a rose. More like a pile of manure."

Gabe regarded her with surprise, then shook his head and chuckled. "You really do see him clearly now, don't you?"

"If I didn't, shame on me," she said, then cautioned, "That doesn't mean I want my kids disillusioned about him, at least not until they figure out what he's all about on their own. I think Tomas made that discovery today." Sadness settled over her. "His awakening came a little sooner than I might have liked, though."

"I'm sorry if I contributed to that," Gabe apologized.

"Don't go there. I meant what I said before. You said all the right things. You put a smile back on his face." She grinned then. "How'd the painting go, by the way?"

He gave her a rueful look. "The painting went great," he claimed. "The cleanup, not so much."

"So you're saying my son probably doesn't have a career as a housepainter in store."

"Not unless someone's after a decor that looks as if it was painted by Jackson Pollock. Tomas can splatter with the great modern artists of all time."

"Maybe I'll get him some canvases and some washable paints for his birthday and nudge him in that direction," she said, laughing. "Though personally I prefer to know what I'm looking at when I see a painting."

"Oh, you will when you see his," Gabe said. "Chaos."

She let her gaze linger on his face. "You just did it again," she said.

"What?"

"Put a smile on someone's face after a difficult day. Thank you for that."

He ran his thumb over her lips, lingered at the upturned corner of her mouth. "Glad to help. I wonder if I can do the same thing without words."

Even before he lowered his mouth to claim hers, Adelia murmured, "I'll bet you can."

In fact, just as she'd anticipated, Gabe turned out to be very good at silent communication, too.

CHAPTER FIFTEEN

Because it was a family tradition and because her children begged to go, at least the younger ones, Adelia agreed to return to her mother's for Sunday dinner that week. Even so, when she arrived, she wasn't anxious to face all the judgmental looks from her sisters and their husbands. Instead, she urged the kids toward the backyard, where their cousins were already playing.

Karen, who'd never been comfortable — or, to be honest, welcomed — in the kitchen with the other women, was sitting on the patio with the baby in her arms. Elliott, as usual, was in the thick of the games the kids were devising. Adelia sat beside her sister-in-law, then nodded toward her brother.

"He really is just a big kid himself, isn't he?" she said, amused.

Karen laughed. "I know that's why Daisy and Mack loved him from the instant they met him. It takes a man with real confidence to risk looking silly." Karen turned her gaze on Adelia. "You must feel the same way about Gabe. I saw the picture from the tea party."

Adelia laughed. "That picture is destined to haunt him forever."

Karen studied her worriedly. "Adelia, are you deliberately hiding out from your mother and sisters?"

"How'd you guess?"

"I recognize the signs," Karen said. "I tend to avoid the house and head straight back here. It gives me time to prepare for all that Cruz togetherness."

"It's not the togetherness that bothers me," Adelia confided. "It's the way my sisters and their husbands still look at me as if I'd committed a sin. I'm tired of defending my actions to them."

"Welcome to my world," Karen replied lightly.

"Why do you keep coming back?" Adelia asked, genuinely wanting to know. She was well aware that for months she'd been part of the problem, no more understanding with Karen than her sisters were being with her now.

"For Elliott's sake, of course. And I want my children to be part of this family. I have no issues with your mom. Not anymore, anyway. And I can tolerate the judgment and unwelcoming looks from the rest of them. They'll either come around to give me a chance as you and your mother have, or they won't." She shrugged. "I can't control that. I've given up trying to. As long as there's nothing overt said that might hurt my family, I can deal with whatever they might direct at me."

Adelia regarded her with deepening respect. "I hope I get to that point. As disappointed as I am in them, I'd still like us to be as close as we once were."

"I can understand that," Karen said. "It's different for you. You've had a lifetime of being close to your mother and sisters. It has to be incredibly hard to feel they've turned on you."

Once again, Adelia thought, Karen had surprised her. "That's exactly right," she admitted. "It feels as if I don't even know the people I've loved and trusted my whole life. Or as if they don't know me. Either way, I feel uncomfortable in the house I grew up in. It's hard, too, seeing Mama caught in the middle. She's doing her best to be supportive of my decisions, but I don't think she can quite bring herself to call Carolina and Maria to task, because on some level she agrees with them."

"Same with me," Karen said. Her expression brightened. "But we have Elliott and we have each other, at least if you want my backing."

Adelia reached over and squeezed her hand. "I count on it," she said, realizing it was true. "Now, hand over my nephew. I need to hold a sweet, innocent baby and forget all about this complicated family drama."

Karen shifted the baby to her. He whimpered but then settled trustingly in Adelia's arms. "I've missed this," Adelia whispered, eyes closed as she drew in the baby powder scent and felt the weight of the child in her arms. She'd never really aspired to be anything more than a great mom. While she was discovering that she had strong business skills, her real passion was her family.

"It's not too late to have another one," Karen said, regarding her with amusement.

"Are you nuts?" Adelia asked, her eyes snapping open. She handed the baby back as if pregnancy could be brought on by the power of suggestion. "I have four children already and no man in my life."

Karen grinned. "That sure wasn't the way it sounded at margarita night. By the time you left Raylene's, I thought you were ready to give Gabe a second chance."

319

Adelia glanced around to be sure her brother wasn't close enough to overhear her. "I have," she told Karen in a hushed voice, unable to stop the smile that spread across her face at the admission.

"Well, there you go," Karen said. "He's most definitely all man. Seems like he might make good daddy material."

Elliott walked over just in time to overhear his wife's comment. A frown settled on his face. "Did you just suggest that my sister and Gabe have a baby?"

Karen didn't seem the least bit intimidated by Elliott's scowl. "I was merely suggesting that if she wanted another baby, there was a candidate who might prove helpful."

Elliott turned his disapproving gaze from his wife to Adelia. "I told you to give the man a chance, not to let him father your children."

Adelia bit back a smile. "Nobody's going to father any children with me," she soothed, then allowed herself a grin. "At least not right this minute. And this conversation is exactly why I discouraged Mama from asking Gabe to join us for dinner."

Elliott looked as if he wanted to launch into a protective, brotherly lecture, but just then the back door opened and their mother announced that dinner was ready.

"Time to face the music," Adelia said, getting to her feet.

Karen handed the baby off to Elliott, then put an arm around Adelia's waist. "Come on. I'll protect you."

"And who's going to protect you?" Adelia asked.

"You, of course. And that big, strong man carrying my baby. Nobody in church heard it on the day we got married, but one of his vows was to stand between me and his family."

"I've got your back," Elliott confirmed, giving her a doting look. He winked at Adelia. "Yours, too, if you'll let me."

"You already have your hands full, little brother. I can take care of myself," Adelia told him.

She allowed herself just a moment of envy at the bond between Elliott and Karen. She wondered if she'd ever have that sort of bond again. While she was starting to trust Gabe around her kids, she wasn't quite ready to trust him with her heart. After all, she'd known Ernesto for years and never suspected he was a serial cheater. How could she possibly trust any man after just a few weeks?

In Cruz family tradition, the children had

all been served at their table. Now the adults said grace and began passing around the familiar bowls of rice and beans, fried plantains and fragrant pork. Adelia absorbed the temporary calm and goodwill and almost allowed herself to relax.

Within minutes, though, she realized that there was an underlying tension in the room and that, for once, it had nothing to do with her. She glanced across the table and saw that Carolina was fighting tears while her husband sat back in his chair with a dark expression on his face. This time there was no ignoring her gut feeling that something wasn't right there.

Since everyone else was studiously avoiding the obviously angry couple, Adelia did, as well, but she resolved that after dinner she'd make another attempt to reach out to her sister, despite the harsh words they'd exchanged on their last encounter.

Maria tried to fill the silence with idle chitchat, but no one seemed interested in helping her out. Adelia glanced at her mother and realized that she was clearly at the end of her rope. She didn't like dissension in the family in general and especially not at these Sunday gatherings.

"Carolina, could you help me in the

kitchen?" their mother said, suddenly standing up.

"But, Mama —" Carolina started to protest, only to be cut off.

"Now!"

Adelia started to stand, as well, but her mother gestured for her to stay.

When mother and daughter had gone into the kitchen, all eyes turned angrily on Enrique.

"What's going on, Ricky?" Elliott demanded of his brother-in-law.

"Nothing but hormones," Ricky replied, as if his wife's mood were of no consequence. "You know how women get."

Adelia almost came out of her seat at that. "Don't take that condescending tone about my sister," she snapped, sitting down only because Karen reached out, then shook her head. Confronting Ricky about his attitude would only stir the pot. And Adelia knew, as did Karen, that little good would come of that, not with these old-school men who believed their wives were more possessions than partners.

"Let your mother get to the bottom of this," Karen whispered.

Elliott looked as if he was no more inclined to listen to that advice than Adelia was, but he sat back in his chair, as well.

323

"For now," he said, a heated warning in his voice as he stared hard at Ricky, who was fingering an unlit cigar as if nothing at all were wrong in his world.

Adelia turned to her brother. "I have no idea what's going on between those two, but I would give anything to wipe that smug look off his face," she said, speaking in an undertone she hoped wouldn't be overheard.

"Don't tempt me," Elliott replied.

Just then their mother returned to the dining room alone. She turned a gaze on Ricky that startled Adelia. She looked as if she was furious and fighting to contain it.

"Your wife isn't feeling well," she said tightly to her son-in-law. "She's waiting in the car. I suggest you take her home. The children will be staying here."

Ricky looked as if he might balk at what could only be interpreted as an order, but after a quick glance around the table, during which he obviously spotted no allies, he finally shrugged and stood.

"Lovely as always," he said sarcastically.

Elliott was on his feet before the remark was finished, but after a stern look from his mother, he didn't go after Ricky.

"I believe we've had enough drama for the moment," his mother said. "Leave the two of them to work this out."

Elliott didn't look happy, but he nodded. "Whatever you say, Mama."

Maria glanced at her husband, but Marco seemed to be avoiding her gaze. For once, without an ally in the room, he apparently had nothing to say, either. Adelia couldn't help thinking that he must have a good idea about what was going on, but he'd never betray Ricky, any more than either of them had revealed Ernesto's secrets. It was as if the three brothers-in-law had taken a pact of unity.

Adelia kept her own thoughts to herself until after dinner, when she volunteered to help her mother clear the table and deal with the dishes. Alone with her mother in the kitchen, she asked quietly, "Is Carolina okay?"

Her mother sighed heavily. "She's more troubled than I imagined," she admitted. A tear spilled down her cheek. "What is happening to my family?"

Adelia gave her a fierce hug. "Nothing you are responsible for, Mama. We all made our own choices, and each of us must decide how we want to move forward."

"I've always believed marriage vows to be sacred, that it should be forever. I harbored what was apparently an illusion, that problems could always be worked out," her mother said, a plaintive note in her voice. "That's the way it should be. It's the way I taught all of you to live your lives. Now you're divorced." She met Adelia's gaze. "And rightfully so. As for Carolina . . ." Her voice quavered and she sat down, then lifted her sad gaze to Adelia. "There are bruises. Ricky hit her, Adelia. That man hit my child."

Adelia was indignant. Beyond indignant. She wanted to rip into Ricky herself. "And you let her leave here with him?"

"I didn't let her. She insisted."

Now Adelia was actually stunned. "Carolina wanted to go home with him after that?"

Her mother nodded, her expression helpless. "Did I teach her too well? About honoring her vows, I mean. Is it my fault that she won't walk away from a man who abuses her?"

Adelia thought it might, indeed, be about that, at least to some extent. She knew firsthand how eager they all were for their mother's approval. She also knew that some women couldn't make that break from an abusive man for far different reasons.

"What did she say?" she asked her mother. "Did she admit that he was responsible for the bruises?"

"Yes, but she said they were her fault, that she'd upset him and that he'd apologized. Over and over, she said, as if that made up for it."

Adelia knew that was the classic response of far too many women. "I'll talk to her," she told her mother. "Better yet, I'll have Raylene talk to her. Raylene knows how that kind of abuse can escalate. Maybe she can get through to Carolina that it's never okay, not even the first time." She was struck by a terrible thought. "Was it the first time?"

"I don't know," her mother responded. "I couldn't get her to open up. I swear I wanted to walk into the dining room and swing a cast-iron skillet straight at his head myself." She held Adelia's gaze. "I had it in my hand. I've never felt that kind of rage before. I wanted to send my girl upstairs and tell her she was grounded and not allowed to leave this house."

Adelia smiled at that. "Carolina's thirty-eight, a little old for grounding, but I totally understand your wanting to do just that. I want to go over there and snatch her out of that house myself. God help us if Elliott gets wind of this. I've kept him from laying a hand on Ernesto, but I doubt there's anything any of us could say to keep him from going after Ricky."

"Which is why we won't say a word to anyone," her mother said. "Not unless it becomes necessary to protect Carolina."

"Well, I'm going over there now," Adelia said. "Who knows how Ricky might react if he finds out Carolina's told you the truth?"

"You can't," her mother protested. "What if that makes him even madder?"

"Then he'll have two of us to deal with. May my children stay here? If you already have too much on your hands, I can ask Elliott to take them, or call Gabe to pick them up."

"No, no. They'll be fine right here. Looking after them will help to take my mind off of all this. I'll bake them cookies."

Adelia knew that baking was her mother's best stress reducer. That worked out nicely for her appreciative, always hungry grandkids. She leaned down and gave her a hug.

"I'll be back soon," she promised. "Hopefully I can persuade Carolina to come with me."

"I'll pray for that," her mother said, but her sorrowful expression suggested she didn't believe that particular prayer would be answered.

Adelia slipped out of the kitchen door, hoping that no one would notice her departure.

The fewer explanations she had to offer, the better. She doubted she could contain the anger she was feeling toward Ricky right now or the pity she felt for her sister.

Though she'd suspected that Carolina's marriage was in trouble, she hadn't guessed something like this. When Adelia had suggested he might be cheating, Carolina had even let her believe she'd gotten it right. Obviously she'd been too ashamed to admit that it was even worse than that. While Ernesto's behavior had been its own form of abuse that she'd tolerated for far too long, Adelia had always believed that she'd have the strength to walk away the first time any man ever laid a hand on her. From talking to Raylene, though, she knew that wasn't always the case, that the situation could sometimes be too complex for a quick, easy solution.

Adelia drove into Carolina's neighborhood of modest but well-kept homes. Her sister's passion for gardening was evident in the small, lushly landscaped lawn that was edged with fragrant roses in full bloom. Baskets of bright flowers hung from the porch ceiling and more pots lined the steps. The cheerful riot of color was a far cry from what Adelia expected to find inside.

On the way over, she'd come up with a

reason for the impromptu visit, one that might be believable to both her sister and Ricky. Pressing the doorbell, she drew in a deep breath and prepared to sell her hastily devised story.

When Carolina opened the door, her eyes were puffy from crying, her expression dismayed. "This isn't a good time," she said, stepping outside and closing the door behind her.

Relieved to be able to speak to her sister alone, Adelia kept her voice low. "Mama told me," she said. "Come with me, Carolina. Please don't stay here."

"This is my home," Carolina said stubbornly. "It's where I belong."

"Just for tonight," Adelia pleaded. "Stay with me if you don't want to go to Mama's. The kids, too."

Her sister regarded her miserably. "I can't. It will only make him angrier."

"Who cares how angry he gets?" Adelia said. "And if your visiting your sister is all it takes to set him off, you don't belong here."

"How can you possibly understand? You had a man who gave you everything. You had a beautiful home. Your children had whatever they needed. You could spend your days at home. Your life was perfect, and you threw it away. For what?"

Adelia held her gaze. "My self-respect," she said softly. "That's more important than any of the rest."

"And do you have your precious self-respect now with your reputation ruined because of a man you've known for, what, a few weeks?"

"My reputation isn't ruined, except, perhaps, in your eyes. Gabe's a good and decent man. I can't say the same about Ernesto." She dared to touch her sister's cheek. "This has nothing to do with me, Carolina. I'm here because of you. This situation isn't acceptable. Please let me help you."

Carolina shook her head. "I don't need your help. Ricky was angry. He didn't mean it." She said it almost by rote, as if she'd repeated it to herself a thousand times to justify what was happening to her.

"And how many times has he told you that?" Adelia asked her, holding her gaze. Her sister blinked and looked away. "I thought so. This isn't the first time, as Mama had hoped."

"It will get better," her sister argued. "It always does. I just have to try harder."

"And how long will things be better? How many weeks or days or hours does it take before he finds another excuse?"

"Stop it," Carolina said angrily. "It's not his fault. It's mine."

Adelia felt her temper flare at the way Ricky had managed to manipulate Carolina into believing that she'd done anything to justify the abuse. "You're being abused," she told her heatedly. "That is never, ever okay, Carolina. Will you at least go with me to talk to Raylene? She's been through this. There are people ready and willing to help you. If you don't want to talk to her or me or even Mama, there's a wonderful counselor who can help. Don't let this escalate. Don't let yourself be a victim for a second longer. Think about what happened to Raylene."

Since everyone in town had heard Raylene's story and was aware that her ex-husband had come to town to try to kill her after his release from jail on abuse charges, Carolina did flinch at the mention of Raylene's name.

"It's not the same," she insisted to Adelia. "Ricky's a good man. He just has a quick temper."

"And a willing target, apparently," Adelia said, hoping to provoke her sister. Maybe straight talk would snap her out of this destructive, accepting attitude she seemed to have adopted.

Carolina regarded Adelia with real heat in her eyes. "That's not fair. You don't know what it's like."

"Thank God for that," Adelia said. "But you shouldn't know what it's like, either. You shouldn't be living like this, in constant fear of your husband's moods. This isn't a marriage."

Just then Ricky bellowed from inside. "Carolina, get back in here! Tell that troublemaking sister of yours to mind her own business."

Panic immediately spread across Carolina's face. "I have to go."

"Come with me," Adelia repeated. "Get away from here."

A faint smile touched her sister's lips, but it was gone in a heartbeat. "Do you think I'd be safer at your house or Mama's?" she inquired. "Never. I'd just be putting you in danger, too."

Her words were more alarming than anything she'd said before. Adelia regarded her with growing dismay. "All the more reason to leave. If Ricky's that dangerous, you have to get away. We can protect you. Elliott, Gabe, there are others, too, who'll see to it that no more harm comes to you. Carter Rollins can arrest Ricky. You know he has no tolerance for domestic violence."

"What about my children?" Carolina asked. "What would they think if I sent their father to jail?"

"That you'd stood up for yourself." She looked her sister in the eye. "And for them," she added.

"Ricky would never touch them," Carolina responded, looking genuinely shocked by the suggestion. Once more, she was clearly deluding herself.

"Are you so sure?" Adelia asked more gently, seeing an opening that might make Carolina see reason. "And even if he never lays a hand on them, how do you think it makes them feel to know their father is abusing you?"

"They don't know," Carolina insisted.

Adelia regarded her incredulously. "Maybe not the younger ones, but I'll bet Joey knows," she told Carolina. "And sooner or later he will either get dragged into the middle of it to protect you or he'll wind up believing that it's okay for a husband to hit a wife."

Carolina looked deeply shaken by Adelia's words, but she backed away just the same. "I have to go inside."

"Please don't," Adelia pleaded one last time.

"I have to," Carolina said, her expression

defeated.

She darted inside, leaving Adelia standing on the porch, tears streaming down her cheeks and fury burning in her heart.

CHAPTER SIXTEEN

Gabe had never had a problem with loneliness before. After years of the chaos of living with his mom, he'd craved a peaceful lifestyle. He'd lived mostly on his own for years now, found female companionship when he wanted it or created distractions that kept him occupied whenever he had time off.

Since coming back to Serenity, though, he'd discovered that Sundays seemed endless. Mitch flatly refused to let him work at the Main Street site. He claimed the churchgoers in town wouldn't approve, that Sundays were meant for church and family.

Though he considered himself to be a man of faith, Gabe hadn't set foot in church since the one time his mother had dragged him to a service, only to be subjected to searing looks of disapproval that didn't seem to him to be very Christian or welcoming.

As for family, he figured Mitch had seen more than enough of him weekdays. Though he had a standing invitation to Mitch's, he didn't want to interrupt his cousin's family time just because he was at loose ends.

That left Adelia's. The renovations were coming along, even with the scant amount of time he had to devote to them. That didn't mean that the occasional Sunday on the job wouldn't help to speed things up. If he caught a glimpse of her or got to spend time with the kids, so much the better.

As he headed to Swan Point, he called to make sure it would be okay with Adelia for him to put in a few hours. He didn't get an answer and assumed she was off somewhere with her family. Since he had a key and her permission to work whenever he could, he went on over.

He'd just pulled into the driveway and was about to go inside when he spotted Adelia's car coming down the street at a breakneck pace. She skidded to a stop in front of the house, at least a foot from the curb. To his surprise, though, while she cut the engine, she didn't get out. She sat where she was, arms braced on the steering wheel, her head lowered onto them. Gabe doubted she'd even taken note of his presence. Something definitely wasn't right.

His heart thudding, he walked over and tapped on the window. She jumped, then regarded him with dismay. He took in her pale complexion and the tears streaming down her cheeks and grabbed the door handle. Opening the door carefully, he kneeled beside her and rested a hand lightly on her thigh.

"What is it? What's happened?" he asked, keeping his tone gentle.

She shook her head, the tears coming harder than ever. Her pain was enough to break his heart.

"Is it one of the kids? Is someone hurt? Is it your mom?"

Again, she could only seem to shake her head.

For a minute he couldn't think what to do. Then it occurred to him that sitting here in the car sobbing where anyone could see probably wasn't something she'd want if she were thinking clearly.

"Is it okay if I take you inside?" he asked, sensing that she was so fragile right now, he didn't dare do anything without her permission.

"Please," she whispered. "I can't seem to move."

He snagged the keys from the ignition, then gently picked her up and cradled her against his chest. It took only a few strides to carry her up the walkway and open the door. Inside, though, he hesitated.

"Living room? Kitchen? Your bedroom?" The last came out on a husky note. "Do you need to lay down?"

"Just hold me," she said, snuggling closer.

Gabe knew she was distraught, that she'd never be all over him if she were thinking straight. He vowed not to take advantage of her while she was in this state, not even if it killed him. He at least had to get to the bottom of her distress first.

Since that was the immediate goal, he decided they'd better steer clear of the bedroom. She was obviously vulnerable, and he'd never been called a saint.

He strode into the living room, sat on the sofa and held her close. Though it was a warm day and the air-conditioning wasn't running in the house, she shivered. He rubbed his hands up and down her arms to try to get the circulation going. She shivered even more, though it was hard to tell if it was from a chill or a reaction to his touch.

"Talk to me," he pleaded. "What's going on?"

She drew in a deep shuddering breath and then the words began to tumble out. He tried to follow, but she was so upset and speaking so quickly, he could barely piece together what had happened.

"Your sister's husband is abusing her?" he asked, to be sure he'd heard right.

"I tried to get her to come home with me, but she won't." She gave him a heartbroken look. "How can she stay there, Gabe? Was I wrong to leave her in that house with him?"

"It sounds like you did everything you could," he said slowly. He thought of the times his mother had tolerated being slapped around just to keep some man in her life for a few more days or weeks. He'd tried intervening with them, even taking a punch himself on occasion. He'd tried pleading with her, but nothing had worked. She'd made her choices. The irony, of course, was that the men had eventually left, anyway, taking her self-respect right along with them. "You can't make her do something she's not ready to do," he said based on experience.

A sudden thought crossed his mind. "Does Elliott know?"

She shook her head. "Mama and I agreed he can't find out. He'd kill Ricky."

"Secrets like this always come out," Gabe warned. "I think you need to fill him in." He held her gaze. "And Carter at the same time. If Carter's aware of the situation, maybe that will be enough to keep your brother from going off the deep end."

"I can't take that chance," she said at once. "And if Carter knows, won't he have to do something? I know if he tries to arrest Ricky, Carolina will deny anything's happened. She's already said as much. She's convinced herself — and tried to convince Mama and me — that this is all her fault."

"What about her kids?" Gabe asked. "Are they in danger?"

"They're at Mama's," Adelia reported. "Hopefully Carolina will let them stay there."

"And your kids? Are they at your mother's, too?"

She nodded. "I called when I left my sister's and told Mama that I hadn't had any luck changing Carolina's mind. My kids are fine with Mama for another couple of hours. She's baking cookies. They get to lick the bowl and eat the cookies straight out of the oven. I doubt they're even aware I'm gone. I needed some time to pull myself together before they come home. I'll pick them up later or she'll bring them home."

Even in her distressed state, she'd thought of her children, made sure they were okay. Gabe tried to imagine what his life would have been like if his mother had ever put him first.

"Is there anything I can do?" he asked Adelia, wanting to share this burden with her, to ease it if he could.

"Stay here with me, Gabe. You don't need to be mixed up in this. You don't even know my sister."

"She matters to you, so she matters to me," Gabe said without hesitation.

She regarded him with wonder. "You really mean that, don't you?"

Gabe was almost as surprised by that as she was, but it was true. It might not be his problem to resolve, but he hated what it was doing to this woman he cared about. If he could pummel Ricky and solve anything, he'd do it in a heartbeat. It was ironic really how many people he'd wanted to punch out on Adelia's behalf or Mitch's lately, but he'd managed to resist the urge. Maybe he really had grown up and realized there were always better choices.

"I really mean it," he told her.

"I've never had a hero before," she murmured, her eyes drifting closed as she finally relaxed in his arms.

"Oh, darlin', I'm nobody's hero," Gabe protested, but she was beyond hearing him. She'd fallen asleep, obviously worn-out by the day's traumatic events.

As he sat there holding her, Gabe realized something else. The loneliness he'd felt earlier in the day had vanished. Even with Adelia asleep and a very real crisis threatening to erupt, he felt more at peace than he had in a long time, maybe ever.

When Gabe was satisfied that Adelia was sleeping soundly, he covered her with a soft blue afghan that was on the back of the sofa and slipped away. First, he went out and pulled her car closer to the curb to lessen the risk of it being struck by another driver. Then he considered going upstairs to work, but he was afraid any noise he made would wake her. Instead, he went into the kitchen to see if there was anything basic that he could fix for dinner.

He'd just pulled salad ingredients and hamburger meat from the refrigerator when Selena came in. Her eyes widened when she saw him.

"You're making dinner?" she asked.

He smiled at her incredulous expression. "I thought I'd give it a try. Want to help me?"

"Sure," she said, taking over with the salad ingredients. "Mom's asleep in the living room. How come? She left *Abuela*'s early and never came back. Is she sick?"

Sick at heart more likely, Gabe thought. To Selena he said only, "I think she was tired."

"She does work awfully hard," Selena said. She gave Gabe a worried look. "Do you think it's too much for her? I know she was determined not to take any help from my dad, except for the money he gives her for us. She puts that into a college fund, though. Maybe she should be spending it, instead, so she doesn't have to work so hard."

"I may not know your mom very well yet, but I think she wants to provide for you guys. I think she takes a lot of pride in it."

"I guess," Selena said, setting aside the bowl she'd filled with lettuce, peppers, grape tomatoes and croutons. "But if she's worn-out, that can't be good."

"I think it just hit her today," Gabe said. "I don't think it's anything you need to worry about. Where are your sisters and brother? I thought you were all over at your grandmother's."

"We were, but we wanted to come back here. *Abuela* wanted us to stay, but I told her I could look out for the kids." She flushed guiltily. "I guess maybe she knew Mom was here resting or with you. I probably should have listened to her, but Uncle

Elliott was leaving and he said he'd drop us off."

Gabe smiled. "It's good you're home. I think your mom will be glad to see you when she's awake. Where are Tomas and your sisters now?"

"Out back. When I saw that Mom was asleep, I sent them outside to play. Tomas didn't want to go, because he saw your truck. He wanted to come in and help you."

"He can help me with the burgers on the grill," Gabe said. He gave Selena an approving look. "I hope you know what a big help you are to your mom by looking out for Tomas, Natalia and Juanita."

She blushed at the compliment. "I'm grounded. What else do I have to do?"

He smiled at that. "It's more than that. You're mature enough to see that your mom could use a little help and you've stepped up."

"Does being mature mean I have to keep doing this, like, forever? Even after I'm not grounded?"

Gabe laughed. "Oh, I imagine your mom will reward you with some time off for good behavior."

"I hope so, 'cause I really, really miss hanging out with my friends."

He studied her for a minute. "Are you allowed to use your cell phone yet?"

"Only for emergencies," she said despondently. "And for maybe fifteen minutes, if Mom thinks I've been extra good."

"If she were awake, I think she'd let you use it for fifteen minutes right now," he said. "The salad is made. You have a little time before the burgers will be ready."

Her eyes brightened. "Really?"

"I think so."

"But what if you get in trouble for letting me?" she asked worriedly.

"My problem," he said, then grinned. "Maybe she'll ground me, too."

Selena laughed at that. "Thanks, Gabe."

"Fifteen minutes," he warned. "Not a second longer."

"I promise," she said and ran from them room, already making a call.

He was about to go outside when he saw Adelia standing in the doorway, hands on hips and what he hoped was a mock scowl in place. "Did I just hear you give my daughter permission to use her cell phone?"

He winced. "Sorry. She'd been really helpful." He gestured toward the counter. "She made the salad. She shooed the younger kids outside so they wouldn't wake you. And she admitted she wasn't allowed to use the phone except when you gave her permission." He shrugged. "I made an executive decision."

"And what if I did decide to ground you for it?" she asked, her lips twitching. "How do you see that working?"

"I'd have to stay here," he told her solemnly. "For as long as you want."

Her eyes sparkled. "For some reason, when you say it, it doesn't sound so much like a punishment."

"That depends on where you let me sleep," he teased.

"Gabe!" she protested, giving a quick glance around to make sure none of the kids were nearby.

He stepped closer. "Any thoughts about that, Adelia?"

She swallowed hard. "I can't think about anything when you're this close."

He grinned. "Exactly what I was going for," he said. "That and getting some color back in your complexion. Mission accomplished."

She touched a hand to his cheek. "I meant what I said earlier, you know. You are my hero. And I won't let you deny it now, the way you did then."

"I thought you were asleep and didn't hear me."

"No, I heard you, but it wasn't worth

arguing about. I know the truth and that's what counts."

For the first time in his entire life, Gabe actually realized what it felt like to be someone's hero. He wasn't sure he deserved the label, but it felt darn good just the same.

Adelia did her best to put her sister's situation out of her mind and to focus on her own family for the remainder of the evening. She smiled when Selena bounced back downstairs after exactly fifteen minutes and put her cell phone down on the kitchen counter with a dramatic flourish.

"Right on time," Selena announced, then regarded her mother worriedly. "Gabe's not in trouble for letting me use it, is he?"

"No, I think he showed good judgment," Adelia told her. "You've been a huge help to me lately. You deserved a break. And the fact that you acknowledged to him that you weren't allowed to use the phone without permission showed me something, too."

"What?"

"That you respect my rules, even if you don't always agree with them," Adelia told her. "You're growing up, Selena." She grinned. "A little too fast for my taste, but I do appreciate the maturity you've been demonstrating lately."

To her surprise, Selena gave her a fierce hug.

"I don't want to let you down, Mom." She glanced around. "Where's Gabe?"

"Outside cooking hamburgers, or trying to. Last time I looked, he was trying to keep Tomas from flipping them onto the ground."

"Dad was never patient enough to let Tomas do anything," Selena said. "I think it's cool that Gabe is."

"So, you really have changed your opinion of him?" Adelia asked carefully.

"He's a good guy," Selena conceded, then frowned. "I just don't know how I feel about him being with you. It's still kind of soon."

"Remember that feeling when I try to tell you who you can date," Adelia said, deciding it wasn't worth some long and serious discussion since things were far from settled between her and Gabe. One official date was hardly a relationship, though he did seem to be increasingly a part of their lives.

Selena grinned at her comment, just as Adelia had intended. "Good point," she said. "How about I promise not to butt into your life and you don't butt into mine?"

Adelia laughed. "Nice try, but I'm the mom. I get to butt in anytime I want to." She tugged gently on a strand of her daughter's hair. "And you have to listen."

"Not fair," Selena declared, but her eyes were shining. "Do you think Gabe will want to do game night with us?"

Adelia regarded her with surprise. "We haven't had a game night in a long time." It had been a Sunday night tradition for years, though Ernesto had rarely joined in the games. With all the commotion of the past few months, the tradition seemed to have died.

"I know," Selena said. "I kinda miss it. We could play team Scrabble. I could play with either Juanita or Natalia, you could play with the other one and Tomas could play with Gabe. It might be fun."

"Why don't we bring it up at dinner?" Adelia suggested. "We can see if everyone wants to play that or something else."

"As long as it's not Candy Land," Selena said, rolling her eyes. "I think I played that about a million times."

Adelia laughed. "I think maybe everyone's beyond that now. You should be safe."

Just then the younger girls came running inside, announced that the burgers were ready, then raced off to wash their hands.

Gabe was right on their heels with the platter of hamburgers, toasted buns and, to her astonishment, some grilled vegetables, as well.

"Gabe says everything tastes better when it's cooked on the grill," Tomas announced. "We did peppers and squash and even some onions." He wrinkled his nose at that.

Gabe caught his expression and chided, "But we're all going to try everything, right? Because that's the only way to know if we really like it or not."

"I guess," Tomas said, his expression doubtful. "But I don't have to eat it if it's yucky. That's the deal."

Gabe nodded, fighting a smile. "That's the deal."

"It's a better deal than I ever got," Adelia told him as he set the platter on the table. She turned to Selena. "Bring in the ketchup and mustard, please. I forgot those."

As soon as they were seated, Adelia realized she was starving. She'd lost her appetite at her mother's earlier and eaten very little of the food on her plate. Now, surrounded by her laughing kids and with Gabe across the table, she finally let herself relax.

As the platter was passed, she noted that Gabe put a little of everything on Tomas's plate. She hid a grin as her son reluctantly tried tiny bites of each vegetable. He looked up at Gabe with a shocked expression. "They're really good," he announced.

"Told you," Gabe said.

Her son's reaction had the desired effect and she noted that everyone's plate was quickly piled high with grilled veggies. She met Gabe's gaze. "Miracle worker," she mouthed.

He laughed at that.

When everyone was starting to slow down, Selena announced, "I told Mom I think we should have a game night. How about it?"

Juanita and Natalia immediately bounced eagerly in their chairs and shouted their agreement. Tomas looked skeptical.

"Daddy hated game night," he said.

"Oh, so what?" Selena said. "It's fun. I thought we could play team Scrabble." She gave her brother a sly look. "You could play with Gabe."

Tomas immediately looked more interested. "Are you gonna play, Gabe?"

Adelia waited almost breathlessly for his response.

"Sounds as if I've been drafted," Gabe said. He leaned toward Tomas. "But you're going to have to teach me. I haven't played a lot of Scrabble."

"I can do that," Tomas agreed. "My spelling's not so good, but I know strategy and stuff."

"Then we should make a good team," Gabe told him. "I got A's in spelling."

"Seriously?" Tomas said, wide-eyed. "Daddy always said it didn't matter, that that's what spell-check on the computer was for."

"Well, in my day, we had to learn to spell the old-fashioned way," Gabe told him. "We practiced and practiced."

"Could you practice with me sometime?" Tomas begged. "I get new words every week."

Gabe nodded. "Get your list. Maybe we can use them in the game."

"Okay, it's settled then," Adelia said. "Kids, I want to see your homework before we start to make sure it's ready for school tomorrow. While you get that, I'll clean up the kitchen."

Gabe automatically picked up dishes and carried them into the kitchen. Adelia frowned at him. "You don't need to do that. You cooked, after all."

"Maybe I'm looking for a few more points," he said solemnly. "Or a couple of minutes alone with you away from prying eyes."

She flushed at his teasing. "Why would

you need to be alone with me?"

He backed her up toward the counter, then braced his hands on either side of her. "For this," he said, brushing his lips over hers. "And this." He settled in for a longer taste, then stepped away at the sound of footsteps running in their direction.

"Guess that'll have to do for now," he said, pulling away. He winked at her. "Fair warning, though. If I win at Scrabble, I expect a really, really nice reward."

She laughed at the impudent comment. "Winning should be its own reward."

"You might be able to convince your kids of that, but I know there are things that matter more. There's a whole lot I'd do for a few more stolen kisses."

"Gabe Franklin," she said a little breathlessly, "if you keep this up, you're going to turn my head. Is that your intention?"

He seemed surprised by the idea, but then a smile stole across his face. "You know, I think maybe it is."

Adelia was shaken by the intensity she heard in his voice. How long had it been since any man had wanted her? Even more, how long had it been since one had openly put his heart on the line? After so many years of being viewed as the woman who raised Ernesto's kids and kept his house spotless, but little more, it was heady stuff to be seen as a desirable woman.

Suddenly she couldn't wait to put this Scrabble tournament behind them. In fact, she might even throw a game or two Gabe's way just so she could see how clever he was about claiming his rewards.

CHAPTER SEVENTEEN

The Scrabble board had been put away. The exhausted kids had gone to bed. Gabe could see that Adelia was completely drained, but there was a brightness in her eyes as she held the score sheet up for him to see.

"This tells me you bamboozled us," she accused. "You know a whole lot more about playing Scrabble than you let on."

"Just luck," he claimed. "I got great letters and your son has killer instincts about how to make the best use of them."

"He might have the instincts, but you're a very good coach. I actually have high hopes that he might pass his spelling test this week."

Gabe gave her a long, speculative look. "So, you're saying I not only won, but that you're pleased with how I got Tomas to study for his spelling test?"

"You have a definite knack for both," she agreed.

He stepped closer. "So, any thoughts about what sort of reward I deserve?" He ran a finger along the curve of her jaw and down her neck. He felt her pulse jump and her skin heat. She gave him a surprisingly innocent look, though there was an unmistakable twinkle in her eyes. "I'll buy you an extralarge coffee in the morning," she offered.

Gabe shook his head and traced her lower lip with his thumb. "Not quite what I had in mind."

She swallowed hard. "Pastry?" she suggested in a choked voice. "I'll buy your pastry, too. Two, if you want. Even three."

"Nope. I want something sweeter," he said softly, his gaze holding hers. "And more immediate."

"What if . . ." Her voice shook. "What if that's not available?"

"Isn't it? What I want, what I need is standing right here, right now." He lowered his head and claimed her mouth. After barely more than a heartbeat of hesitation, she surrendered to the kiss, parting her lips, taking him in. Gabe lost himself in the sweetness of the moment. This woman who'd been through so much, not just today, but for months now, was trusting him, welcoming him. He suddenly felt ten feet tall.

Still, this wasn't the time or the place to claim all he wanted from her, not with her children right upstairs and her so exhausted she might not be thinking clearly. Reluctantly, he took a step back, still holding her lightly.

"I want even more than that, Adelia," he told her candidly. "Not because of some game, but because I don't think I'll ever get enough of you."

She looked as if she desperately wanted to believe him, but he could see the doubts crowding in and wanted, yet again, to curse Ernesto for planting those seeds in her head. If he were being honest, he'd probably added to those doubts with his repeated warnings that he didn't do the whole forever thing. Since he couldn't take back his words, he focused on her shaky self-confidence.

He brushed her thick dark hair back from her face and kept his hands gentle on her cheeks. "You don't believe me now, but you will," he told her. "I'll make sure you start to see yourself as I do."

"And then what?" she blurted, then covered her mouth with her hand, obviously embarrassed.

"Then we'll see," he said, his expression

sobering as she called him on the very thing he'd been trying to avoid. "I won't make false promises to you, Adelia. Not ever. This is new to me, too. I'm not sure I know how to do a real relationship. I don't know if I can."

"Oh," she whispered, looking shaken by the repeated warning.

"Look at me," he commanded. When she dared to lift her eyes to meet his, he said, "But you make me want to try, Adelia. No woman's ever done that before. Lately, spending time with you, with your family . . ." He fell silent, almost afraid of the thought, much less of expressing it. Nights like tonight had been nonexistent in his past. He'd never known how happy being with a family could make him. On the rare occasions when he and his mom had been included in family events, any joy had been overshadowed by anger and recriminations and judgment. Tonight had given him a taste of something far different, something he found himself longing to claim.

When he was about to say more, she touched a finger to his lips. "It's okay, Gabe. There's no rush. I'm not exactly ready to jump into anything too serious, either."

Perversely, that made him want to do the opposite, to jump straight into wherever this might be taking them. Instead, though, he let her have the last word on the topic.

"You need to get some sleep," he said. "You've had a long and stressful day."

"You made it better," she told him. "You really did. Thank you for being here for me and for being so good with my kids."

"Anytime, darlin'. And that really is a promise."

He left then, because he didn't entirely trust himself not to make more promises or to ask for more from her as he'd just been so tempted to do. If he did either of those things and then bailed, as he feared he someday would, he'd never forgive himself for disappointing her.

Adelia took a late morning break, put a sign on the boutique's door and ran next door to the bakery for coffee. She could barely keep her eyes open. Between worrying about her sister and thinking about Gabe, she'd barely slept a wink the night before.

Lynn took one look at her and poured her a large cup of coffee to go. "If you don't mind me saying so, you look beat, and that's coming from a woman who knows a thing or two about exhaustion." Lynn studied her speculatively. "Is it too much to hope that you had a late night with Gabe?"

"Gabe was over, but it wasn't like that," Adelia told her. "We played Scrabble with the kids. It was a relatively early evening."

To her surprise, Lynn grinned. "Ah, so that's it. Frustration is what kept you awake."

Adelia laughed. "What is it with you Sweet Magnolias? Your minds are always on romance and sex."

"Because we have men who make us very happy," Lynn said, her own contentment plain. "We want that for everyone. And maybe since we're all settled into our old married ruts, we want to live vicariously through the courtship rituals."

"Well, there's no courting going on," Adelia insisted, though she feared the heat she could feel in her cheeks would give her away.

"Not buying that," Lynn said, dismissing the claim without a second's hesitation. "Gabe's no fool. I also think he's the kind of man who'll go after what he wants. And all the signs point to his wanting you."

"What if I'm not sure I can handle what he wants?" Adelia asked, unable to keep a plaintive note from her voice.

Lynn's teasing expression sobered at once. "Do you know what he wants?"

"Well, he says he wants me, but I think he

means in an uncomplicated, casual fling sort of way. Last night he was tossing around all sorts of warnings about not making promises. It was nothing he hasn't said before, so I have to believe he means it."

"He probably thinks he does," Lynn said, looking exasperated. "I suppose he's trying to play fair, the idiot."

Adelia smiled at the disgust she heard in her friend's voice. "Being fair doesn't make him an idiot. It probably makes me the idiot for wanting to plunge in headfirst, anyway."

Lynn's expression brightened at that. "You want to plunge in?"

"Well, sure. The man can kiss like it's an Olympic event and he's going for the gold. And the way he is with my kids, well, let me just say that after the way Ernesto all but ignored them, seeing Gabe with them fills my heart with happiness. So, yes, I start fantasizing just a little about what the future could be like. But down that road disaster's waiting to happen, so I've put my defenses firmly in place."

"Oh, boy," Lynn said. "I thought you might have a little crush, but it sounds to me as if you're way beyond that."

"Absolutely not," Adelia said hurriedly. "Expecting anything more would be crazy.

Gabe's warned me again and again about that."

"I didn't say you expected it, but I do think you want it."

Adelia sighed. "Maybe I do. And, given all the signs that it will never happen, that definitely makes me an idiot."

"Just because he warned you off?" Lynn asked, clearly trying to follow her logic.

"No, because men like Gabe don't fall for women like me. Not in some forever kind of way, anyway."

Lynn stared at her incredulously. "That is absolute hogwash!" she said emphatically. "Women like you? What does that even mean? Are you talking about bright, beautiful, sexy, caring, generous women? Any man would be lucky to have you. Gabe might be oblivious to what he needs in his life, but he's not oblivious to the fact that you're incredible."

Adelia let the praise sink in, then stood up. Between the pep talk, overly optimistic though it may have been, and the coffee, she felt much better.

"Thank you, Lynn," she said. "Maybe you should get a degree in psychology and dispense wisdom with your coffee and pastries."

"And exactly when would I fit those

classes into my day?" Lynn asked, laughing. "Maybe I could do that instead of, say, laundry. Or dusting." Her expression brightened as if she might actually consider that. "I really hate dusting."

"Ditto," Adelia said. "I'm just saying I came in here feeling wiped out physically and emotionally, and now I feel as if I just might be able to cope with the rest of the day."

"Okay, then. Happy to help," Lynn told her. "For you the advice is always free."

Adelia's step was lighter when she went back next door, at least until she saw her brother leaning against the wall, obviously waiting for her. Since she knew Elliott wouldn't willingly set foot in a place as girlie as the boutique unless he was on a mission, her heart plunged. Still, she forced a smile.

"Well, this is an unexpected surprise," she said as she unlocked the door and led the way inside.

"Really?" he said, his expression dark. "I would have thought you'd be expecting me."

"Why is that?"

"Because something was going on at the house yesterday and you and Mama were doing everything in your power to keep me from finding out what it was."

"If you believe that, then what makes you

think I'll tell you anything now?"

"Because I've taken the afternoon off and I can sit here all day until you decide to open up."

When he deliberately settled his tall, muscled frame onto a dainty little chair as if to prove his intentions, Adelia had to fight a smile.

"I'm surprised you aren't more worked up over finding Gabe at my house when you brought the kids home from Mama's," she said in an attempt to deflect his attention.

"We'll get to that," he said direly. "First I want to know what you're keeping from me."

"Nothing you don't already know," she claimed. "Carolina was having a bad day. Mama and I were worried about her."

"Is she sick?"

Adelia considered lying and saying yes, but the lie wouldn't hold up for more time than it took Elliott to rush over to their sister's.

"No, not the way you mean."

"Then her marriage is in trouble," he guessed. "I'm right, aren't I? I should have punched Ricky yesterday, when I wanted to."

Adelia saw little point in denying that much. "Yes, but she insists she wants to work it out herself," she told him. "You punching out her husband wouldn't solve anything."

Though she genuinely regretted that she couldn't tell him the rest, that comment about starting a fight proved she was right to remain silent. That was for his protection as well as their sister's. The last thing Carolina needed was to have Elliott taking on Ricky in what was bound to be a messy and likely public brawl. For now the situation needed to be dealt with in a calm way, at least until that was no longer safe or reasonable.

"Show her that respect," she advised her brother.

"Is that what you were doing when you went over there?" he asked. "And don't even pretend that wasn't where you headed when you snuck out Mama's back door."

She managed a weak smile. "But that's because I'm the calm, rational one. You'd go in there ready to start something and only wind up making things worse." Come to think of it, she wasn't entirely sure she hadn't done the same thing. She should have called Carolina first thing this morning to be sure she was okay. She resolved to do that the instant Elliott left.

"I'm not buying any of this," he told her.

"If I find out you're hiding something serious from me, something I should have handled, I swear, Adelia . . ." His voice trailed off.

"What will you do, Elliott? Yell at me? Berate Mama? How come you're not over there asking her all these questions?"

"Because she's already told me to stay out of it," he admitted, his expression chagrined. "Once yesterday afternoon and again earlier today."

"And you thought I'd be made of weaker stuff?" Adelia asked, amused. "I am my mother's daughter, after all. You can't bully me into talking."

Her brother sighed heavily. "I just want to help." He held her gaze. "Does Carolina need my help, Adelia? The truth?"

"Not yet," Adelia said, praying it was true. "But the minute she does, I promise you I'll come to you. Can you let that be enough for now?"

"You swear it?"

She sketched a mark across her chest. "Cross my heart."

"Okay, then."

He stood up, and Adelia thought she might be home free, but he turned back. "Is this thing between you and Gabe getting serious?"

"I haven't even confirmed there is a thing with Gabe."

"I'm not blind or stupid," he said. "And as long as he's good to you, I'm in your corner."

"That's very sweet," she told him. "But you have nothing to worry about. Just concentrate on your own family."

"You're my family, too. So is Carolina. I have plenty of time to worry about all of you."

She walked over and gave him a hug. "And that's why you'd win brother of the year in this town every single time if we had such a contest. In fact, I think that's why no one's ever suggested it. It wouldn't be fair to have the same winner over and over."

Elliott gave her a wry look. "The flattery's nice, but I see through it, you know. You just want me gone."

She grinned. "How'd you guess? I have work to do. Love you."

"Te amo," he said.

How lucky was she? she thought as he walked away. It seemed she had two men in her life she could count on in a crisis. The only thing worrisome was how soon she — or Carolina — might need them.

Once Elliott had gone, Adelia started worrying in earnest about Carolina. She couldn't shake off the feeling that she ought to check on her, not by phone but in person. It would be far too easy to lie over the phone.

She went into the boutique's office and called Raylene. "Are you busy?"

"Not unless you count sitting around with my feet up to try to make the swelling in my ankles go down as work," Raylene said, then lamented, "I used to have such nice ankles."

"And you will again," Adelia assured her. "In just a few more months."

"I suppose. So, what's up? Did you need me for something?"

"Could you come in for an hour? I need to check on someone."

"Absolutely," Raylene said eagerly. "Give me fifteen minutes to walk over there."

Adelia hesitated. "Raylene, I'm not taking advantage, am I? This isn't the first time I've called you to cover for me lately."

"Who else should you call?" Raylene said. "It's my business. I count on you to handle way more than you should have to. Covering for you when something comes up will never be a problem, unless I'm in labor or something."

"Well, thank goodness you're not in labor

just yet," Adelia told her.

While she waited for Raylene to get there, she totaled her receipts for the day so far and made a note of that. Raylene would need the figures if Adelia turned out to be gone longer than she expected to be.

The second her boss came in the door, Adelia grabbed her purse. Raylene stopped her before she could leave, her expression worried.

"You don't have to tell me if you don't want to, but is everything okay? I never thought to ask on the phone if there was some sort of crisis."

"I hope there's not," Adelia told her, then drew in a deep breath. "Actually it is something I'd like to discuss with you, but could we do it when I get back?"

"Of course," Raylene said. "Do you need backup? I could call someone to go along with you. Or to stay here, so I could go. Any of the Sweet Magnolias would be happy to help."

"Thank you so much, but I'll be fine. It's just a bit of a family situation. I won't be gone long. I promise."

"Take as long as you need," Raylene said, her expression still concerned.

"I'll call if I'm going to be gone more than an hour," Adelia promised.

Grateful that she'd driven her car to work this morning, rather than walking, she headed for Carolina's. Her sister's car was in the driveway, but when Adelia rang the bell, no one answered the door. Adelia pulled out her cell phone and called her sister, first on the house phone, then on her cell. Both went to voice mail. Adelia tried the cell phone again.

"What?" Carolina finally snapped.

"Where are you?" Adelia asked, keeping her own voice level. "Your car's in the driveway."

"Maybe I went for a walk."

Since her sister's aversion to exercise was even greater than Adelia's own, the response didn't ring true. "Did you?"

"What do you want, Adelia?"

"I want to see you."

"It's not a good time."

"That's what you said yesterday. I understood then that you were trying not to anger Ricky, but what about now?"

"Just go away, Adelia. I'm not your problem."

"You're my little sister. You will always be my problem. And in case there's any doubt in your mind, our brother is worried about you, too. You're a whole lot better off dealing with me than you would be with Elliott.

If he finds out what's going on, Carolina . . ." She drew in a deep breath. "Well, I don't have to tell you what will happen then."

"Elliott can't find out about any of this," Carolina said, real panic in her voice.

"Then let me in," Adelia said emphatically. "Once we've talked and I'm satisfied that you're okay, I'll do what I can to keep Elliott out of this."

"What if I'm not okay?" Carolina asked, her voice barely above a whisper.

Now Adelia was the one in a panic. "What do you mean you're not okay? Let me in this minute, Carolina, or I swear I will call Carter Rollins and have him break down the door. That will put an end to all of this. Maybe it's what I need to do, anyway."

"No, please," her sister pleaded, opening the door a crack. The chain on it remained in place. "Let it go, Adelia."

"Sweetie, I can't do that. You know I can't."

"Okay, but don't freak out. Promise me you won't freak out."

The plea wasn't enough to stop Adelia's gasp when the door opened and she caught a glimpse of the black-and-blue marks on her sister's face. "Oh, my God," she whispered, even as rage tore through her. "Ricky

did this to you? Because I was here yesterday?"

"No," Carolina said at once. "I thought
about what you'd said. I told him that I
wasn't going to take it anymore. It's because
I listened to you and tried to stand up for
myself. He lost his temper. He said he
wouldn't have you interfering in our marriage, that you needed to learn your place."
Fresh tears spilled down her cheeks. "He
said Ernesto was lucky to be rid of you."

"And then he hit you?" Adelia whispered.
"To teach you a lesson, so you'd know what
to expect if you tried to leave?"

Carolina nodded.

"And you stayed after that?" Adelia asked
incredulously.

"What choice did I have?" Carolina asked,
her tone flat and defeated.

"What about this morning, after he'd left
for work? You could have packed up then
and taken off."

"Where could I go like this?" Carolina
asked. "To Mama? It would kill her. She
flipped out over a couple of bruises on my
arm when she caught a glimpse of them
yesterday."

"You could have come to me," Adelia said,
brokenhearted that her sister didn't realize
that.

"And listen to you gloat?"

Adelia merely stared at her, wondering how things between them had deteriorated so badly. There'd been a time, when they were young, that they'd been so close. She'd dried Carolina's tears when she'd scraped her knees falling off her bike, when her first boyfriend had broken up with her.

"I'm so sorry you feel that way," she told her sister. "Do I seem to be gloating now? Carolina, I love you. It tears me apart to see what's happening here. I just want to help."

"Then go away. That's the only way to help. Stay out of it."

"You know I can't do that, not after this. Come with me. Raylene's at the boutique. She can tell us how to get help. Or we can go straight to Carter. With pictures of your injuries and your statement, he'll handle Ricky. Your husband will never hurt you again."

"You're so naive," Carolina said. "My marriage is all I have. I'm not strong like you. I don't have job skills. Ricky would fight me for custody of the kids and he'd probably win. I'd be all alone."

"Never," Adelia said fiercely. "Helen would make sure you have sole custody. No judge would award those children to a man who's beaten his wife."

"Okay, let's say you're right," Carolina said. "Then what? Should we all move in with Mama?"

"We can figure all of that out," Adelia assured her. "The first step is to leave."

"I can't."

"Of course you can. You must. You have children," Adelia reminded her. "Do this for them. Walk away, while you still can. They need their mother."

"They need both parents," Carolina contradicted. "The way it was meant to be."

Adelia was struck by a sudden sickening thought. "What exactly has Ricky told you would happen if you tried to leave him? Did he threaten to kill you, Carolina?" she asked, thinking of Raylene's ex-husband, who'd gone beyond threats to actually trying to kill her.

"No, of course not," Carolina replied unconvincingly.

"I don't believe you. He hit you last night. Tell me the truth. Has he threatened to do worse?"

"It doesn't matter," Carolina said, sounding thoroughly defeated. "I'm staying."

One of the blessings and, it seemed, curses of being born a Cruz was pure stubbornness. Adelia knew she was fighting yet another losing battle. She reached out and gently stroked a finger along the bruised and swollen curve of her sister's jaw.

"It makes me physically ill that you're allowing him to do this to you," she said softly. "You're too good to be treated this way, Carolina." She sighed. "But if you don't want to go, I can't drag you away from here."

Carolina didn't reply, but she held the front door open a little wider, as if to encourage Adelia to leave.

Adelia hesitated on the front stoop. She faced her sister and took a risky but necessary stance. "I will warn you about one thing, though. If I ever see another bruise on you, I will unleash the hounds of hell on Ricky myself."

Alarm flashed in her sister's eyes. "You wouldn't dare."

"Oh, yes, I would," Adelia told her. "I'm already terrified that I'm waiting too long as it is. Next time I won't ask you first. I won't plead with you to leave. I'll just make sure that Ricky gets what's coming to him. I don't know if you're staying out of fear or some twisted idea of love, but either way, perhaps you'll reconsider and get out before he winds up in jail or you wind up in the hospital. Those are only two of the potential consequences of staying."

Carolina frowned. "What could possibly be worse than sending my husband to jail?"

"Letting him take out his anger on one of your children," Adelia suggested. "Or letting our brother in on what's going on in your marriage."

"Ricky would never hurt the kids," Carolina said again, but she didn't sound quite as convinced as she had the day before. "And you would never tell Elliott about any of this."

"Wouldn't I? Try me."

"But if Elliott did something crazy to defend me, he'd be the one in jail. You wouldn't take that risk."

"I think Elliott might agree with me that it would be worth it," Adelia said. "Don't test me, Carolina. If you won't accept help from me, ask someone else. But don't let this escalate. Please. Think about your kids. Think about Mama. But most of all think about yourself."

It took every bit of resolve Adelia possessed to turn and walk away then. She still wanted desperately to throw her arms around her sister and forcibly drag her from the house. Since that would be only a temporary solution, good only as long as it took Carolina to break free and go back home, Adelia resisted the temptation.

What she needed now was Raylene's advice on the next step. Thankfully that was waiting for her just a couple of miles away.

CHAPTER EIGHTEEN

Gabe wandered into the boutique hoping to catch Adelia, but found Raylene there instead.

"Looking for a special gift?" Raylene taunted, her eyes filled with mischief. "Or were you looking for a special someone?"

"I had a few things to discuss with Adelia," he improvised quickly. "About the renovations at her place."

"Really?" Raylene asked, her skepticism plain. "And these things came up out of the blue overnight?"

He frowned at her. "What are you suggesting?"

"Just that I happen to know you were over there last night. Were the two of you especially busy, too busy to discuss these important things?" There was an unmistakable and worrisome twinkle in her eyes when she said it.

Even though Gabe recognized that Raylene was deliberately baiting him, he reacted with exactly the sort of exasperation he knew she was hoping for. "And how would you know a thing like that? Were you out spying on your friends?"

Rather than taking offense, she chuckled. "Carter and I went for a long walk, just like we do every night. We strolled through Swan Point," she explained, then added pointedly, "just like we do every night." Her smile spread. "And your truck was parked in Adelia's driveway, the same as it has been on a lot of nights lately." She gave him an innocent look. "Or did it just break down there?"

Gabe's scowl deepened. "How is this any of your business?"

It seemed his annoyed tone finally registered with her. Her expression sobered at once.

"Adelia's my friend," she said with a hint of defiance. "As are Lynn and Mitch. I'd like to think we'd be friends, too, if I knew you a little better. So, yes, I pay attention."

"And you feel entitled to poke around in our lives?" he concluded.

Her winning smile returned. "Pretty much."

Gabe shook his head. "I knew this would happen sooner or later. This town is going to drive me nuts. This is exactly why I left all those years ago. People didn't know how to mind their own business."

Somehow all those years of moving from place to place had lulled him into thinking that maybe Serenity hadn't been as bad as he'd thought, that his memories were tainted by the pain of a kid constantly in trouble for defending his mom against gossip. Since it had been the last place he'd had any family to speak of, he'd wanted to give the town another chance. It occurred to him now that he'd been yearning for family even before he'd met Adelia and fallen for hers.

The gossip and meddling, though? He hadn't been yearning for that.

"Maybe I need to start thinking about moving on again," he said, not even trying to hide his frustration.

"Don't say that," Raylene protested urgently, clearly regretting having pushed him too far. "There are great people here, Gabe. You have family here. And Adelia's here."

"Sometimes I have to wonder if that's enough," he said. "Just tell her I dropped by, okay?"

"You don't want to wait?"

"And let you pry some more? I don't think so."

The bell over the door tinkled merrily as he left, the sound oddly jarring given his suddenly sour mood.

This was the Serenity he remembered, a town where people poked their noses where they didn't belong. Things were already complicated between him and Adelia. How could they possibly figure anything out, if everyone started interfering?

Gabe could respect the fact that Elliott cared about his sister. He could even deal with Mitch and Lynn and their questions. They were family, and he actually believed they might want the best for him.

But everybody else? Didn't they have better things to do than dig around in his personal life? Pressure wasn't going to help anything. He was already stressed out enough over feelings he didn't quite understand and wasn't sure he wanted to be experiencing. If he and Adelia were constantly under a microscope, no matter how well-meaning, he figured they were pretty much doomed.

He worked himself into a real lousy mood just between the boutique and the bakery. He should have turned right around and gone back to the work site down the block, but instead he opted for coffee. With any luck, he could pour himself a cup, leave some money on the counter and get out before Lynn was even aware of his presence.

Naturally that was not the way it went. When he opened the door, Lynn was standing right there, a phone in her hand and a speculative gleam in her eyes. She carefully returned the cell phone to her pocket.

"Raylene says she's sorry," Lynn reported, her eyes narrowing. "What does she have to be sorry about?"

"Nothing," he said tightly, unwilling to open that particular can of worms.

Lynn nodded knowingly. "It must have had something to do with Adelia then."

"Don't go there," Gabe warned.

"Why? Because you can't take being teased?"

Gabe was about to snap back a quick denial, when he realized the evidence would contradict him. Whatever Lynn had heard or guessed clearly suggested that he'd lost it over something that had only been spoken in jest. And he'd overreacted, because he was suddenly very sensitive on the topic of Adelia.

"I'll go next door and apologize," he muttered.

Lynn tried unsuccessfully to hide a grin. "There may be hope for you yet."

"What's that supposed to mean?"

"You recognize that you went a little crazy just because a friend dared to tease you."

"I barely know Raylene."

Lynn rolled her eyes. "That's the part of what I said you want to focus on?"

Gabe scowled. "Okay, yes. I went a little crazy. Maybe even a lot crazy."

"I wonder why," Lynn said, studying him speculatively. "Did she hit too close to home, suggesting that you and Adelia are a couple?"

"It wasn't that," he said, accepting the coffee she'd finally poured for him without his needing to beg. He drew in a deep breath. "Suddenly I was a teenager again and people in this town were dissecting my mom's life. I know I came back here to try to put all of that behind me once and for all, but suddenly it smacked me right in the face." He met Lynn's suddenly worried gaze. "To tell you the truth, I'm not sure I can do this."

"Do what?"

"Stay here."

Now there was real alarm in Lynn's eyes. "You want to take off? You didn't just say that to provoke Raylene?"

"I do and I don't," he said candidly. "And here's the real kicker, either way it's about Adelia."

Lynn waved him toward a table. "Maybe Adelia was right," she mumbled as she followed him.

"Adelia was right about what?" he asked, confused by the odd remark.

"She suggested I get a degree in psychology and start holding my sessions right here. Since you're my second client of the day, she might have been on to something."

"Who was your first?"

"Adelia, of course. She's as confused as you are, by the way." She leveled a look at him that held his attention. "And do you know what that tells me? It tells me that whatever's between the two of you matters. Otherwise neither of you would be wrestling with it. You'd give in to the attraction, settle for a fling and then move on."

"I'm not having a fling with Adelia," Gabe said heatedly, outraged by the suggestion. He had more respect for her than that. He frowned at Lynn. "After everything she's been through, don't you think she deserves better than a fling?"

"Absolutely, and I'm thrilled that you recognize that," Lynn said approvingly. "And what do you deserve, Gabe?"

"Not a woman like Adelia," he said at once.

"Oh, for heaven's sake, do I have to sit

here and list all your attributes the way I did for her?"

"You were trying to sell her on my good points?"

"No, on her own," Lynn said impatiently. "Neither of you seems to have a lick of self-esteem, and, frankly, I think that's just pitiful."

"I imagine there are a few people who'd tell you my ego's in pretty good shape," he replied.

"Well, they're not here, and I am. From where I'm sitting, you don't seem to be giving yourself half enough credit for the decent, honorable man you are. Let me ask you something, and I want you to think about the answer for a minute."

"Okay, shoot," he said agreeably, though there was little doubt that he couldn't stop her if he wanted to.

"You think Adelia is an admirable woman, correct?"

"Of course."

"Smart?"

"Absolutely." His eyes narrowed. "Where are you going with this? Do you want me to realize she's too good for me?"

Lynn merely rolled her eyes. "No, my point is that she likes you. She's been spending time with you. She seems to be at least a little bit infatuated. Maybe you should trust her judgment about how worthy you are. She obviously sees something in you that you don't see in yourself."

She'd gotten Gabe's attention at last. "Okay, let's say I'm a great guy, in her eyes, anyway. And we know she's terrific. That still doesn't mean we're a good match."

"No, it doesn't," Lynn agreed.

Her candid reply caught him off guard. "I thought you were a big booster of this relationship."

"Not exactly. I'm a big booster of the two of you getting out of your own way and finding out if you're a good match. She needs to stop throwing up her defenses and you need to stop looking for ways to bail." She stood up and held his gaze. "And that is all I intend to say about that. Mull it over."

Gabe sat where he was and let Lynn's advice sink in. It didn't take long for him to realize she had a point. Maybe more than one. So maybe he wouldn't leave Serenity just yet. Maybe he'd hang around and see how things played out, at least for a little while longer. The grand prize — marriage and a family he'd never dared to envision — just might be within his grasp after all.

■ ■ ■ ■

Adelia had barely walked in the door at the boutique before Gabe stuck his head in.

"Hey," she said. "You coming in?"

He looked uncomfortable. "I was looking for Raylene."

"I'm here," Raylene called out, stepping out of the office.

"I just wanted to apologize for jumping down your throat before," he said. He glanced at Adelia. "I'm sure Raylene will explain. I'll see you at the house later?"

"Sure," Adelia said, though she was thoroughly confused and wanted answers now.

Gabe nodded. "Later, then."

"Well, that was odd," Adelia said, watching him back out and take off down the block.

"Not from where I'm standing," Raylene said, a grin on her face.

"What on earth happened while I was gone?"

A guilty expression passed over Raylene's face. "I might have freaked him out just a little."

"How?"

"By teasing him about whatever's going on between the two of you," Raylene admitted. "I don't think he was quite ready for the full-on Sweet Magnolia treatment. You know, prying inappropriately."

Adelia shook her head. "I can imagine. I'm still having a tough time with that myself." She waved off the situation with Gabe. Right this second it wasn't that important. "Do you need to leave right away or can we talk?"

Raylene regarded her with immediate concern. "Of course we can talk. Sounds as if we should have some privacy for this. Not that the office is all that private, but it's better than out here where anybody could walk in and overhear something they shouldn't."

When Raylene was seated at her desk, Adelia had no choice but to sit on the folding chair next to it. There was no room for the nervous pacing that might have made the conversation easier.

She filled Raylene in on what was going on with Carolina, then concluded, "She needs help, but she doesn't want it. I'm way out of my depth here. I don't know what else to do."

"The sad reality is that there's not a lot you can do," Raylene said. "If your sister won't admit what's going on to Carter or agree to press charges, his hands are tied. I think if he got a call to the house and saw evidence of the abuse, he could act, even if she denied it, but she's not going to call, is she?"

"I don't think so," Adelia said. "She keeps saying it's all her fault, as if she's triggering Ricky's rage and, therefore, his reaction is acceptable."

"Been there, done that," Raylene said wearily. "My husband was very good at isolating me, making sure I understood that no one would listen to me, the little nobody from Serenity. Because he had this sterling reputation in Charleston and an important family, I believed him."

"I think that's exactly what Ricky is doing," Adelia said.

"Well, sadly it took losing the baby I was carrying before I finally had the courage to get out and to file charges," Raylene said. "I didn't think there was a chance the charges would stick given his reputation and ability to wiggle out of tight spots, but some doctors stood up and testified about what they'd seen, not just that awful night, but on other E.R. visits. Not even his expensive lawyers and doting parents could save him at that point. These were respected colleagues speaking out, not just me."

"I don't want it to take something terrible for Carolina to wake up," Adelia said.

"Then be there for her as much as you can be. Don't let her push you away. Keep reminding her that help's available, that she has family who loves her, that her kids deserve a mother who doesn't tolerate abuse, that she needs to set an example for them."

Adelia nodded. "That's what finally did it for me with Ernesto. I realized Selena was losing all respect for me because I stayed after finding out about his affairs. And I didn't want Tomas to grow up thinking that men had some inalienable right to cheat. It's surprising how much strength you can find when you see how your decisions are affecting your children."

She thought about Joey and his tendency to lash out with hurtful comments. "I think the situation is taking more of a toll on her oldest than I realized," Adelia said. "I've thought for some time that Joey was just a brat, but now I wonder if he's not acting out either because he's hurting or, even worse, because he's mimicking his father's attitude."

"Give me an example," Raylene suggested.

Adelia described his deliberately mean remarks to Selena about the kiss Adelia and Gabe had shared.

"Maybe you need to tell Carolina about

that," Raylene suggested. "Or did you?"

"No. I let it pass. I was more concerned with Selena's reaction."

"I think you need to tell Carolina," Raylene said. "It's a concrete example of how her son is being affected by what's going on. She's a mother first. That instinct to protect her kids is strong."

"She doesn't think they're in danger," Adelia lamented.

"Maybe they're not, physically," Raylene said. "But that doesn't mean the situation isn't harmful to them. Just what you described about her oldest suggests that much."

"I'll try bringing that to her attention," Adelia said. "Thanks."

"Don't thank me," Raylene said. "I owe a lot of people for standing by me. If I can do even half as much for someone else, it'll go at least a tiny bit toward paying back that debt." She held Adelia's gaze. "Don't stay away, no matter how hard Carolina tries to push you out of her life. When things get worse, and there's little doubt in my mind that they will, she'll remember that she can come to you."

Adelia sighed, thinking of her conversation earlier, the one in which her sister had expected her to gloat. "I hope so," she said softly. "I really hope so."

For the second day in a row, Adelia went home exhausted and emotionally drained. Just inside the front door, she paused and listened to the laughter coming from the kitchen. The happy sound washed over her, easing just a little of the tension she'd been feeling ever since her visit to Carolina.

She walked into the kitchen and found the girls once more around the kitchen table doing homework. Selena jumped up and hugged her, then bounced toward the refrigerator.

"I'll put dinner in the oven now," she said. "I've set the dining room table already."

"Mama, look at the A I got on my book report," Juanita said, interrupting them.

"And I got a B plus on my math test," Natalia chimed in, eager to share her own success. "It's the first time ever!"

Adelia smiled at them. "Then we need to celebrate." She turned to her oldest. "And how did you do on your history test?"

Selena made a face that had Adelia's heart dropping. Then her daughter grinned.

"An A minus," Selena said, then confided, "It's because Gabe helped me."

"He helped us, too," Natalia said.

That came as a surprise to Adelia. "How

did he help?"

"He came up with a way for me to remember all those dates," Selena said. "While he was working, he'd play this game he made up, sort of like *Jeopardy* only just about history. For the first time ever, history was actually fun."

"He showed me what I was doing wrong on my math problems," Natalia revealed. "He never once said I was dumb for not getting it."

Adelia's temper stirred. "Who told you that you were dumb?" she asked. "You know that's not a word I like you to use."

"The teacher," Natalia said.

"She actually said that you were dumb?" Adelia pressed, increasingly infuriated.

"Kinda," Natalia said, backing off a little. "The other kids laughed."

Adelia vowed to have a talk with that teacher first thing in the morning. Nobody should be telling a student, any student, that they were dumb just because they were having trouble grasping a concept.

Biting back her annoyance, she turned to Juanita. "Did Gabe help you, too?"

Juanita nodded. "He asked me to tell him what my book was about," she explained. "Then he told me I should write the report just the way I'd told him. So that's what I did. The teacher said it was the best book report she'd heard all day."

How had she not been aware of any of this, Adelia wondered. She joined her children at the kitchen table. "So maybe we should have more than a celebration," she suggested. "Maybe you could think of some way to thank Gabe for his help."

"We already did," Juanita said, bouncing in her seat. "Show Mom, Selena."

Selena rolled out a banner they'd made: Gabe, you're the best! The colorful letters were decorated not just with bright drawings of balloons and streamers, but with an assortment of tools. There was even a sparkling tiara over his name.

Adelia touched a finger to that tiara and smiled. "Nice touch."

She glanced around. "Where's your brother, or do I even need to ask?"

"Helping Gabe, of course," Selena said.

"And his homework?"

"He did that first. Gabe said if he didn't get it finished, he couldn't help. Now Gabe's working on his spelling words with him."

Amazing, Adelia thought. She couldn't recall a single time when Ernesto had even asked to see homework, much less helped any of the kids with it. That, he'd insisted, was her responsibility.

"What's Gabe working on today?" she asked as she rose to go upstairs and check on him.

Selena smiled. "I think it's a surprise. You should probably stay here. I'll go check."

Though Adelia wanted to argue, a part of her couldn't resist the prospect of a surprise, especially one that put a smile on her daughter's face. Most of the surprises that had come her way lately had been less than positive.

"I'll check the freezer for ice cream while you're gone," she told Selena. "Then we can celebrate after dinner."

"There isn't any," Selena said. "I checked." She regarded Adelia hopefully. "Instead, maybe we could walk to Wharton's after we eat."

"Yes, please," Natalia said. Her plea was echoed by Juanita.

Adelia looked into their happy, expectant faces and realized how far they'd come in just a few weeks. "Wharton's it is," she agreed.

"Great. I'll tell Gabe," Selena said, bounding off.

Shaking her head at her daughter's burst of enthusiasm, Adelia wondered if Gabe had any idea of the role he'd played in the miracle that was happening in her home. He still thought he wasn't cut out for family life, but around here, it sure seemed he was slowly becoming the center of hers.

Gabe looked around Adelia's bedroom worriedly. He'd tried to put it together in the way he thought she'd want it, but he was a guy and he was pretty sure she'd have her own ideas. Selena walked in the door and uttered a gasp. He turned to look at her.

"Was that an 'oh my gosh what a mess' gasp?" he asked, frowning.

"No, it was a 'you got it exactly right' gasp," she said, grinning at him. "Mom's going to love it."

"I hope so. She did pick out the color."

"It's not just about the paint," she told him. "It's all the stuff you got, the pretty pillows, the new comforter." She gestured toward the nightstand. "The flowers. I can't remember Mom ever getting flowers before."

Gabe didn't find that especially reassuring. Sure, Ernesto was a jerk, but maybe she was allergic. Maybe she didn't like flowers.

"She doesn't have an allergy to flowers, does she?" he asked worriedly.

"No, she loves them," Selena said. "You should have seen our garden at the old house. She was out there all the time. Sometimes she'd pick this huge bouquet and make a centerpiece for the dining room table. It was as pretty as anything I've ever seen in a magazine."

"Maybe this won't seem like much, then," he said, unable to stop himself from fretting. It was ridiculous. It was a bouquet of flowers, not a declaration of some kind.

"Gabe, she's going to love them," Selena reassured him. She glanced around the room. "Is everything ready? Can I let her come up?"

He surveyed the room one more time and concluded it was as ready as he knew how to make it. "Send her up."

Selena nodded and beckoned for Tomas. "Come downstairs with me."

"But I want to be here when Mom sees the surprise," he protested.

"It's Gabe's surprise," she said emphatically. "Let him show Mom. Otherwise, I'll tell her you don't deserve to go with the rest of us for ice cream after dinner." She glanced at Gabe. "That's one reason I came up here, to tell you we're going out to celebrate all the good grades we got. You have to come, too."

Gabe chuckled at her enthusiasm. "Absolutely."

Though he was tempted to tell her Tomas could stay, just to have a buffer, he let Selena coax her brother from the room.

Gabe walked around after Selena and Tomas had gone, checking things that didn't need to be checked again, his nerves shot. What had made him think he could pull off something like this? He had no idea what sort of frilly things women liked.

"Gabe!"

He whirled around at the stunned tone of Adelia's voice. "Is it okay?" he asked, annoyed at how insecure he sounded. "I have all the receipts if you want to take anything back. Selena gave me some ideas, but I've never shopped for stuff like this before. She unpacked all the boxes and put all your clothes in the closet. I think she even ironed a few things. She wanted to be part of the surprise."

"It's perfect," Adelia whispered, tears filling her eyes. "Nobody has ever done anything this sweet for me before."

"Then you like it?" he asked again, just to be sure. "And you're not mad because I overstepped or something?"

"I love it. And if there weren't a bunch of kids downstairs desperate to know if I like it, I'd show you just how much."

Gabe's lips curved at that. "Really?" He

crossed the room and stood in front of her. "You sure we couldn't take just a minute?"

"It would be a risk," she said, a twinkle in her eyes. "They're very anxious."

"We could call Selena's cell phone and bribe her to keep them down there," he suggested hopefully.

"First, she's not allowed to answer her cell phone," Adelia said, struggling to keep her expression stern. "Second, I do not want my teenage daughter wondering what you and I might be doing up here. And, third, if we try it, I sense there will be a rebellion. Tomas was already putting up a struggle about having to be downstairs and missing the surprise. He's probably sitting on the top step right this second."

Gabe sighed dramatically. "Another time then?"

"Most definitely," she said.

There was a heated promise in her eyes that left him a little bit desperate.

"Maybe after dinner —"

"And a walk to Wharton's for ice cream," she reminded him, not shooting him down exactly but postponing any reward even longer.

"Right. I forgot all about the celebration. Maybe after that, if either of us can even keep our eyes open, we can steal a little alone time to talk about things."

"Things?"

"Us. Our days. You know, the stuff I assume couples talk about at the end of the day."

She regarded him with obvious surprise. "We're a couple?"

"I'm beginning to think we might not have a choice in the matter," he said, his tone resigned.

"You sound so cheery about that," she teased. "It makes me all warm and fuzzy."

"Hey, I'm just getting used to the idea, but something Lynn said finally got through to me."

"What was that?"

"That we needed to get out of our own way."

Adelia smiled. "She said much the same to me. Something tells me tomorrow I'll owe her a very big tip."

Gabe laughed. "Let's see how her advice works out first."

She gestured around the bedroom. "It's already resulted in this. I'm obviously a lucky woman."

"No, sweetheart. I'm the lucky one," Gabe said. And he had no idea what he'd done to deserve it.

CHAPTER NINETEEN

When Adelia, Gabe and her children walked into Wharton's, Adelia didn't miss the speculative look Grace cast at them. She wondered just how long it would take before word of this outing spread through town.

"Well, this looks like it might be some sort of special occasion," Grace said.

"We're celebrating," Tomas piped up. " 'Cause we all got good grades in school and Gabe helped us."

Grace's eyes lit up. "Is that so?" she said, regarding Gabe with approval. "Times surely have changed."

Adelia wasn't sure she cared for Grace's implication, but Gabe didn't seem to be taking offense, so she, too, let it pass.

"What does this celebration call for?" Grace asked. "Cones? Hot fudge sundaes?"

Tomas's eyes lit up. "I want a hot fudge sundae," he said eagerly. "Or a banana split."

"That's too much for you," Adelia told him. "You'll never finish it."

"Gabe can share with me," he said, then turned to his newfound hero. "Wanna?"

"Sure," Gabe said, then looked to Grace. "Do you still make those small banana splits?"

"I sure do," she said.

"But I want a big one," Tomas protested.

"A small one that you share with Gabe or none," Adelia told him firmly.

Though he wore a pout on his face, Tomas grudgingly agreed.

The girls ordered cones and then Grace turned to her.

"How about you, Adelia?"

She thought of how hard she'd fought to take off the pounds she'd gained after carrying each of her babies. Ice cream had been off-limits for months now. As if he were reading her mind, she realized Gabe's gaze was on her.

"I think you deserve a hot fudge sundae," he told her solemnly.

"But —"

"I'll eat what you don't finish."

She laughed at his hopeful expression. "Are you thinking that half a small banana split won't fill you up?"

He leaned closer and whispered in her ear,

"No, I'm thinking of how much I'm going to enjoy watching you savor every bite of that sundae. Maybe I'll even get to lick a little hot fudge off your lips later."

Adelia felt an instant rush of heat into her cheeks. She quickly turned to Grace. "A very small hot fudge sundae," she requested, a breathless note in her voice.

Grace chuckled. "Good choice."

Because there were six of them, they took two booths, with the girls seated in the one behind Adelia, Gabe and Tomas. Apparently her disappointment at not being alone with Gabe showed in her face, because within seconds after their ice cream had been served, Gabe put down his spoon with a dramatic sigh.

"That's it for me," he announced. "Tomas, you can take the rest and finish it up with your sisters."

Adelia saw the storm clouds darkening her son's eyes, but before she could second Gabe's suggestion, he held her son's gaze. "Please," he said quietly. "I need a few minutes to speak to your mom alone."

"Okay," Tomas grumbled, his tone resigned.

She studied Gabe with a sense of wonder as her son took his ice cream to the neighboring booth. "Do you have some kind of

404

magic touch? I was expecting a full-blown tantrum."

He shrugged. "He usually listens to me."

"Because you have something he wants," she realized.

Gabe looked confused. "What?"

"Tools," she said. "And the willingness to spend the time to teach him how to use them. I imagine to Tomas that's a pretty good bargaining chip."

"I've never resorted to bribing your son," Gabe protested with a touch of indignation.

"Haven't you? I heard that just this afternoon you told him he couldn't help you till his homework was done. Well done, by the way."

Gabe regarded her with a startled expression. "I was just trying to be responsible."

"An excellent parental attitude," she commended him. Before she could lose her nerve, she asked, "Gabe, you've told me you didn't think you were any good at relationships. Didn't you ever want kids?"

He seemed taken aback by the question. "I never thought about it," he claimed.

"Why?"

"Because I didn't have a very good example in my life. My mom did her best under the circumstances, but her best wasn't so great. I never even knew my dad, and the men who paraded through her life weren't exactly role models. I didn't want to take any chances about messing up some kid's life."

"You're certainly not doing anything to mess up my kids' lives. They're happier than they have been in months. They're doing well in school, something I'd despaired of seeing this school year. A lot of the credit for that goes to you. And in my book that makes you great parent material."

Gabe looked shaken by the comment. "Adelia, I don't know. I'm still grappling with whether I can give you what you need, much less your kids."

"First of all, you're already giving them what they need, your love and attention. Second, we're a package deal. You can't separate me from my kids."

"No, of course not," he said at once. "I guess I was just compartmentalizing."

"How so?"

"I thought maybe we could figure out the whole relationship thing. Then if that's going okay, we'd start thinking about the rest."

She laughed at his naïveté. "Then I think you've done things backwards. You already have my kids thinking you hung the moon. Even Selena has come around a lot more quickly than I'd anticipated." The implications of that suddenly had her sobering. "I wonder if that's been a mistake."

Gabe frowned. "What do you mean?"

"What if this thing between us doesn't go anywhere?" she asked. "What is wrong with me? I never should have let this happen. I just saw how the kids seemed to be blossoming under your attention and stood by and let them start to care about you. Even when you and I split up so they wouldn't get ideas about us, I still let them spend time with you. Naturally they were going to get attached."

Gabe reached for her hand and gave it a squeeze. "I won't let them down," he promised. "No matter what happens between us."

"I don't think it will work that way," she said. "If we can't figure things out, they're bound to be crushed."

"So, what are you saying?" he asked, a frown on his face. "Do you want to call it all off, after all?"

Before she could respond, he added, "If you do, just say the word. I can probably rearrange things with Mitch so I can work while they're at school. Or with most of the work already done, someone else could finish up. I can ease out of their lives, if that's what you think is best."

"It's not best," Adelia said, thoroughly

frustrated by his willingness to end things before they even got started. Was he really that skittish? Or was she that unimportant to him? Or was this another one of those misunderstandings that could easily spiral out of control and have them making decisions they'd come to regret.

She sighed, determined not to let that happen. "It's already too late to do what's best, Gabe. They adore you. I don't know about the younger ones, but Selena's already getting ideas about the two of us. You should have seen how excited she was helping me get dressed for our date and that was before she fully approved of me being with you at all. Then again today when you'd planned that surprise for me, I think she was almost as excited as you were."

Gabe regarded her with confusion. "Help me out here, Adelia. I'm getting mixed signals. What exactly do you want me to do?"

She'd never felt so utterly helpless in her life. Anything she suggested would wind up hurting someone she loved. Her kids. Gabe. Even herself. "I honestly don't know."

"Is this one of those times when we should be listening to Lynn's advice?" he asked. "Are we getting in our own way, complicating something that doesn't need to be that complicated?"

"I have to think about my kids," she said stubbornly.

But wasn't that the rub? If she pushed Gabe away now, her kids would be miserable. If she let him stay in their lives and they grew even more attached and he left eventually, they'd be devastated.

Gabe shoved a hand through his hair, his expression filled with obvious frustration. "This sure wasn't how I envisioned tonight going," he told her.

"Me, either." She studied him, sensing she didn't have the whole picture. "I know about the reward thing you were hoping for later. Was there more?"

He nodded. "After listening to Lynn and putting up with Raylene's commentary, I was ready to make it official."

Adelia's heart thudded. "Official?"

"To tell you I wanted us to be a couple, or at least to try to be. I figured we could go on more dates, hang out in public." He gave her a rueful smile. "Let those Sweet Magnolia friends of yours have a field day."

She knew exactly what it was costing him to express a willingness to submit to all that well-meant teasing and interference. And here she was suggesting they take not just a step back, but maybe call it off entirely. Talk about crossed signals.

Her dilemma must have showed on her face, because he leaned forward and kept a tight grip on her hand. "What do you want, Adelia? Forget the kids for a minute. Forget all the potential complications that may or may not happen. What do you really want?"

She thought of the kisses they'd shared, the way Gabe made her feel, as if she were incredibly special. "You," she said, her voice barely above a whisper. She dared to meet his gaze. "I want you."

"Are you sure?"

She nodded. "But what if —"

A smile broke across his face. "Too late for what-if," he declared, cutting her off. "You've already said you want me. I heard you."

"But —"

"Nope, too late," he said again. "We're in too deep for what-if. Your kids are already invested. We need to play this out. If we don't, if we cut and run because you're scared for them or because I'm just plain terrified, it would be wrong. We're going to do the adult thing and see where this goes."

He sounded so sure, so confident, but Adelia could see the uncertainty in his eyes. Ironically, it was that uncertainty and his willingness to rise above it that gave her the courage to nod. "We'll do the adult thing, then," she said softly. "At least we can be terrified together."

He nodded. "Sounds like a plan."

Despite all her reservations, despite the panic that she was barely keeping at bay, she had to agree. It sounded like an amazing plan.

"I warned you!"

Gabe's head snapped up at the threatening tone. Ernesto Hernandez was just inside the doorway at the construction site, his voice echoing across the cavernous room. Every worker in the place had gone silent. Gabe gestured for them to resume working, but they ignored his words and kept a careful gaze on Ernesto as Gabe crossed to stand in front of him. Apparently his maturity was about to be tested again, because he wanted like crazy just to slug the man.

Instead, refusing to let the scene escalate if he could help it, he said mildly, "Something I can do for you?"

"You can stay away from my kids," Ernesto said. "You don't get to parade them around town as if they're yours."

"When have I ever done that?" Gabe asked, barely restraining the desire to remind the man that he wasn't exactly filling up the hours of their days with his attention.

"Last night," Ernesto said. "I heard all about your little outing to Wharton's. What was it you were celebrating? A few good marks at school? The kids are supposed to make good grades. That's their job. There's no need to reward them for it."

"Their mother doesn't seem to agree," Gabe said.

Ernesto shrugged off the comment. "She'll ruin them before she's done. I have half a mind to get Tomas out of her house."

Gabe's temper kicked up another notch at the threat. "Adelia is a wonderful mother. No court would take that boy away from her."

"Are you so sure about that? Even after they hear about the kind of man she's allowing to influence him?" He pulled his cell phone from his pocket. "I have my lawyer on speed dial. Maybe we should ask him."

"Be sure to remind him why you're divorced in the first place," Gabe suggested.

The remark hit home. Now Ernesto looked as if he wanted to throw the first punch. A part of Gabe actually hoped that he would. It was plain, though, that even Ernesto recognized that doing it in front of witnesses wouldn't help his cause. Gabe's crew, led by Henry Davis, had moved a little closer just in case Ernesto dared to start something. Or maybe they'd moved so they could hear better. Either way, their presence kept things from turning even uglier.

"This isn't over," Ernesto warned him. "I can still make Adelia's life hell."

"Worse than you have already?" Gabe inquired.

Ernesto leveled a cold look straight at him. "Watch me." He turned then and left, leaving Gabe both shaken and furious.

One of his men edged closer. Gabe turned to meet Henry's worried gaze.

"Boss, you don't want to mess with him," Henry warned. "He's a nasty, self-important son of a gun."

"I've noticed," Gabe said.

"He'll get to Adelia by going after you," Henry said. "I know his type. It took a strip out of his pride when she left him. He's been waiting for a chance to get even."

Gabe had figured out that much for himself. "Thanks, Henry. I'll watch out for Adelia."

The older man smiled. "I don't doubt that, but who's going to be watching out for you?" He held Gabe's gaze. "You might want to sit down with Helen Decatur-Whitney. That woman has a good head on her shoulders. She tangled with Hernandez once and I'm pretty sure she'd be eager to take him on again."

Gabe nodded. "I think I'll do just that. Can you handle things here for an hour or two?"

"I've got it," Henry said at once. "And I know how to reach you or Mitch if anything comes up I can't handle."

Gabe walked the few blocks to Helen's office, using the time to try to cool down. He was not going to let a slime bag like Ernesto make Adelia miserable or ruin what they'd just agreed to try to build together.

Unfortunately, when he walked into Helen's waiting room, it was packed. Her secretary, a woman he thought he recognized from working in the high school office years ago, scowled when she saw him.

"I know you don't have an appointment, Gabe Franklin," Barb told him. She gestured to the crowded waiting room. "Helen doesn't have time for you. You might just as well turn around and leave."

Since he didn't want everyone in the waiting room in on his business with Helen, he leaned down and tried to practice some of that charm he was supposed to possess. "Darlin', I know I don't have an appointment, but this is a little bit of an emergency."

414

"Are the police on your heels?" she asked. "It wouldn't surprise me a bit."

Gabe bit back his annoyance. "No, but they could be my next stop. Ernesto Hernandez is making threats about trying to take Adelia's son from her. I thought Helen ought to know about it."

Barb's expression went from annoyance to dismay in a heartbeat. "He wouldn't dare."

"Not if he has half a brain," Gabe agreed. "Do you think he does?"

"Hardly," she said, clearly concluding that whatever her beef might be with Gabe, he was the lesser of two evils. "Give me a minute and I'll squeeze you in."

"Thank you, darlin'."

"Stop calling me that. It won't work on me."

Gabe gave her an innocent look. "No idea what you mean."

She shook her head, but for an instant, he thought he saw her expression mellow just a little.

He stood off to the side and waited. The second Helen's current client exited her office, Barb stood up and headed in. In less than a minute, she was beckoning for him.

"Fifteen minutes," she warned both Gabe and Helen. "Not one second more or I'll

415

have a rebellion on my hands out there."

Helen's serious expression reflected Gabe's mood. "Tell me," she said.

Gabe described the incident and the threat. "It's the second time he's warned me to stay away from his kids and suggested he'd take Adelia to court to make sure I couldn't be a bad influence on them."

"He doesn't have a leg to stand on," Helen said. "I know all about the trouble you got in back then. It was kid stuff. I'll check, but you never spent a single night in jail or even had a charge against you that stood up, right?"

"Not a one," Gabe said. "It doesn't mean I didn't cause my share of trouble. I don't want that to be used against Adelia."

To his surprise, Helen grinned. "Spoken like the honorable man I've been hearing a lot about recently. Stop worrying, Gabe. I'm on this."

He didn't believe it could be as easy to keep Ernesto in check as she was making it sound. "But —"

"Gabe, I am very, very good at what I do," Helen assured him quietly. "And what I do, among many other things, is neutralize threats against my clients, especially when it comes to their kids."

Gabe saw the fire in her eyes and realized

this was not a woman he'd want to go up against in court, not when she thought she was on the side of right and justice.

He nodded, satisfied. "I'll leave it in your hands then."

"By the way," she said, a smile on her lips. "Good job in not punching the guy's lights out. It might have been satisfying, but it wouldn't have helped."

"I figured as much. If he hurts Adelia, though, I can't promise I'll show the same restraint."

"Try," she said. "But if you do lose control, and frankly I could hardly blame you, call me. I'll bail you out and represent you pro bono for doing what a whole lot of us would like to do to that man."

Gabe chuckled. "Now you're just tempting me."

She held up a hand. "Last resort, okay? Promise."

"Last resort," Gabe confirmed. Somehow knowing the kind of friend Adelia had on her side made it a whole lot easier to swear to that and mean it.

At the sound of the bell, Adelia glanced up from the catalogs she'd been marking while waiting for any customers to turn up at the boutique. To her surprise Selena stood hesitantly in the doorway, her expression dark. It had been weeks since Adelia had seen that particular look on Selena's face.

"What's wrong?" she asked at once.

"Is it okay that I'm here? Are you busy?"

"It's fine. I've told you before that you can come by here whenever you want to. Where are your sisters and brother?"

"Next door at the bakery," her oldest reported. "It'll take them forever to pick out cupcakes. I needed to talk to you when they're not around."

Adelia beckoned her in. "What's going on? Did something happen at school today?"

Selena nodded. "Daddy was waiting outside of school when I got out," she said. "He was with that woman again."

Adelia wanted to utter a curse, but she refrained. "What did he want?"

"He said we needed to get to know each other because she'd be our stepmother and we'd all be living with them soon."

Adelia's control vanished. "He said what?" she asked, stunned by what she was hearing.

"Mom, he was lying, wasn't he?" Selena asked, real panic in her voice. "He can't make us come and live with them. I'll run away if he does that. I swear I will."

"You're not going to live with your father,"

Adelia said flatly, already reaching for her phone.

Selena's eyes widened. If anything, she looked even more frightened. "You're not going to call him, are you? I don't want you fighting again."

"I'm not calling him. I'm calling Helen."

Selena immediately looked relieved. "She'll fix it, won't she? She'll stop him before he says anything to Tomas and the girls, right? I know they're supposed to spend the day with him Saturday, but he's never shown up before." Her panic suddenly returned. "What if he does this time and gets them all worked up? Or even worse, what if he won't bring them home?"

"Not going to happen," Adelia said fiercely. She held up a hand to silence Selena when Barb answered the phone in Helen's office. Adelia quickly explained the situation and was put right through.

"Blast it all!" Helen said when Adelia had filled her in. "I was afraid of something like this. I thought I had time to deal with it before Ernesto did something stupid. I guess I underestimated how angry he was."

"Angry? What are you talking about?" Adelia asked.

"Gabe was here earlier. Apparently Ernesto confronted him at work earlier."

"Why?"

"He was furious about your outing last night to Wharton's," Helen explained. "It must have triggered some sort of macho pride thing because he told Gabe he was going to take Tomas away from you. He didn't say anything about the girls as far as I know. Obviously after giving it more thought, he concluded that Selena would be a great target to stir things up even more. He knows she's never forgiven him. By going to her, he's escalated the situation and gotten her to panic."

"You have no idea," Adelia said, as Selena leaned into her side, tears on her cheeks. She kept a firm arm around her daughter's waist. "What can we do?"

"You said his mistress was with him when he spoke to Selena?"

"That's what she said."

"I know this is personal, but have you and Gabe slept together? I know it's what we've all been hoping for you, but it could complicate this situation."

"Not yet," Adelia said, cheeks flushed.

"Keep it that way for now. I want to be able to use the way Ernesto flaunts his mistress in front of his children. I'm calling the judge's office now to set an emergency hearing. Try not to worry, okay? He's not going to take your kids. He hasn't even exercised the right he was granted for visitation, has he?"

"Not more than a couple of times way back at the beginning. He doesn't even call, as far as I know."

Selena nodded. "He's never called me. Not even once."

Adelia started to repeat it, but Helen said, "I heard. I'll let you know the minute I have that hearing scheduled."

Adelia uttered a sigh of relief. She knew she was in good hands. Helen's reputation as a barracuda in the courtroom wasn't an idle designation. She'd tear Ernesto apart if he tried to hurt Adelia's kids. In fact, she'd probably do a better job than Adelia could ever do on her own.

When she hung up, she looked into Selena's worried gaze. "Helen's going to fix this?" her daughter asked.

"Absolutely."

"Mom, is this because of Gabe? Did I hear Helen say something about Dad going after him?"

"It's nothing for you to worry about," Adelia insisted. "Helen's got it."

"But it's not fair that Dad would try to hurt Gabe," Selena protested. "All he's done is be nice to us and to you."

"I know, sweetie. You don't need to worry about Gabe. He can take care of himself."

"But he shouldn't have to," Selena protested.

No, Adelia thought. *He really shouldn't have to.* Perhaps last night's decision had been premature. Perhaps this was just one more sign that their attempt to form some sort of relationship was a really bad idea.

CHAPTER TWENTY

Gabe was stunned when he received a call from Helen just as he was about to leave the work site on Main Street.

"I need you in court tomorrow morning at nine. Can you be there?" she asked.

"This must be about Ernesto."

"Of course. After he paid a visit to you this morning, he waited at school for Selena," she explained, her voice filled with disdain. "He wanted her to get to know her potential new stepmommy. He told her they'd all soon be living together. Naturally that sent her into a tailspin."

Gabe felt his free hand close into a fist. "I can't believe even he would be so insensitive."

"Of course he is. The man's either delusional or an idiot. Either way, it played right into my hands. I intend to prove to the judge that this demonstrates that he's completely unsuited to be a parent. He's using those children as a weapon. If I have my way, he'll be stripped of visitation rights, at least until the kids are old enough to decide for themselves if they want to spend time with him. If I can't convince the judge of that, then I at least want the visits supervised."

Despite the seriousness of the situation, Gabe was reassured by the determination in Helen's voice. Whatever she needed from him, she had it. "What can I do?"

"Just tell the judge about the threats Ernesto made to you," she said.

"Done," Gabe said at once. "And I have witnesses. Would they help? You may not want my whole crew traipsing into court, but how about Henry Davis? He heard every word for sure. I know he'd be willing, maybe even eager, to testify about what he saw and heard."

"Good idea," Helen said. "Henry's a good guy and he'll be viewed as impartial, at least when it comes to the custody matter. I may not need him, but it won't hurt to have backup just in case."

"We'll be there," Gabe promised. "I'll give him a call right now."

As soon as he'd hung up, he tracked down Henry and got his commitment to be at the courthouse before nine.

Gabe had intended to head to Adelia's, but under the circumstances he had to wonder if that was such a good idea, at least tonight. Maybe they should be more circumspect, at least for the next twenty-four hours. He was still debating with himself about that when Adelia appeared on the sidewalk outside the space he was renovating. Gabe stepped out and locked the door behind him.

She studied his expression, then sighed. "You've already heard?"

Gabe nodded. "I'm so sorry that I seem to have triggered this."

"You didn't do anything wrong. Neither did I. This is just Ernesto's way of trying to prove he's still got control of my life. I swear I actually hate him for this," she said, the look on her face filled with loathing.

"Up till now I've managed to stand up for him with the kids." She shook her head. "Why did I even bother? I've even encouraged them to spend time with him, not that he's taken advantage of that. I'm done, though," she declared forcefully. "He's crossed a line. I won't let them be his pawns and I certainly won't let him force that woman on them, not unless it's court-mandated that I have to."

"Good for you," he said, desperately wanting to reach for her but knowing it was a bad idea.

"Are you coming over?"

Gabe shook his head. "I was just thinking we should probably take a time-out, especially with this court date in the morning."

She heaved another sigh, clearly disappointed. "You're probably right. Ernesto probably has a private detective stationed across the street from the house, ready to snap pictures. That would be just like him."

Gabe regretted that he'd already locked up. He wished he could drag Adelia inside and kiss her until she lost that anxious expression. It wasn't something he could do out here on the street, though. That private eye she was so worried about could just as easily be right here on Main Street. He settled for tucking a finger under her chin.

"It's going to be okay," he promised. "Helen's exactly the person I'd want on my side in this situation. She impressed the daylights out of me when I spoke to her earlier."

She smiled a little at that. "No question about it. She kept me sane during the divorce. Nothing rattles her."

"Then don't let it rattle you," he said. "I'll see you first thing in the morning. If you need me before then, call."

"I'm sorry you got dragged into this," she

426

said again.

"Hey, don't you dare be sorry," he replied. "You didn't do the dragging. We can both thank Ernesto for that."

"But you like things easy and uncomplicated."

"Seems as if that's been a lost cause since I met you," he said, then winked at her. "I'm starting to think easy and uncomplicated are highly overrated, anyway."

She laughed, just as he'd intended.

"Night, darlin'." He regretted he couldn't put some color in her cheeks with a kiss, but the endearment seemed to have almost the same effect.

"Maybe I'll call you later just to say goodnight again," she said, then added in a low, surprisingly sultry voice, "After I'm in bed."

He swallowed hard at the twinkle in her eyes, then chuckled. "Who knew you were a big ol' tease, Adelia Hernandez?"

"I know," she said, smiling brightly at last. "Who knew?"

To Adelia's surprise just that few minutes with Gabe right on Main Street where anyone could see was enough to settle her nerves over tomorrow's court date. Of course, the realization that she'd been flirting outrageously with him caused its own share of jitters. What had she been thinking? She couldn't think of a single time in her life that she'd tossed out daring innuendoes the way she had with him.

As she remained standing on the corner after he'd gone, her kids came running out of the bakery to join her. Given the amount of frosting on their faces, she had a hunch they'd be on a sugar high for most of the evening.

"Mommy, we had cupcakes," Juanita announced happily. "I had one with chocolate frosting and sprinkles and one with pink frosting."

"Yes, I can see that," Adelia said, taking a tissue from her purse and wiping away the evidence. She beckoned for Natalia, then wiped her face. "Only chocolate?"

Natalia nodded. "But I had three."

Adelia put her hands on her hips and turned to Tomas. "And you, young man? I see chocolate frosting and vanilla," she said as she scrubbed his face with the tissue. "And what's this?"

"Caramel," he said happily. "Lynn said it was new. I still like chocolate the best, though."

She glanced over his head at Selena.

"Sorry, Mom. I didn't think they had enough money for more than one, but Lynn

428

floated them a loan. I paid her when I got back over there."

"What about you?" she asked Selena. "Didn't you want a cupcake?"

Her daughter, who'd always loved sweets, shook her head. "I wasn't hungry."

Adelia understood exactly why. "How about one to take home? You might feel more like it later."

Selena shrugged off the offer. "That's okay."

"Well, I doubt these three are going to be hungry anytime soon. What about you? Anything special you'd like me to fix for dinner?"

Again, Selena shook her head. Adelia decided to let it drop for now.

At home she sent the three younger children into the yard to run off some of their excess energy, then gestured for Selena to join her in the kitchen.

"Sweetie, I know you're worried, but you don't need to be," she told her.

"How can you say that?" Selena demanded with surprising anger. "Dad's going to ruin everything again."

Startled by her vehemence, Adelia reached for her hands. "Nothing's ruined."

"How can you say that? Gabe's not here, is he? I don't hear him upstairs and his truck's not in the driveway. That's because of Dad."

"In a way, yes," Adelia said, unable to deny it. "But Gabe and I agreed it would be for the best if he stayed away just for tonight. Once we see the judge in the morning, things can go back to normal."

"What if they can't?" Selena asked. "You don't know for sure what the judge is going to say. He could be on Dad's side. He could make us live with him."

"He could, but he's not going to," Adelia said with more confidence than she actually felt. "Helen won't let that happen."

"I know Helen's a really, really good lawyer, but she's not the judge," Selena said, unappeased. "Dad could bribe the judge or something."

While Adelia doubted Ernesto would be above doing just that, she had faith in Helen and, for that matter, in the judge. "I think it would only land your father in a lot of hot water if he tried anything like that," she told Selena. "There are pretty serious consequences for crossing that line."

"I guess," Selena said.

Adelia heard the skepticism in Selena's voice and realized the toll the past months had taken on her daughter. At only thirteen, she was bitter and cynical. Adelia wondered

430

if there was any way at all to recapture just a little of that lost innocence.

"Look, I understand why you find all of this upsetting," Adelia told her gently. "I really do."

"No, you don't," Selena said. "Lately we've been like a real family, or the way a family's supposed to be. We have dinner together. Gabe helps us with homework. We even had game night again. Now it's all messed up. What if Gabe goes away and we never see him again?"

"Not that long ago you didn't want him around here," Adelia reminded her.

"That was before," Selena said.

"Before what?"

"Before he made you laugh again and before he was so nice to Tomas and to me, Natalia and Juanita, too." She gave Adelia a plaintive look. "He reminds me of the way Uncle Elliott treats Daisy and Mack. I was so jealous of that for so long. Then Gabe came along and I thought maybe we'd have someone who treats us like that, like he really cares about us."

Adelia smiled, even though her eyes were stinging with tears she didn't dare shed. "Gabe does care about you," she agreed. She wasn't sure if even he was aware how much.

"You'd hate it if he went away, wouldn't you?" Selena asked.

"Sure I would," Adelia admitted. "But I don't think Gabe plans on going anywhere right now. And he certainly wouldn't take off just because your dad's being a bully."

"He left town once before," Selena said, her voice hesitant. "Joey told me. He said Gabe was always in trouble when he was a kid and that when things got bad, he just took off. Joey says he'll probably do it again."

"Joey doesn't know what he's talking about," Adelia said angrily, though she knew that wasn't exactly the case. For once he did have the basic facts right. He just wasn't taking into account the man Gabe was today.

"Did Joey lie?" Selena pressed.

"Not exactly," Adelia conceded. "There were people who were mean to him and to his mom back then. He got into some fights trying to stand up for her. After his mom died, he did leave Serenity. Who could blame him? Nobody wants to be where they've been mistreated."

"But that's exactly the same as what's happening now," Selena protested.

"But Gabe isn't the same person. I believe he'll stay right here, at least for as long as we need him," Adelia said, aware that she was putting her faith in him. There were so many reasons she needed to believe he wouldn't let them down.

Selena frowned. "What does that mean, for as long as we need him?"

Adelia didn't dare look too far into the future. Now was all she could count on. "It means that he's not going to bail on us because of anything your dad does."

Apparently Adelia wasn't as good at hiding her own fears as she'd hoped to be. Selena, rather than looking relieved, seemed more worried than before. Apparently she was a little too good at reading between the lines.

"But you think he will leave eventually, don't you?" Selena asked, proving Adelia's point.

"It's a possibility," Adelia admitted reluctantly.

"But I thought he really liked us," Selena said plaintively. "You just said so yourself. And I thought he might even be falling in love with you."

"Sweetie, life's more complicated than that. Even if both of those things are true, it doesn't always mean that things will work out," Adelia said.

"Well, that just sucks," Selena said, pushing away from the table and racing from the room in tears.

Adelia sighed, hating that she'd managed to make things worse for Selena by trying to be honest with her. Selena was right about one thing, though. Sometimes facing reality was the pits.

Lynn's temper stirred as she listened to Helen's description of what was going on with Ernesto and his attempts to wrest custody of his kids from Adelia.

"What can I do?" she asked at once.

"Normally I'd call the Sweet Magnolias myself, but I'm swamped with pulling everything together for tomorrow's hearing," Helen said. "I need a huge show of support for Adelia in the courtroom."

"Consider it done," Lynn said. "I'll start making calls right now."

"Call Maddie first," Helen suggested. "She had her share of tough custody issues back in the day. She'll help you make the calls."

"I'm on it," Lynn promised, then hung up and turned to Mitch and filled him in. "You might want to look for Gabe. I imagine he's busy blaming himself for this."

Her husband nodded. "Only if you promise me that you'll get your nap the second you've made those calls."

Lynn regarded him with dismay. "You know about the naps?"

Mitch chuckled. "Sweetheart, only a robot could keep the hours you keep without a nap." He gave her a long look. "Maybe it's time we talked about that."

"Not until this mess with Ernesto is resolved," she said. "Then I promise I'll listen to whatever you have to say." She held his gaze. "Have I told you lately how glad I am that you're my husband?"

"Right back at you."

Lynn watched as he left the house to go in search of his cousin, then picked up the phone and made that first call to Maddie Maddox.

Within an hour they'd reached out to every one of the Sweet Magnolias. Adelia would have some of the most prominent women in town in court in the morning. Even if Helen never called a single one of them to the stand, the show of support would speak for itself.

Gabe retreated to his regular table at Rosalina's for a lonely meal, drawing a surprised look from his old waitress.

"It's been a while," Debbie said. "I thought you'd deserted us for good. Word around town is that you've found somebody to share your meals with."

Gabe wasn't about to confirm or deny that. "I just took a temporary reprieve from the pizza," he said.

"Then I suppose you want your usual," Debbie said, clearly disappointed that he wasn't willing to reveal more details.

"Sure. Why not?"

While he was waiting for his order, his cell phone rang. He considered ignoring it, then saw Adelia's name on the caller ID.

"What's up?" he asked at once. "I thought we were going to talk later."

"I think you need to come over here, after all," Adelia said, sounding worried. "Selena's totally freaked out about what's going on. Her cousin, who seems to thrive on taunting her these days, told her you took off from Serenity years ago because you were sick of being bullied. Now she's afraid her dad is going to chase you off again. I tried to be honest with her, but I only made it worse."

"What did you tell her?"

"That I didn't think her dad could chase you away, but that it was always possible that you could leave eventually."

Gabe immediately saw the dilemma. "You know I can't come over there and deny that," he said. "Neither of us has any idea what could happen down the road."

"I know," she said with obvious frustration. "I just don't think Selena was ready for quite that degree of candor. I could shake Joey for planting these seeds of doubt in her head, but he has his own share of issues at home right now. I'll deal with him later."

She drew in a deep breath. "Please, Gabe, can you stop by? I think it would help if Selena could just see you tonight and know that you're not planning to abandon us because of this mess."

"I'll be there in a few minutes," he promised. "I just ordered pizza. I'll double the order so there will be enough to share."

"That sounds great to me and maybe we can coax Selena to eat, but don't count on the little kids," Adelia warned him. "They overdosed on cupcakes. Right now they're running off all that excess sugar in the backyard. I'm going to take a stab at getting them in bed before you get here, so we can focus on Selena."

He laughed at her optimism. "I'll make it a half hour, then, though I doubt even that will be enough time for you to round them up and herd them into their beds."

"I'll make it long enough," she said with

grim determination. "And remind me tomorrow to thank Lynn for caving in to their pleas for all those cupcakes."

"Hey, business is business."

"They didn't even have enough cash on them," Adelia retorted dryly. "She floated them a loan till Selena came back for them. I hope this new baby when it comes doesn't sleep a wink at night for a month."

Gabe stifled a chuckle. "Now that's just mean."

"It's called payback," she said. "It's perfectly fair."

"Remind me not to cross you," Gabe said. "I hate to think what you'd consider to be a fitting punishment."

"I'll have to give that some thought," she said. "If I'm clever enough, maybe I can keep you in town."

Gabe almost admitted that she was close to ensuring his presence for good now, but he had enough remaining doubts to keep silent. "See you soon," he said instead.

Before Gabe could collect his pizza and take off for Adelia's, Mitch walked into Rosalina's with his stepchildren, Lexie and Jeremy. As soon as he caught sight of Gabe, he handed over a bunch of quarters and sent them off to play video games.

As soon as Mitch sat down, Gabe warned him that he was about to leave. "I'm heading over to Adelia's."

Mitch frowned. "After what happened today? I heard Ernesto paid a visit to you and tried to stir up trouble. Lynn just got a call from Helen, who filled her in on the rest. I figured you'd be steering clear of her for a few days till things settled down. In fact, I tried looking for you at the inn and at the work site before I picked up the kids and headed over here. I thought you might want to join us for dinner."

"Not tonight," Gabe said. "Something just came up. Adelia needs me over there."

"Is it important enough to risk getting Ernesto all worked up again?" Mitch asked, his worry plain.

Gabe thought of Selena and what she'd been through today. "It's important enough," he declared. "And if Ernesto tries to stir up more trouble, I can handle that, too. I kept my cool today. I can do it again."

Mitch nodded. "Your crew thought you behaved a lot better than he deserved. Henry said you did go over to Helen's office to fill her in."

"And now Henry and I are going to testify about what happened at an emergency hearing in court first thing in the morning,"

Gabe told him.

Mitch regarded him with surprise. "Henry didn't mention that."

"He probably didn't know about it when he spoke to you. I just filled him in a little while ago that it would be a help to Helen if we were both there." He met Mitch's worried gaze. "I'm sorry about getting one of your men involved in all this drama."

"Hey, stuff happens. Ed Morrow tried to haul me into the middle of his divorce from Lynn. She was falling all over herself apologizing. What she didn't get was that I'd have done anything for her. Ed's fussing didn't worry me. The only thing I cared two hoots about was whether he could use me to hurt Lynn."

"Same with me," Gabe said. "Helen seems to think Ernesto overplayed his hand. After he caused that scene with me, he took his mistress to see Selena and told her they'd all be a family soon."

Outrage spread across Mitch's face. "I don't think Helen mentioned that part to Lynn. That just proves that as low as I thought Ernesto was, I was overestimating him. He's even lower than slime."

"No doubt about it," Gabe agreed. "By the way, have there been any repercussions from those lies he was spreading about you and the business?"

Mitch shook his head. "Nothing I couldn't handle."

"Meaning there were some," Gabe guessed. "Blast it all, Mitch, you need to sue him."

"I took care of it," Mitch said. "No harm, no foul. In fact, I imagine if anyone lost business over it, it was Ernesto. The guy Ernesto went to had been planning to work with him on a new development outside of town. Once Conway heard the whole story, he opted to go with another developer." Mitch grinned. "And I'll be hiring more men to handle the construction."

Gabe slapped him on the back. "Good for you."

Mitch's expression immediately turned serious. "Which is why it's more important than ever that you stick around, Gabe. With all this work and a baby on the way, I need you right here. I hope you're not getting any ideas about moving on. Lynn said you'd mentioned it."

"I was having a bad day when I told her that. For now, I'm staying," Gabe assured him.

"I'd feel a whole lot more confident about that if you'd start looking for a place to live, instead of staying in that room at the

441

Serenity Inn." His cousin gave him a sly look. "Or are you hoping if you do make a move, it will be into Adelia's house in Swan Point?"

Gabe frowned. "Nobody's suggesting that, least of all me. It's way too soon."

"One thing I've learned over the years is that there's no such thing as a timetable when it comes to love," Mitch told him. "I waited for years before Lynn and I got together."

"And spent a lot of those years happily married to someone else," Gabe reminded him.

"True," Mitch said. "And if Amy hadn't died in that accident and Ed hadn't finally owned up to being gay and asked for a divorce, who knows if Lynn and I would ever have gotten together? I'm just saying that fate works in its own mysterious way. If this thing with Adelia is right, it could be as right after a few weeks as it would be a couple of years from now."

"Well, we're opting for slow and steady," Gabe told him.

Mitch smiled. "Only because anything else terrifies you."

"If you're trying to suggest I'm a coward without saying the word, I'm not denying it," Gabe countered. "I prefer to think of it as old habits dying hard."

"The old habit being to avoid commitment at all costs," Mitch guessed.

"Exactly."

"A piece of advice?"

"As if I could stop you," Gabe said.

"People have a way of clinging to old habits long past the time when they're useful. Something to think about, okay?"

Fortunately Debbie arrived with Gabe's pizzas before he had to respond to his cousin's advice.

"Gotta go," Gabe announced, relieved.

"Have a good evening," Mitch said, a twinkle in his eyes.

Gabe thought of what awaited him at Adelia's, the thankless task of trying to cheer up a teenager. Then again, he'd get to spend some unexpected time with Adelia, so perhaps the night wouldn't be a lost cause after all.

CHAPTER TWENTY-ONE

Gabe wasn't sure what sort of chaos he might find when he got to Adelia's. To his surprise the house was eerily quiet when he used his key to get in. Apparently she'd somehow managed to get the younger children to bed before his arrival.

He carried the pizza into the kitchen and was getting three plates down from the cupboard when Adelia finally came in. Judging from her harried expression, he concluded the kids hadn't gone to bed willingly.

"Everything under control?" he asked, pausing to drop a quick kiss on her cheek before setting the plates on the table. At least that kiss put some color in her face, he thought, satisfied with the effect. It was startling how much he was coming to appreciate the impact of bestowing these little acts of affection. Until recently he'd always considered sex to be the endgame. Lately he'd been developing a whole new fondness for intimate gestures and foreplay.

"I suppose it depends on how you define control," she replied dryly. "Tomas is crying because he heard your truck and I wouldn't let him come downstairs to see you. Juanita just threw up. Natalia is under the covers reading with a flashlight, which is normally against the rules and which she apparently assumes I didn't notice. I was just too tired to start a fight with her."

"Come here," Gabe said, opening his arms. Adelia practically sagged against him, letting her head rest on his shoulder. That she gave in so easily told him exactly how draining the day had been for her. He held her close. "After tomorrow everything will settle down again."

"We don't know that," she said wearily. "The little kids don't have any idea about what's going on. What if the judge rules in Ernesto's favor and I haven't prepared them?"

Gabe took a step back and looked her in the eye. "The only way any judge would rule in Ernesto's favor would be if he concluded I were a worse influence on them than Ernesto is. Helen doesn't believe that will happen, but if it does, I will back off. You can take out a restraining order to make it official if that's what it takes."

Adelia looked shocked. "I could never do that. It would suggest you've done something wrong and quite the opposite is true."

"If it's the last resort, you could," Gabe stated flatly. "I mean it, Adelia. You do whatever you need to do to keep your kids right here where they belong."

"But that would be so unfair," she protested.

"Hopefully it won't come to that, but I do not want to be the reason your kids are not with you. I'll pack up and take off before I'll let that happen."

Naturally that was the precise instant that Selena chose to join them. Alarm spread across her face.

"You're leaving? Just like Joey said you would?" Her eyes filled with tears. "I knew I shouldn't trust you. I *knew* it. I was right all along. I hate you!"

She whirled around and was about to run, but Adelia caught her arm. "Not until you let Gabe explain," she said quietly.

"Explain what? That he's no better than Dad?"

Adelia looked as if she'd been slapped. "You know that's not true," she said furiously. "And I won't have you talking to Gabe or about him like that."

"Then let me leave before I say something

even more rude," Selena said, trying to pull free.

Gabe decided it was time to step in and stand up for himself. Adelia had more than enough on her plate without trying to handle his battles.

"Selena," he said quietly. "You're almost an adult and part of being grown-up is giving people a chance to explain, especially when you only heard part of what we were discussing."

"What if I don't want to hear anything you have to say?" she asked angrily. "I'm sick of everybody lying to me."

"I will never lie to you," Gabe said. He gestured toward a kitchen chair. "Please, sit down and listen. Just a few minutes. That's all I'm asking."

"Sweetie, you owe him that much," Adelia said. "Think about everything he's done for you."

"I guess," Selena said sullenly.

"Gabe brought pizza," Adelia added. "Wouldn't you like some? You haven't eaten a thing."

Selena shook her head. Even so, Adelia put the box on the table and moved one of the plates and several napkins so they were right in front of her daughter.

"Just in case you change you mind," she

told her.

"I won't," Selena said stubbornly.

Gabe pulled out the chair opposite her and sat. "What did you hear when you walked in here?"

"That you're going to leave, just like Joey said you would."

"But you didn't hear why I said that, did you?" Gabe asked.

"Because it's what you do — you run away," she said bitterly.

"I did once," Gabe conceded. "But this time I would only go if the judge thinks I'm a bad influence on you kids and sides with your dad. I would only leave town to protect you and make sure you can stay here with your mom."

Selena looked shaken. She turned to Adelia. "But you said the judge would never do that."

"I don't believe he will," Adelia said.

"And I don't think he will, either," Gabe added. "This was a just-in-case promise, a way to make sure nothing in your life changes."

The tension in Selena's shoulders visibly eased. Her gaze hopeful, her voice tremulous, she whispered, "Cross your heart? You won't just pack up and go?"

"Cross my heart," Gabe told her, suiting

action to words. "I don't want to leave, Selena."

"But you did once before. Joey told me, and Mom didn't deny it."

"That's true. Have you heard the whole story?"

"It had something to do with your mom," Selena said.

"That's exactly right," Gabe confirmed. "When I was about your age, maybe even a couple of years younger, kids started making really mean remarks about my mom. To be honest, a lot of it was true, but that didn't mean it didn't hurt to hear them say it. My mom did a lot of bad stuff back then. Since it was just the two of us, I figured it was my job to defend her. I started a lot of fights. Eventually I got kicked out of school. Fortunately that was the worst of what happened. Still, your dad wants to bring all of that up to the judge."

"But that's not fair," Selena said. "You were just worried about your mom. I feel the same way about my mom. That's why I got so mad when I heard you might take off. I thought you were going to hurt her by leaving, and it would be even worse if you did, because I was starting to think you're a really good guy and I know she likes you."

He glanced at Adelia, then back at her

449

daughter. "Would it help if I promise that it's not my intention to hurt your mother?"

She was silent for a long time, then said wearily, "My dad promised to love her for always. He didn't keep his promise."

Gabe's heart ached for the pain he could hear in this young girl's voice. She was learning lessons no one her age needed to know. He couldn't help wondering how those would shape the woman she'd become.

"I know," he said quietly. "Adults always mean their promises when they make them, but they can't always keep them."

"Then why should I trust you?" Selena asked with a touch of belligerence.

Gabe gave Adelia a meaningful look. "Because I will never make a promise if I don't think I can keep it," he said, the words directed at Selena but meant for her mother, as well. "And I suppose the only way I can prove that is if you'll give me another chance. Can you do that?"

Again, Selena hesitated. "I guess," she said eventually.

"Thank you," he said, relieved because he knew that without Selena's blessing, his chances for making any inroads with her mother would be nil. Adelia would shift gears all over again and want him out of their lives.

Before he realized what she intended, Selena was out of her chair, her arms tight around his neck. "Please don't leave us. Please. It's been so much better since you came here."

Gabe closed his eyes. Here it was, the test he'd dreaded, because the promise she so desperately wanted was one he couldn't guarantee he could keep. His silence finally registered with her apparently, because she pulled away.

"Why aren't you saying anything?" she asked, her gaze accusing.

"I told you I would never lie and that I wouldn't make a promise I didn't think I could keep," he said quietly. "What I will promise you is that no matter what happens, I will always, always care about you and be around anytime you tell me you need me. No matter where I might be, I will only be a phone call away."

"But you could go away," she concluded, her expression resigned.

"I won't want to, but, yes, it could happen."

"Even if the judge doesn't make you?"

Gabe nodded, though his heart ached. "Even then."

Though Selena was clearly fighting tears,

451

a few managed to leak out and dampen her cheeks. "Will you tell me if you have to go?"

"Absolutely," he said, his own eyes stinging. "I promise."

"Okay," she said in a small voice. She sat back down and took a slice of pizza from the box, picking off bits of pepperoni and tearing them into smaller bits.

Gabe and Adelia waited until she eventually turned to her mom.

"I want to come to court tomorrow," Selena said, her voice filled with determination. "I want to testify."

"Oh, sweetie, I don't think that's a good idea," Adelia protested. "Helen didn't ask that you be there."

"I'll call her myself and tell her I'm coming," Selena said stubbornly. "I was the one Dad brought that woman to see. I can tell the judge that he doesn't care about us. And I can tell him that Gabe does, so much that he'd go away before he'd ever hurt us."

Gabe could see that Adelia was torn between trying to protect her daughter and letting her have her way.

"I think you should talk it over with Helen," he told Adelia. "Let her decide."

Selena gave him a grateful look, then turned back to Adelia. "Please, Mom. I have to do this. I have to stand up for our family."

Adelia finally nodded. "I'll ask Helen."

"Now," Selena prodded.

Adelia stood up and regarded Gabe wryly. "I wonder where she gets that stubborn streak from."

He winked at her. "I think we both know the answer to that. You're no slouch in that department yourself."

After Adelia left the room to make the call, Selena regarded him shyly. "Thanks for backing me up."

"I think you've earned the right to have a say," he told her. "Just remember, it's up to Helen. She knows best."

Adelia returned before Selena could even respond to that. "Helen says it's fine if you're there, but she will only call on you to testify if it seems like the right thing to do or if the judge asks to hear from you."

"I can live with that," Selena said happily.

This time when she picked up her slice of pizza, she actually ate it. Two slices after that, she glanced from her mom to Gabe and back again.

"I guess you'd like to be alone, huh?"

Gabe laughed. "I wouldn't mind."

Selena gave her mother a kiss, then gave him a peck on the cheek, too. Gabe held her gaze.

"All is forgiven?" he asked.

She nodded.

"Then get some sleep. I'll see you tomorrow at the courthouse."

"Good night, Gabe. It's all going to work out," she said, sounding surprisingly confident. "You'll see."

Gabe couldn't help wishing he had the same crystal ball Selena seemed to be looking into.

"You were good with Selena earlier," Adelia told Gabe when they were alone on the back patio after Selena had finally gone upstairs to bed.

"I meant what I said to her. I know where she's coming from," Gabe said. "My mom went through some tough times, a lot of tough times, to be honest." He regarded her curiously. "No one's filled you in on the stories?"

She shook her head. "I only know what you've mentioned."

"I'm surprised. She was certainly the talk of the town back then."

Adelia tried to imagine what it was like for a young man to have his mother at the center of town gossip, then realized that was exactly what Selena had experienced because of Ernesto. She certainly knew the effect that had had. "That must have been so hard on you."

He shrugged. "Thus my reputation as a troublemaker. Just like I told Selena, I was in a lot of fights back then, defending her honor, or at least that's how I viewed it. Maybe she deserved it, maybe she didn't, but I didn't think I had a choice."

"Of course you didn't," Adelia said at once. "She was your mother. Selena feels that same sort of loyalty to me, but thankfully she hasn't felt the need to beat anyone up. I think she was probably tempted to throw a few punches at Ernesto's mistress, but she didn't. I was tempted to do that myself, so I could hardly have blamed her if she had."

"I'm sorry you went through that. I'm sorry Selena did, too."

"It's behind me now," she said, then sighed. "At least I was working on leaving it in the past until this latest mess came up."

"What about the future?" he asked. "Not tomorrow, but way beyond that. What do you see for yourself?"

"I try not to look too far beyond today," she told him. "I'm still at the stage of trying to put one foot in front of the other, making sure the kids are okay, getting this place fixed up." She glanced his way. "What about you? Once you've got your life on an even keel, what's next?"

"I haven't been back all that long," he said. "An even keel feels as if it's a long way off."

"No big dreams, Gabe?"

He met her gaze, held it. "I haven't let myself dream for a long time," he confessed. "I didn't think I deserved to have dreams. Now, since I've met you . . ."

His voice trailed off, but his meaning was clear. It left Adelia shaken but filled with the kind of anticipation she hadn't thought possible just a few months ago.

She shook off her desire to bask in his words. "I should stop this."

"Stop what?"

"Talking about the future as if either one of us has any control over it. Knowing that a judge could change my life forever tomorrow morning is proof enough that I'm not the one in charge of anything."

Gabe scooted closer and put his arm around her. "Have a little faith. You're a great mom. You've done right by your kids. They're healthy and getting happier by the day. You have a good job and the respect of a lot of people in this town. There's not a judge in the world who would choose

Ernesto over you. I'm the complication."

She smiled at his willingness to take responsibility for anything that might not go her way in court. "No, Gabe. You're the good influence. I imagine Selena intends to tell the judge exactly that if she gets the chance. Do you know what she told me earlier?"

"What?"

"That because of you, it feels like we're a real family. I can't argue with that. The past few weeks have been the way I always wanted my family to be. She also said you treat her and my other kids the way Elliott treats Daisy and Mack. Believe me, that's high praise. Even before my brother officially adopted those two, he loved them to pieces. And because he did, even the most judgmental people in my family accepted them, and ultimately Karen, too."

Gabe frowned. "What did they have against Karen? Admittedly, I don't know her that well, but she seems to have an approval sticker from that whole group of Sweet Magnolia women. From what Mitch has said, they're pretty tight-knit."

"Ah, but in the eyes of my family, she has a tragic flaw. She's divorced," she responded.

"But you're divorced, too," he said, clearly

confused.

"I wasn't then. And in fact, my sisters think Karen had some sort of evil influence over me. They're no more accepting of me now than they were of Karen back then."

"What about the one whose husband is abusing her? Carolina, is it? Surely she understands."

"Afraid not. If anything, she hates me even more because I got out of a bad marriage and she can't bring herself to leave hers." She waved off the topic. "Enough of that. It's too depressing and it's not anything I can resolve tonight. I have enough on my mind."

Gabe looked into her eyes. "I wish I could stay right here and distract you."

She smiled at the wistfulness in his voice. "Believe me, I wish you could, too."

"But I should go," he said without making a move to do so.

"You should," she agreed.

He glanced around, as if to determine if there were spies lurking in the bushes, then leaned in close. "Not before this," he whispered, then sealed his mouth over hers.

Once again Adelia lost herself in his kiss. How had she never realized what sort of sweet torment a simple kiss could stir up? Not that there was anything simple about the way Gabe kissed. He teased and taunted, coaxed and demanded, until her body was shouting for a whole lot more. It had been a long time since she'd experienced the sweet torment of foreplay.

"If that judge tries to banish me from your life tomorrow, I may have to pummel some sense into him myself," he said with a moan as he pulled away. "I want a whole lot more than kisses from you, Adelia."

Shaken and breathless, she could only nod.

"You, too?" he asked, clearly amused.

"Oh yeah."

"Still going to call me after you put on your sexy nightie and crawl into bed?" he teased.

She swallowed hard, imagining it. "I don't think so," she said with regret. "I'm going to have enough trouble getting to sleep as it is. If I let you get me all stirred up, I'll be awake and frustrated all night long."

Gabe laughed. "Welcome to my world, darlin'."

When Adelia arrived at the courthouse in the morning, she was stunned to find a whole contingent of Sweet Magnolias waiting in the courtroom, along with her mother.

She addressed her mother's presence first. "Mama, I wasn't expecting you to be here."

"Where else would I be? What I want to know is why you didn't tell me yourself what was happening?"

"You have enough on your mind," Adelia said, then lowered her voice. "Have you seen Carolina?"

Her mother frowned at the question. "She won't open the door for me. That alone tells me things are worse. I'm terrified to even think about how much worse. She has one more day and then I'm taking Elliott over there with me."

Adelia recognized that her mother was at her wits' end if she was even considering involving Elliott. "I'll go with you, Mama. We'll go first thing tomorrow. Maybe if we gang up on Carolina, we can make her get out of that house before things get even worse."

"For now let's focus on seeing that Ernesto gets what's coming to him," her mother said, her expression grim. She beckoned for Selena. "You sit with me. We'll say prayers that the judge is a good and decent man."

Selena grinned. "*Abuela,* I hope you have a lot of pull with God."

"I have enough," she replied. "So do you."

Adelia turned then to Maddie, Dana Sue, Raylene and the other Sweet Magnolias. As far as she could tell the only ones missing were Lynn, who had to be at the bakery, and Sarah, who was on the air at the radio station. She regarded the women with tears in her eyes, then faced Helen.

"I see you rallied the troops," she whispered. "Thank you."

"Lynn made the calls. This is what we do any time one of us is in trouble," Helen said simply. "Every one of those women is prepared to tell the judge what an excellent mother you are. Collectively they carry a lot of weight in this town."

Gabe came in just then, dressed in a suit and tie that made him look as if he'd just stepped off the cover of some slick men's fashion magazine. He'd even shaved off that sexy stubble she'd come to love. She stared at him, practically tongue-tied. He caught her eye and winked as he stopped to speak to her mother, who looked almost as stunned as Adelia knew she must.

Beside her, Helen chuckled. "Something tells me you just had a mental flash of what Gabe would look like on your wedding day."

Adelia turned a shocked look on her. "Don't even say something like that. What if Ernesto overheard you?"

461

"Oh, so what if he did?" Helen said. "It serves him right to have to sit here and see that another man values you the way you should be valued."

"It may serve him right," Adelia agreed, "but is it a good legal strategy?"

Helen grinned. "Anything that rattles him is a good legal strategy," she said, then nodded toward Gabe. "Ernesto didn't expect he'd clean up so well, I'm sure. Just one more lesson in not underestimating the opposition. There's no one in this courtroom right now who looks more respectable than Gabe."

Adelia was taken aback by her assessment. "Did you take him out and buy him that suit first thing this morning?"

"Didn't have to," Helen said. "I just suggested if he owned a suit, this would be a good occasion to trot it out. Sexy as he looks in those tight jeans and T-shirts he usually wears, I told him a suit might give a better impression in court."

"I notice you didn't say the same thing to Henry Davis. He looks as if he came here straight from the construction site."

"Henry's not the one Ernesto is after," Helen reminded her just as the bailiff called the court to order. "He looks exactly like what he is, an honest, hardworking man.

That works nicely in our favor, too."

As soon as the judge was seated, Ernesto's attorney was on his feet. "Your Honor, given that this is a custody issue involving minor children, we move that the courtroom be closed to all but those directly involved."

Helen leveled a withering look in his direction. "My apologies, Your Honor, but when my client's family and friends learned of what her ex-husband is trying to pull today, they all insisted on being here to testify on her behalf. I intend to call every one of them, if Your Honor needs convincing that she is the best person to continue to have custody of her children."

"They may stay," he ruled. "Now let's get on with this. I've looked over my earlier ruling in this case." He turned to Ernesto. "What's changed?"

Once again, Ernesto's attorney stood. "We've learned that their mother has been subjecting the children to the influence of a man known to be a troublemaker. It is no longer a safe environment."

"That's nuts!" Selena shouted, standing up and staring belligerently at her father. "Gabe's a better influence than you ever were."

The judge's gavel slammed down. "Young lady, I won't have my courtroom disrupted."

"How about disrespected, then?" she said, fighting off her grandmother's attempts to pull her back into her seat. "That's what my father's doing. He's in here lying to you."

Helen was on her feet. "I'm sorry, Your Honor. As you can imagine, emotions are running high."

He nodded. He glanced down at the papers in front of him, then returned his gaze to Selena. "You are the oldest child, Selena Hernandez?"

"Yes, sir."

"Come up here," he ordered, then gestured for her to take a seat in the witness box. He glanced at Adelia and at Ernesto. "Any objections?"

Ernesto opened his mouth, but his attorney immediately silenced him.

"Okay, then," the judge said.

Though she looked scared, Selena squared her shoulders and walked forward, casting a defiant look at her father. For once Ernesto actually looked shaken.

Adelia glanced at Helen. "Shouldn't you do something?"

"I don't think so," Helen said. "I think Selena knows exactly what she's doing. I'll intercede if I see a need to."

"Young lady, why do you say that your father is lying?"

464

"Because he's trying to convince you he wants what's best for my sisters, brother and me. He doesn't. All he wants to do is hurt my mom more than he already has."

"Sometimes children don't know what's best for them," the judge said.

"Maybe not, but I'm not exactly a kid. I may be only thirteen, but thanks to my dad I know a lot about the way people cheat and lie and break their vows. If you ask him, I'll bet he'll try to tell you how much he loves us."

"I'm sure he will," the judge agreed. "Fathers love their children."

"Then why hasn't he seen me even once since the divorce? He'll say it's because I took my mom's side, but so what? And what about my sisters and brother? They didn't take sides. And they wait every weekend for him to show up and spend time with them. He did a couple of times, but I can't even remember the last time he didn't break a promise to them."

The judge's expression darkened as he turned to Ernesto. "Is that true?"

"She," Ernesto began, pointing at Adelia, "has turned them against me. That's why I want the custody arrangement changed, so I can get my kids back before it's too late."

"You're the one who doesn't show up,"

Selena retorted. "Mom's never said a bad word against you, not one. In fact, she's told us we should spend time with you. It's not her fault that I don't want to be with a liar and a cheat."

Helen did stand then. "Your Honor, I think you can see that Mr. Hernandez's words and actions don't match. If you doubt that Selena is telling the truth, there are other witnesses here who can back her up."

"I imagine they can," the judge said wearily. "That still leaves the matter of this person that Mr. Hernandez says is a bad influence." Again, he glanced at his notes. "Gabe Franklin, I believe." He glanced around the courtroom until his gaze landed on Gabe. "I believe we've met before. Stand up, if you would."

Gabe stood. "We have, Your Honor."

"Under less than favorable circumstances, as I recall," the judge said, causing Adelia to wince, even as Selena looked indignant.

"I'll bet it was because of his mom," Selena said, jumping to Gabe's defense. "Whatever he did, it was trying to protect his mom, so you can't hold that against him."

The judge actually smiled at her fierce reaction. "No, I can't," he told her gently.

"I just thought you should know," Selena said.

"I've heard only good things about you since you got back to town," the judge told Gabe.

"I hope so, Your Honor," Gabe replied.

"He's the best," Selena chimed in. "He helps us with our homework. He makes my mom laugh. He even wore a tiara for my sisters when they had a tea party."

The judge didn't even try to hide his grin. "I believe I saw a picture of that occasion."

"I know he's not our dad," Selena said. "But it's been like having a real family with him around. Please don't make him go away." She regarded the judge with an earnest expression. "He said he'd go if that's what it took to keep us with our mom. That's how much he cares about us."

"Did he now?" the judge said softly, casting an approving look toward Gabe.

Ernesto's attorney was on his feet. "If this show is over, could we get back to deciding the facts of the situation?"

The judge shot him a daunting look. "I think I have all the facts I need. The custody arrangement will remain as is. However, we will readdress this in three months." He turned to Ernesto and warned, "If you continue to neglect your children or try to use them as weapons in your fight with your ex-wife, I'll consider taking away the visitation rights you do have. Am I clear?"

Ernesto was clearly too furious to reply, so his attorney said, "Yes, Your Honor."

"Then we're done here," the judge said. He turned to Selena. "I've seen adults who didn't understand right and wrong as well as you do, young lady. Good job here today."

As soon as he'd left the courtroom, the Sweet Magnolias erupted into cheers. Selena ran straight to her mother's arms.

Adelia felt tears streaming down her cheeks. She couldn't have been more proud of her daughter. "You saved the day."

"I just told the truth." She looked around. "Where's Gabe?"

Adelia glanced toward the back of the courtroom, but he wasn't anywhere to be found. A sinking sensation settled in the pit of her stomach. She had this terrible feeling that she might have won the war with Ernesto today, only to lose the battle to keep Gabe in her life.

CHAPTER TWENTY-TWO

Gabe had been so moved by what Selena said to the judge, he'd practically run from the courthouse to keep anyone from seeing the tears gathering in his eyes. Sure, she'd said much the same the night before, but hearing her declare it in public had shaken him. There was a lot of pressure in trying to live up to the kind of faith she'd so openly placed in him.

How could he even be thinking about trying to take care of a family when he'd spent a lot of his adult years barely taking care of himself? He'd been rebelling, albeit unknowingly until now, against having so much responsibility heaped on him as a kid. He wasn't convinced he was ready — or even worthy enough — to take on more.

After he went back to the Serenity Inn, changed into his work clothes and headed for the construction site, he stopped by the hardware store to pick up a few things.

"How'd it go in court?" Ronnie Sullivan asked, proving that everyone in town was no doubt up-to-date on Ernesto's latest attempt to turn Adelia's life upside down. "I know Dana Sue was there, but I imagine she went straight to work at the restaurant. I haven't heard from her."

Gabe filled him in, figuring the news would be all over town in the blink of an eye, anyway. "Adelia kept custody of the kids and Ernesto got his wrist slapped by the judge."

Ronnie took off the glasses he'd been wearing to read an invoice, then frowned as he studied Gabe more intently. "Then why do you look so down in the dumps?"

"Just some stuff Selena said in court," Gabe told him. "It hit home how much she's counting on me. I don't know if I can live up to all those expectations. It's one thing for me and Adelia to try to work things out and fail, but I don't think I could bear it if I let those kids down." He met Ronnie's gaze. "They're great kids. They deserve the best — you know what I mean?"

Rather than dismissing his worries, Ronnie nodded. "I get that, Gabe. I really do. The truth is, though, that nobody knows if they're any good at being a parent until they're in the thick of it. If someone tells you they know exactly what to do in any and all conditions, they're crazy. Just when you figure you've handled one crisis, another one will crop up and blindside you."

Since Ronnie was a grandfather now and seemed to have a rock-solid marriage, Gabe listened.

"Just look at Dana Sue and me," Ronnie continued. "Our daughter nearly died because we messed up so bad. Thankfully Annie made it through all the terrible side effects of her anorexia. She's married to her childhood sweetheart and a mom now. Dana Sue and I are back together again and happier than ever for having survived that nightmare. I thank God every day for giving all of us a second chance."

"I hadn't heard about any of that," Gabe said, shaken.

"I'm surprised, even though most of it probably happened while you were gone. The day Dana Sue chased me out of the house with a cast-iron skillet is one of those stories the guys like to repeat when they want to get under my skin."

"She didn't!"

"She sure did," Ronnie said, laughing. Then his expression sobered. "Here's the condensed version. I acted like a fool, Dana Sue kicked me out and our divorce rocked

Annie's world so badly she developed an eating disorder. She was still in her teens, but she actually had a heart attack."

"Annie? Kids don't have heart attacks," Gabe said, trying to imagine how terrifying that must have been for Ronnie and Dana Sue.

"Well, mine did," Ronnie said. "That anorexia is a nasty business. When I found out about it, I thought my own heart would stop. In fact, I prayed it would if that would keep Annie alive. I discovered that God's not interested in making bargains. He has His own plans. That crisis brought me back to town and reminded me that everything I wanted was right here. I never should have left."

He met Gabe's gaze. "What I'm trying to tell you is that you will make mistakes as a parent if you decide to take on Adelia's family. But if your love is strong enough, you get through the tough times together. I know the worst time in my life while Annie was in the hospital turned out to be the best thing that ever happened to me, too, because Dana Sue and I found our way back to each other."

Gabe absorbed what Ronnie was saying. Though Ronnie had obviously intended his story to make the prospect of parenting a

little less scary, Gabe didn't find it reassuring. If a couple as deeply in love as
Ronnie and Dana Sue had been back in the
day could fail so badly, what chance did he
have to get it right?

"You okay?" Ronnie asked, frowning. "I
didn't make it worse, did I? Dana Sue will
have my hide if I did."

"You just said some things I needed to
hear," Gabe told him.

Ronnie's expression turned even more
worried.

"Is there something else?" Gabe asked
him.

"Just that I had a call from a friend of
mine the other day, a man I worked for in
construction while I was away from Serenity.
In fact, he helped me put together the plans
and money for me to get this store up and
running again."

Gabe wondered what that could possibly
have to do with him.

Ronnie hesitated. "I'm not sure if this is
the right time to get into this."

"Why not?"

"Because he's looking for a new construction crew foreman down in Beaufort,"
Ronnie explained. "He'd heard good things
about you and wondered if I knew you."

Gabe stilled at that. Here it was, the

chance to move on, perhaps, to get yet another fresh start away from a community that until recently had held only bad memories.

"What did you tell him?" he asked Ronnie.

"That what I've seen of your work is excellent and that you're the kind of man who'd fit right in with the tight ship he runs. But I also told him that you had some ties that might keep you here." He studied Gabe. "Was I wrong about that?"

Gabe thought of Adelia and the unexpected, amazing way she made him feel. He thought of Selena, Tomas, of Juanita and Natalia. If he left, he'd be giving Selena one more reason not to trust the adults in her life. If he left, who would teach Tomas all the things he was so eager to learn about guy stuff? And who, pray tell, would sit in a feather boa and a tiara at a tea party with Juanita and Natalia?

And then he thought of Mitch, who'd taken a chance on him, who was depending on him as backup now with a baby on the way and more work than ever on his plate. How could he bail on him?

None of that, though, seemed to dull the familiar temptation to take off for yet another fresh beginning in a town where he had no ties at all, no responsibilities except to himself.

"Have him give me a call," he said eventually. "It's worth listening to what he has to say."

Ronnie looked disappointed by his response, but he nodded. "I'll tell him to call. His name's Butch. He gets to town every so often to check on this place. He's Mary Vaughan's uncle, too, so he and his wife like to stop by and watch her trying to juggle her booming real estate career and a toddler. Given Mary Vaughan's type A personality, they consider that to be an excellent form of entertainment."

Since Gabe had watched a very frustrated Mary Vaughan trying to coax her child into her car one afternoon, he totally got that. The kid had more stubbornness than Mary Vaughan, and she excelled at it. She just called it persistence in her own case.

"I appreciate the good word," he told Ronnie.

"Not a problem, but one more piece of advice," Ronnie said as Gabe started to leave. "Think long and hard before you walk away from what you've found here. I didn't think before I left. I let Helen convince me that Dana Sue and Annie needed space, that having me here would only be a reminder of the mistakes I'd made. I came to regret listening to her."

"Believe me, I won't be thinking about anything else," Gabe told him.

He knew what his pattern was. He knew what the old Gabe would have done. There was safety and comfort in that decision. There was nothing safe or comfortable about staying here.

But there was Adelia. There were four kids he'd come to love. And there was family. Was he brave enough to believe in all that and take a chance on something he'd never dared to hope might be in the cards for him?

Dana Sue insisted that the court ruling deserved to be celebrated. "You're all coming to Sullivan's right now," she announced outside the courthouse. "Brunch is on me."

"Who could say no to that?" Helen said eagerly. "I'll get to sneak into the kitchen and hang out with my honey. It'll be like old times."

"Old times?" Adelia asked.

"Erik and Helen got together when I kept finding excuses requiring her to help out in the kitchen at Sullivan's," Dana Sue explained. "She couldn't cook a lick, of course, and Erik got on her nerves because he rightfully thought he should be the boss. It was fun to watch."

"Boy, was it ever," Maddie confirmed. "The only thing more fun has been watching Helen accept that her mom has a boyfriend and that they're living together."

Helen put her hands on her hips and tried to stare down her two best friends. "Are you two through?"

Maddie and Dana Sue exchanged a look, then grinned.

"Probably not," Maddie said, then gave Helen a hug. "Though we probably shouldn't be teasing the woman who saved the day in court."

"Actually it was Selena who saved the day," Helen said, putting an arm around the blushing teenager.

"I am so proud of you," Adelia told her daughter.

"I just told the truth," Selena said, then regarded her hopefully. "Do I get to come to brunch, too, or do I have to go to school?"

"I think you can be excused for the whole day just this once," Adelia told her, then warned, "But don't get any ideas."

"As if," Selena said. "The last time I cut class, you grounded me, like, forever."

"And I'll do it again if I have to," Adelia said emphatically.

At Sullivan's, where new spins on traditional Southern cuisine were the order of the day, Dana Sue and Erik managed to whip up a feast for the impromptu brunch, even though the restaurant was scheduled to open in an hour for lunch and those preparations already had the kitchen in a frenzy.

"This stuffed French toast with strawberries is amazing," Maddie said, sitting back and patting her stomach. "I think I just gained five pounds."

"You still have two little kids and an amorous husband at home," Dana Sue retorted. "You'll work those calories off in no time."

As the oldest members of the Sweet Magnolias exchanged taunts, Raylene slipped into the seat next to Adelia. "You doing okay?"

Adelia frowned. "Who's covering the shop?"

"I put a sign on the door that we'd be opening at one today. This is more important than selling a couple of dresses or a scarf. Now answer me. How are you doing?"

"I'm worried about Gabe," Adelia admitted. "He took off before I could even thank him for what he said to the judge today. Because of him and Selena, I still have my kids with me."

"I saw him when I went to put the sign

on the door at the shop. He was already back in his work clothes and coming out of the hardware store."

"Oh," Adelia said, oddly deflated by the news. She wasn't sure what she'd hoped for, that maybe he'd at least want to congratulate her on today's outcome or share the moment with her. Something told her, though, that he was pulling away. What she didn't understand was why. The judge hadn't even hinted that he was taking Ernesto's claims seriously.

"Stop worrying," Raylene advised, as if she'd followed Adelia's thoughts. "I imagine Gabe hasn't had that many good things said about him in years. He's probably a little shaken by it."

"That's what concerns me," Adelia said. "What if he tells himself that he doesn't deserve any of it? Even though everything turned out okay, he may be blaming himself for the fact that we were in court in the first place."

"Call him," Raylene suggested. "Or stop by the construction site when you leave here. I can handle the store."

Adelia squeezed her hand. "You may be the most understanding boss in captivity."

"I doubt that," Raylene said. "Keep in mind I have an ulterior motive. I need a happy employee to cover for me while I go off and have a baby and then spend a leisurely few months discovering the joys of motherhood."

Adelia regarded her with shock. "A few months?"

"That's what I've been thinking lately. It could be longer if we move forward with the whole partnership thing. Or if I get really infatuated with this new baby of mine and decide Carter and I should have a few more, I might just sell the whole boutique to you."

Adelia waved off that idea. "Forget that. I'm not even sure I can scrape up enough to be your partner."

"Don't panic. It's all down the road," Raylene advised. "I've told you before, with these women in your corner, anything's possible."

Adelia tried putting Raylene's remarks out of her head. Fortunately, she had a bigger worry at the moment. She needed to find Gabe and make sure that he wasn't going to use today's events to bolt on her after all.

Adelia found Gabe exactly where Raylene had predicted she would, in the cavernous space at the end of the block on Main Street. His crew had apparently gone to lunch, because he was all alone, sitting at that makeshift desk of his in the middle of dust and debris, eating what looked to be a tuna salad sandwich and some fries from a Wharton's take-out container.

When he glanced up at the sound of her heels tapping on the concrete floor, his eyes immediately filled with wariness.

"You shouldn't be in here without a hard hat," he said.

"You're not wearing one," she pointed out.

"Because no one's working right now."

She smiled at that. "Then the rules are different for you?"

His lips quirked slightly. "Sure. I'm the boss. And I'm hardheaded, anyway."

Adelia pulled up a folding chair and sat beside him. "Why'd you take off after court? I didn't even get a chance to thank you."

"You were surrounded by all those women," he said. "You didn't need me butting in."

She frowned at his words. "Gabe, don't you know that I would never consider you an intrusion?"

"I'm just saying that you had plenty of support."

"But you're the one I wanted most to speak to," she said. "Or is that the problem? Did today make things a little too real for you? Did you suddenly realize this thing between us isn't some game, that the kids and I count on you, that it's not your usual cut-and-run flirtation?"

She could tell from his startled reaction that she'd hit on the truth. She sighed. "I guess you did."

He drew in a deep breath, then said, "I always knew you were different."

"Different how?"

"Not the kind of woman I could ever walk away from easily," he told her.

Something in his voice told her, though, that he was going to walk away.

"You're going anyway, though, aren't you?"

"I don't know," he said, looking miserable. "Maybe it's for the best. Complications aren't my thing, Adelia."

"Gabe, there will always be complications in life. Some are good. Some are lousy." She held his gaze. "Crazy me, I thought maybe we were going to be one of the best kind of complications. I'm not saying it would be easy or that there won't be a million times when one of us would prefer to run, but I think the rewards of staying will be worth it." She drew in a deep breath. "But if you can't see that, I can't make you."

He'd been tearing apart his sandwich bit

by bit as she spoke, just as Selena had picked apart the pepperoni the night before. The nervous action was almost enough to make her smile, even though what she really wanted to do was cry and shout at him to look at her, to love her enough to stay with her. She had too much pride, though, to say those words, not to a man who was so obviously intent on leaving.

"There's something I need to tell you," he said. "I've had a job offer in Beaufort. Ronnie Sullivan connected me with the guy he used to work for. He just called. I'm going down this weekend to check it out."

Adelia's heart plummeted. "I see," she said, determined to keep the tears suddenly stinging her eyes from leaking out and betraying her emotions. "So that's it, I guess."

"If I were ever going to stay with someone, it would be you," he told her. "I know it doesn't mean much for me to say I love you, but I'm leaving town anyway, but it's the truth, Adelia. I do love you. I'm doing you a favor."

She stared at him in shock. "That's ridiculous! Leaving isn't doing me a favor. It surely isn't doing my kids a favor. The only one benefiting is you." She shook her head as she regarded him with disbelief. "How could I have been so wrong about you? You're a coward, Gabe Franklin, not a hero at all."

She stood up then, spine straight, shoulders squared, and walked away. She was proud of herself for not shedding a single tear in front of him or even on the walk to Chic.

But when she walked inside the boutique and Raylene glanced up from her cell phone, a shocked expression on her face, Adelia crumbled. Tears flowed unchecked.

"You know, don't you?" she whispered brokenly when she could finally speak.

Raylene nodded. "That was Gabe on the phone. He thought you might need me."

"How considerate!" Adelia said bitterly. "You know, it was bad enough finding out that Ernesto was cheating on me and having to hold my head high and pretend it didn't matter." She gave Raylene a plaintive look. "How am I supposed to pretend this doesn't matter?"

"You don't," Raylene said simply. "You cry and scream and shout and curse the man's sorry butt as much as you want to. The Sweet Magnolias will ply you with margaritas, if that will help."

The offer brought a watery smile to her lips. "If those things almost killed me when

I was having a good day, I don't think I'll rely on them now."

"How about the company? I can get everybody together at my place tonight."

Adelia knew they would all come, too, just as they had that morning to be there for her in court. It was an amazing feeling to discover she had real friends. But while they might be able to offer moral support and would willingly listen to her rip into Gabe, that wasn't what she really needed. What she really needed was to go home and find Gabe at her house, the same as he had been so many times recently.

Sadly, though, that simply wasn't in the cards. She needed to accept reality, and then figure out how on earth she was going to explain all of this to her children.

Despite all Adelia's arguments that she needed to stay at the boutique and work, Raylene insisted that she go home.

"You need a long, leisurely bubble bath and a nap," Raylene said. "It's been a stressful day. Take advantage of the couple of hours you'll have to yourself before the kids come home."

Adelia sighed. "You're probably right. Maybe I'll have a brainstorm about what I'm going to say to them, especially Selena.

For her I think this will be worse in some ways than anything Ernesto did."

"From what I saw in court today, she's a very mature girl. She may be devastated, but she'll be more worried about you."

"And isn't that sad?" Adelia said. It was yet more proof that her daughter had had to grow up too quickly.

"Now go," Raylene ordered. "Tomorrow's soon enough for you to be back in here working your sales magic."

Adelia gave in reluctantly and walked home. As she neared the house, she frowned at the sight of her sister's car in the driveway, Carolina behind the wheel. Adelia prayed that she was right about what this meant.

After approaching the car slowly, she tapped on the window. "Carolina?"

Her sister lifted her head, revealing yet another cut on her cheek and bruises that to Adelia's untrained eye seemed fresh.

"Come inside," Adelia said at once, her own worries forgotten.

Carolina climbed out of the car, but when she tried to walk, she could barely limp. Adelia slipped an arm around her waist.

"Come on," she said softly. "I've got you. Do you need to go to the hospital? Is anything broken?"

Carolina shook her head, then asked hesitantly, "Is it okay if the kids and I stay here, just for tonight?"

"You'll stay for as long as you need to," Adelia replied.

"Thank you. After all the things I've said to you, I don't deserve it," Carolina said.

"We're sisters," Adelia told her. "You will always be welcome in my home."

Her sister gave her a weary look. "Don't call Mama, not yet, okay? I'm just not ready to talk to her."

"Whatever you want."

"Is Gabe coming over? I don't think I could bear it if he or anyone else saw me right now."

"You don't need to worry about that," Adelia said, her tone wry.

Inside, she settled her sister gingerly on the sofa, then took her one small suitcase upstairs. When she came down, she asked, "Is there more?"

"I didn't stop to pack much. What's in there is for the kids."

"Do they know to come here? Do I need to pick them up at school?"

Alarm filled Carolina's eyes. "I didn't think of that. They'll take the bus home from school. I should be there."

"Absolutely not," Adelia told her. "I'll call

Helen. She'll know what to do."

"I'm not ready to talk to a lawyer," Carolina said, panic in her voice.

"You don't have a choice," Adelia said firmly. "You have to think about doing what's best for your kids. The only other alternative is for me to call Mama and have her get the kids and bring them here or take them home with her."

Carolina seemed to be struggling between hiding what was happening from their mother or relying on her in this crisis. "Maybe that would be best," she said at last. "You talk to her, though. Ask her to keep the kids with her for a day or two. They have clothes at her house."

"What do I tell her when she asks about what's going on? She will, you know."

"Just that I need a couple of days to think about things. That will give these bruises time enough to fade some more."

"Haven't the kids already seen what Ricky has done to you? I know Mama has."

She shook her head. "I told Joey I was sick and probably contagious, so I was staying in the guest room. I asked him to keep an eye on his brothers. I couldn't let him see me. He'd have gone after Ricky himself."

Adelia regarded her sister with compassion. "You've done the right thing, Carolina.

I know how hard it is to walk out on a marriage, especially after the way we were raised. But God wouldn't want this to go on. I know He wouldn't."

"God might understand, but what about Mama?"

Adelia ran a comforting hand over her sister's head. "She'd want what's best for you, the same way she did for me. It's going to be okay. I promise. You've taken the most important step toward getting your life back."

"It feels more like I've just jumped off a precipice and there's no going back. There's nothing to grab on to going down, either."

Adelia smiled at the first tiny hint of her sister's sense of humor. "Been there, done that," she told her. "But just like me, you're going to land on your feet."

Chapter Twenty-Three

Gabe had rushed into a lot of short-term relationships over the years. He'd even had one or two that had lasted well beyond those impulsive first weeks of heat and passion. This long, slow buildup to something with real potential he'd experienced with Adelia was new to him and he didn't mind admitting that it scared him to death. That's why he was going to Beaufort to talk to Ronnie's friend. That's why he thought the only smart thing to do was to leave before anybody got hurt or at least hurt worse than they would be if he bailed now.

Early Saturday morning he drove down to Beaufort to meet with Butch. They talked over a big country breakfast of eggs, bacon and grits and drank about a gallon of coffee to wash it down. He instinctively liked the older man and was intrigued with the construction projects he had going on.

"Do you have time to ride around and

take a look at some of the sites?" Butch asked. "I can show you plans, too."

"Sure," Gabe said.

The projects ranged from several historic renovations to a new development in the suburbs. All were being done with diligent attention to detail, just the way Gabe liked to work. In the end, though, he couldn't figure out why he wasn't more excited by what he'd seen.

After the tour they went back to Butch's office, a far simpler place than that ostentatious building Ernesto had built for himself. Butch, just like Mitch, was obviously a man who put more energy into the work his company was doing than into his own comfort or a pretentious show of success.

"Sorry about the mess," Butch said, as he swept some blueprints off a sofa and gestured for Gabe to have a seat. "I'm never in here long enough to clean this place up. And my secretary reminds me just about daily that it's not what I'm paying her to do."

Gabe chuckled, liking the man more and more. He was a straight shooter, just as Ronnie had described him.

"Now, then," Butch began. "I like what I've seen and heard so far. If you're interested, here's what I'm prepared to offer."

The package of pay and benefits was a

good one, more than Gabe could expect to make from Mitch, at least until that new construction project he'd mentioned broke ground. The work sounded challenging.

"What do you think?" Butch asked. "I'll be candid. You're the first person I've talked to, but I have a list of other candidates. Since I need someone who can be on the job in a couple of weeks or a month at the outside, I can't wait around for long while you make a decision."

Gabe told himself he should jump at this chance that had fallen into his lap, but reservations he didn't totally understand kept him from a quick yes.

"Let me go back to Serenity and think it over," he suggested. "I'll get back to you tomorrow, or first thing Monday morning, if you don't like dealing with work issues on Sunday."

"The sooner the better," Butch told him. "Do you mind telling me what's holding you back from saying yes now?"

"I have some people I need to consider," Gabe hedged. "I'm working for my cousin right now. He's got a baby on the way and he's counting on me."

Butch studied him and nodded. "I appreciate that you want to be fair to him. That's another admirable trait." A gleam lit his eyes. "Something tells me there's more, a woman, maybe. With a decent man as good-looking as you, there's always a woman."

Gabe laughed. "There might be a woman."

"One you're running from or one you're considering staying with?" Butch asked perceptively.

"That is the dilemma," Gabe admitted.

Butch sighed. "I know I'm going to regret telling you this, but one thing I've learned over the years is that a man should never walk away from the possibility of love. Jobs come and go, but the right woman? That's something you should hang on to tight. Given the number of years I've been happily married to the same woman, I think I know what I'm talking about. She'd tell you the same thing."

Gabe felt the knot in his stomach slowly start to ease at Butch's words. It wasn't as if the advice was anything new, or anything he hadn't considered. It just suddenly made sense. Adelia had a hold on his heart. That wouldn't change if he stayed or if he ran.

"Thank you," he said holding out his hand. "I don't think I need to wait after all. I appreciate the offer, but I'm turning it down."

Butch looked disappointed, but he nodded. "Much as I hate to say it, it sounds as if it's the right decision. If it turns out not to be, give me a call."

"I'll do that," Gabe promised.

With luck, though, that would be a call he'd never have to make.

"Can I ask you something personal?" he asked Mitch over coffee on Monday morning. He'd spent the rest of the weekend debating his decision with himself, but not a single one of his many moments of panic had managed to shake his conviction that coming back to Serenity and Adelia was exactly the right choice.

Mitch leveled a look into his eyes. "Maybe first you should tell me about this job offer I hear you've had."

Gabe swallowed hard at the dismay in his cousin's eyes. "I'm sorry. I should have mentioned that I intended to check out another opportunity," he admitted.

"Yes, you should have," Mitch said, his gaze unrelenting.

"My only excuse is that it came up unexpectedly. I felt I owed it to myself to check it out."

"And?"

"I'm staying, Mitch, that is, if you'll still

494

have me."

Relief washed over Mitch's face. "That's good then. We don't have to say another word about it. I assume you had your reasons for even going down to Beaufort."

"Of course I did," Gabe said. "I was running from everything I've been feeling about Adelia."

Mitch smiled. "But you changed your mind and decided to stop running?"

"I did. That brings me back to that personal question I wanted to ask."

"Sure. Shoot," Mitch said.

"How did you know Lynn was the right woman for you?"

Mitch laughed. "You mean back when we were fourteen and the only man she cared about was Ed Morrow? We might be able to chalk that up to teen lust."

"I was thinking about more recently, when you actually got together," Gabe said.

Mitch was silent for several minutes. "I think maybe it was because we did go down those very different paths. When we started running into each other when I was working at Raylene's next door, it just seemed natural to be with her. She was going through hell with her divorce from Ed. I wanted to be the person she leaned on. Not that she did. She was determined to get through that tough time on her own. I think I fell even more in love with her because of that."

"Okay, so there were old feelings, friendship, that leftover lust from when you were fourteen, I assume."

"Oh yeah, there was that," Mitch said, glancing toward the back of the bakery as if to catch a glimpse of Lynn. A smile landed on his lips when she passed by the open doorway into the kitchen. He turned back to Gabe. "What is this really about? Are you wondering if what you feel for Adelia is real?"

Gabe nodded. "We haven't even slept together, if you can believe it. That's the only sort of relationship with a woman I've ever known how to have. Despite that, I feel closer to Adelia than I ever did to those other women. There's something deeper, even more intense between us."

He wasn't sure if he was explaining it right, so he tried again. "Adelia's at the heart of it, though. I feel as if it's hard to breathe when she's not around. It's like I found this piece of myself I never even knew was missing." He gave his cousin a bemused look. "She's in my blood, you know what I mean?"

Again, Mitch glanced toward the kitchen.

"Believe me, I know. If you're asking what I think about what you have with Adelia, it sounds real to me, but you two are the only ones who can really know. How do you feel about having an instant family?"

Gabe smiled. "Well, I'm not entirely over the panic, that's for sure. But when Tomas follows me around and looks at me as if I know all the answers in the universe, it does something to me. The girls . . ." He shook his head. "They scare the daylights out of me. I want to make sure they avoid all the mistakes my mother made. I feel so blasted protective, and then I wonder when that happened."

"It's called being a dad," Mitch said, regarding him sympathetically. "And girls are definitely different. I raised two sons. I totally get Lynn's boy, Jeremy, but Lexie? She's a whole different ball game. She's smart and sassy and tough, but I'm terrified every time she mentions going on a date. So far Lynn's insisted that she only do the group thing, but that won't last much longer. Then I might consider locking her in her room. I have a selection of deadbolts in my truck, just in case."

"I can understand that," Gabe said. "I just know that's how I'm going to be when Selena discovers boys." He gave Mitch a surprised look. "But I want that in my life."

"Okay, here's what I see, Gabe. The same instincts that got you into trouble as a kid, being loyal and looking out for your mom the only way you knew how, those instincts have made you into a good man. You'll do whatever it takes to keep anyone from hurting the people you love. And my gut tells me you've learned that brawling isn't the answer."

"Will it shake that belief to know that I still wouldn't mind catching Ernesto Hernandez in some dark alley and punching his lights out?" Gabe asked, not entirely in jest.

"Not a bit, because you haven't done it."

"So you think I wouldn't make a mess of the whole happily-ever-after thing?"

"It doesn't matter what I think," Mitch said. "It only matters what you believe, how willing you are to dedicate yourself to being a good husband and father. You weren't just running from the past all these years. You were running from too much responsibility, too soon. Only you can decide if you're ready to take on the whole passel of responsibility that comes with marrying Adelia."

Gabe sighed. "After what happened the other day, when I told Adelia I was probably leaving, mine may not be the vote that counts. She may not believe I'm ready, no matter what I say now."

Mitch stood up then and gave his shoulder a reassuring squeeze. "But you came to your senses in the nick of time. I have faith in your powers of persuasion. If Adelia's the woman you really, truly want, there's not a doubt in my mind that you can win her over. It may take more patience than you'd like, but I've seen the way the woman looks at you. Play your cards right and you'll have everything you ever dreamed of."

After Mitch had gone, Gabe sipped his cup of coffee and thought about what his cousin had said. He walked over to the counter and called out to Lynn. She came out of the back, wiping her flour-covered hands on a towel.

"I have an idea," he said. "Think you can help me out?"

"Does this have something to do with what you and my husband were discussing?"

"You overheard?"

"I just heard you mention something about Adelia," Lynn said. "It got my hopes up, especially since you're still here in town, instead of down in Beaufort. Thank you for that, by the way. I know Mitch is relieved. He's counting on you."

"I know that. It's one of the reasons I

turned down the job."

"And the other is Adelia?"

He smiled. "The other is Adelia," he confirmed. "Now, here's what I'm thinking," he said, watching her face as he described his idea. A smile spread as she listened, so he concluded that just maybe he'd gotten it right.

"It's perfect," she said. "When do you want to do this?"

Now that his mind was made up, he knew waiting would kill him. "How long will it take you?"

Lynn laughed. "So you're going for broke today?"

Gabe faltered. "Do you think that's a mistake? Do I need to lay some groundwork? Mitch said something about patience, but it's not my strong suit."

"Personally, though I've had to practice it a time or two, I think patience can be highly overrated. Come back at closing."

"Perfect," he said. "That'll give me just enough time."

Now that he'd made up his mind to reach for the future he'd never let himself imagine, he wanted to get on with it. The end of the day would give him just enough time to check on things at the work site, then get back to the inn to shower and change into

500

something a whole lot more presentable than his work clothes. A man couldn't very well ask the most important question of his life while covered in dust and wearing denim.

Adelia had just hung the closed sign on the door of the boutique and was about to turn the lock when she saw Gabe approaching wearing that perfectly tailored suit again and carrying a huge pastry box. He beckoned for her to open the door.

"What on earth?" she asked, her eyes wide. "Is it somebody's birthday? Where are you going all dressed up and carrying a cake?"

"Lock the door," he told her, his gaze never leaving her face.

"Gabe?" she whispered questioningly, even as she did as he'd requested. "What's going on?"

He set the box on the counter, then suddenly, charmingly looked as if he wasn't quite sure what to do with his hands. He nodded toward the box.

"Red velvet cake," he began. "Lynn says it's your favorite."

"It is."

"The kids like it, too?"

"Sure."

He swallowed hard. "You and I, we haven't known each other all that long."

"True."

"But I feel as if it's been forever." He hesitated. "Do you know what I mean?"

She drew in a deep breath, suddenly terrified about the direction in which he was heading, yet thrilled just the same. "I do," she said, her voice shaking.

"Your divorce is still new," he said. "So maybe you're not where I am yet." He regarded her questioningly.

"Where are you, Gabe? I thought you were taking off."

"I changed my mind," he said, shocking her.

"Why?"

She waited while he seemed to be struggling with the answer.

"Because I'm in love with you," he finally blurted, as if he needed to get the words out in a rush. "I sure didn't expect it, but that's what makes life interesting, right? The surprises. You were a total surprise, Adelia. The best kind. And those complications we talked about? This is the best kind of those, too."

Relief washed over her. She gave him an encouraging smile. He seemed to need reassurance and suddenly she felt calmer and more composed than she had at any time since she'd left her cheating ex-husband.

"You came as a surprise to me, too," she said. "Definitely the best kind."

He looked as if he hadn't really expected her to admit to the same feelings. She laughed. "You look surprised."

"It's just that I'm not used to getting what I want. I want you, Adelia. I don't mean just in my bed or just for a night. I mean forever. I want to marry you, to be with you and your kids. Who knows, maybe it's not too late for us to have one of our own. Will you marry me? I don't think I'm a bad bet, not anymore. And I'll do everything I can to make sure you're happy. That goes for the kids, too. I won't try to be their dad. They have one. But I think I'm ready to be a good influence on them." He held her gaze and waited, then prodded, "So, what do you think?"

Adelia reached behind her and felt for the stool that was always right behind the counter. She sat down hard at the unexpected question. She hadn't dared to let herself even imagine that marriage was where he was heading.

"You want to marry me?" she repeated to be sure.

Hearing the words, even though she'd

been anticipating some sort of dramatic declaration for a few minutes now, stunned her. It was a giant leap from what she'd been thinking. She'd expected maybe a request that they spend more time together, see how it went. Apparently once Gabe made a decision, he was all in. She realized that was something she'd come to appreciate about him. He put what he was thinking, what he wanted, right out there. There were no guessing games about where she stood with him. Even when he'd been thinking of leaving, a move he knew would hurt her, he'd put his cards on the table and told her the truth.

"I do want to marry you," he stated quietly. "More than anything, but I can wait if you need more time. Or if the kids need to adjust to the idea."

"The kids will go a little crazy," she said, then grinned. "But definitely in a good way."

"What about you?"

Her expression sobered. "I need to be clear about a couple of things."

"Okay."

"No more talk about leaving town, getting a fresh start someplace new? Are you really sure you want to stay here in Serenity, crazy gossip and all?"

"Leaving *was* the plan," he said. "I'm apparently a lot more adaptable than I'd realized. *This* is the fresh start I want, Adelia. Right here, with you and your kids, with all those Sweet Magnolia women meddling and their husbands trying to beat my butt in basketball."

"And the red velvet cake? Where does that fit in?"

He grinned, looking more relaxed now that he clearly assumed the conversation was going to go his way. "Answer me first," he countered. "I'm not sure how I feel about being less important to you than a cake."

"Trust me, this cake doesn't hold a candle to you and your proposal," she said. "I just wondered."

"You're stalling," he accused. Then his expression faltered. "Is it because I'm rushing you? I meant it when I said I'd wait till you caught up with me."

She drew in a deep breath, steadied herself, then walked around the counter until she was standing right in front of this man who'd come to mean the world to her, this man she trusted in ways she'd never expected to trust again. She put her hand on his clean-shaven cheek and smiled.

"You're all dressed up and you even shaved," she whispered as if she'd just noticed.

"It's not the kind of question a man asks when he's covered in drywall dust," he said. "And you're still stalling."

"Just drawing out the moment," she said. "I want to savor it."

"So the answer is . . ."

"Yes," she said, moving into his arms. Then she was surrounded by all that heat and strength and his lips were on hers in a kiss that stole her breath away.

When she could speak again, she repeated her answer with even more emphasis, "Yes, Gabe Franklin, I will marry you." Then she nudged him in the ribs. "Now tell me about that cake."

He laughed and lifted the lid on the box. "I thought maybe we'd have something to celebrate tonight," he explained. "At least I hoped we would."

In flowing script across the top of the decadent red velvet cake, it said, "Your mom said yes!"

Adelia laughed. "Awfully sure of yourself, weren't you?"

"Darlin', until I met you, I hadn't been sure of anything for a very long time. This, it was just a matter of time. If you hadn't said yes tonight, that cake would have gone in the freezer until you were ready."

"But it's so much better when it's fresh

out of the oven," she said. "Let's take it home and celebrate."

As she said it, she smiled. With Gabe by her side, the house she'd chosen for her future really was going to be a home. And they were going to be a family, the kind she'd always dreamed of, the kind Gabe had never had.

Of course, it might be a little crowded for a while now. She probably ought to mention that to make sure the presence of her sister and her kids wouldn't give Gabe cold feet.

"I should probably fill you in about something before we take this cake home," she said.

"Is it something that might be a deal breaker?" he asked worriedly.

"I hope not."

"Then tell me."

"My sister's staying with me."

Gabe's eyes widened. "Carolina finally left her husband?"

Adelia nodded. "I'm still hoping to convince her to file charges against Ricky, but she's not there yet."

"At least she got away from him. How are her kids?"

"They're at my mom's for another day or two, but they could be moving in, too.

Carolina needs to be someplace she can feel safe and figure out what comes next. The good news is that Cruz women are never down-and-out for long. I have faith that she's going to find her way, just like I did."

Gabe looked vaguely shaken, but all he said was, "Seems I could be getting even more family than I bargained for."

"And that doesn't terrify you?"

"As long as you're there, I can't think of a thing that would scare me off." He gave her a long, slow look that made her toes curl. "But we might need a very long, very private honeymoon."

Adelia laughed. "That is definitely something I can get behind. I imagine Mama can take over and keep the family on track for a week or two. How soon were you thinking we ought to take this honeymoon?"

He regarded her hopefully. "Well, the minute Mitch's baby is born, I'm going to be busier than ever. And when Raylene's arrives, you're going to have a boatload of responsibility at the boutique. So, I was thinking we'd better get this done before either of those kids gets here."

"And before you can have second thoughts?" she asked.

"Not a consideration," he said adamantly. "It's all about those babies."

"In that case, how about next week? I'm pretty sure at least one of those babies is going to be early, so there's not much time to waste."

To her delight, there wasn't even a flicker of panic in Gabe's eyes at her suggestion.

"Next week is good," he agreed at once.

"The kids are going to complain about not getting to go on the honeymoon," she warned him.

"Too bad," he said, pulling her close for one of his bone-melting kisses. "We'll promise them a family vacation next summer."

Adelia regarded him with approval.

"What?" Gabe asked.

"You're going to be excellent at this parenting thing," she told him. "The promise of a delayed reward can get a parent out of many a tight spot."

"As long as it gets me alone with you for a couple of weeks on a beach somewhere, I'm good," Gabe told her.

"A beach? You've already picked a spot for the honeymoon?"

"I heard that was one of the groom's responsibilities, but if you want a say, speak up. We're going to be an equal-opportunity couple."

Adelia looked at Gabe with her heart in

her throat. How had this man she'd known such a short time understood exactly the right thing to say?

"Thank you," she whispered against his cheek.

"For what?"

"For making me believe in love again."

"I'm going to do my best to make sure you never stop believing again," he promised.

"And I'll do the same," she told him. "I think we're going to be very good together, Gabe."

"I don't have much to compare us to, but I think we're going to be amazing!"

Suddenly Adelia could hardly wait to find out just how amazing life with this man could be, so wasn't it lucky that she only had to wait a week? In no time at all, they'd start an adventure that she was convinced was destined to last forever.

ABOUT THE AUTHOR

With her roots firmly planted in the South, #1 *New York Times* bestselling author **Sherryl Woods** has written many of her more than one hundred books in that distinctive setting, whether it's her home state of Virginia, her adopted state, Florida, or her much-adored South Carolina. Now she's added North Carolina's Outer Banks to her list of favorite spots. And she remains partial to small towns, wherever they may be.

Sherryl divides her time between her childhood summer home overlooking the Potomac River in Colonial Beach, Virginia, and her oceanfront home with its lighthouse view in Key Biscayne, Florida. "Wherever I am, if there's no water in sight, I get a little antsy," she says.

Sherryl loves to hear from readers. You can

visit her on her website at www.sherryl woods.com, link to her Facebook fan page from there, or contact her directly at Sherryl703@gmail.com.

www.SherrylWoods.com